The Open University

MST209 Mathe

Block 4

Contents

The Open University, Walton Hall, Milton Keynes, MK7 6AA.

First published 2005. Second edition 2008.

Edited, designed and typeset by The Open University, using the Open University TEX System.

Printed and bound in the United Kingdom by Charlesworth Press, Wakefield.

ISBN 978 0 7492 5284 7

1.1

UNIT 13 Modelling with non-linear differential equations

Study guide for Unit 13

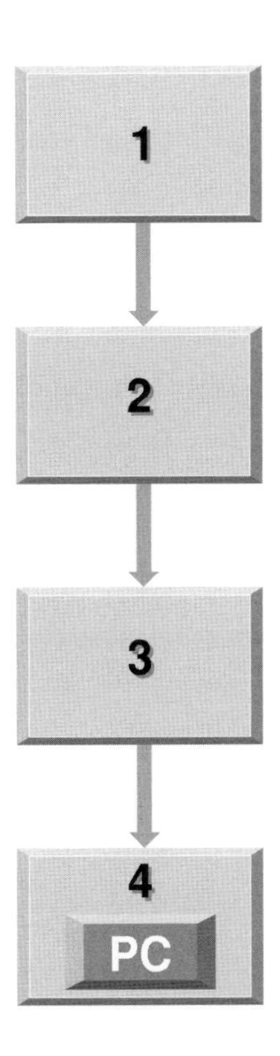

This is the last unit in this course devoted to the analytical solution of ordinary differential equations. We considered the solution of first-order differential equations in *Unit 2*, then in *Unit 3* we looked at linear constant-coefficient second-order differential equations, and in *Unit 11* we studied simultaneous systems of both first-order and second-order linear differential equations. In this unit, we shall be looking again at systems of first-order differential equations, but we shall be concentrating on systems which are *non-linear*.

You will need to be familiar with the techniques developed in *Unit 10* for finding eigenvalues and eigenvectors, and in *Unit 11* for the solution of systems of first-order linear differential equations.

We recommend that you study one section per study session. However, the main ideas of this unit are developed in the first two sections. You could sensibly decide to spend two study sessions on Section 1, spending one study session on Subsections 1.1 to 1.3, and the second study session on Subsections 1.4 to 1.6. If you are short of time, you should devote more time to the first two sections than to the later sections. You will need to use your computer for Section 4, which is entirely devoted to computer activities using the computer algebra package for the course.

The material discussed here is introduced in the context of the interaction of animal populations, but it is applicable to many areas involving systems of non-linear differential equations. The motion of pendulums is also discussed.

Introduction

In this unit we study the mathematical models associated with two physical systems:

- the growth of two interacting populations, one a predator and the other its prey;
- the motion of a rigid pendulum.

At first sight these systems appear to be unrelated, but each can be sensibly modelled by a non-linear differential equation or a system of such equations.

- The interaction between two populations is modelled by the Lotka–Volterra equations

  $$\dot{x} = kx\left(1 - \frac{y}{Y}\right), \quad \dot{y} = -hy\left(1 - \frac{x}{X}\right),$$

  where h, k, X and Y are known constants, and $x = x(t)$ and $y = y(t)$ represent the two population sizes at time t.

The equations are non-linear because of the xy terms.

- The unresisted motion of a rigid pendulum is modelled by the second-order differential equation

  $$\ddot{x} + \omega^2 \sin x = 0,$$

  where ω is a constant and $x = x(t)$ is the angle the pendulum makes with the downwards vertical at time t.

The equation is non-linear because of the $\sin x$ term.

When you studied linear differential equations in *Units 2, 3* and *11*, the emphasis was on finding an explicit equation for the solution. For non-linear equations this is rarely possible; even when it is possible, the solution is usually difficult to interpret. As we shall see in *Unit 26*, it is often possible to find a solution using a numerical method, but such a method may give a solution that is equally difficult to interpret — and this will also be true for any graphs that the solution produces. For these reasons, when studying a system of non-linear differential equations, we often concentrate on a qualitative approach; that is, we try to obtain useful information *about* the solution, rather than trying to find the solution itself. This information may be in the form of a diagram. For the Lotka–Volterra equations, we look at the paths defined by $(x(t), y(t))$ in the (x, y)-plane. In the case of the pendulum, we again discuss paths in the plane, but while one axis is still used to represent $x(t)$, the second axis is used for $\dot{x}(t)$, so that paths are defined by $(x(t), \dot{x}(t))$.

We use the notations x or $x(t)$, $\dot{x}$ or $\dot{x}(t)$, etc., interchangeably to suit the context.

We shall see that a common feature of these two models is the relevance of a constant solution, which, in each case, describes an equilibrium state of the system. For example, a constant solution $x(t) = X$, $y(t) = Y$ to the Lotka–Volterra equations describes a situation where the two populations are in equilibrium. Near such a solution, we shall see that some useful information can be obtained by replacing the original non-linear equations by linear approximations to the differential equations. The equilibrium states and the behaviour of the system when it is nearly in equilibrium play a major part in obtaining a qualitative overview of the behaviour of the model.

We begin in Section 1 with the Lotka–Volterra equations, which apply to a pair of interacting populations, and see how these equations can be linearized near an equilibrium state. The resulting systems of linear differential equations were discussed in *Unit 11*, but here, in Section 2, we concentrate on the graphical representation of the solutions. Section 3 looks at models for the motion of a pendulum: second-order differential equations are transformed to systems of first-order equations, and the techniques developed earlier in the unit are applied to find and interpret graphical solutions.

One feature of all the differential equation models that appear in this unit is that the independent variable, usually t, does not appear explicitly in the differential equation, and the system takes the form

$$\dot{x} = u(x, y),$$
$$\dot{y} = v(x, y).$$

The important point is that the functions on the right-hand sides of these differential equations are independent of t.

Systems of this form, where t does not appear explicitly, are said to be *autonomous*.

1 Modelling populations of predators and prey

In this section we shall develop a model for the first type of system listed in the Introduction: populations of a predator and its prey. A predator population depends for its survival on there being sufficient prey to provide it with food. Intuition suggests that when the number of predators is low, the prey population may increase quickly, and that this will result in turn in an increase in the predator population. On the other hand, a large number of predators may diminish the prey population until it is very small, and this in turn will lead to a collapse in the predator population. Our mathematical model will need to reflect this behaviour.

It is not possible to find algebraic solutions to all such models, so we shall introduce you to a geometric approach, based on the notion that a point $(x, y) = (x(t), y(t))$ in the plane may be used to represent two populations $x = x(t)$ and $y = y(t)$ at time t. As t increases, the point $(x, y) = (x(t), y(t))$ will trace a path that represents the variation of both populations with time. In particular, we shall discuss the equilibrium values for such a system, and a linear approximation to the system near these equilibrium values.

1.1 Exponential growth of a single population

Before we consider a system of two interacting populations, we shall first develop a simple continuous model of the growth of a single population, which is called the exponential model. This will allow us to develop some of the concepts of population models in a simpler context.

Here we model the population size x, which we shall usually simply refer to as the population x (omitting the word 'size'), as a function of time t. This function cannot take negative values (since there are no negative populations), but we shall allow it to take the value zero. We shall normally assume that t is measured in years. We deal with a continuous model, rather than a discrete one, so the derivative $\dot{x}$ represents the rate of increase of the population, which we shall often refer to as the **growth rate** (even when, if $\dot{x} < 0$, it actually represents a decay rate — compare the use in mechanics of 'acceleration' to cover both of the everyday terms 'acceleration' and 'deceleration').

A population x can take only integer values, so we say (as in *Unit 1*) that x is a discrete variable. It is often convenient to approximate a discrete variable by a variable that can take any real value, referred to as a continuous variable.

In the exponential model, we make the assumption that the growth rate $\dot{x}$ is proportional to the current population x. (This means that if the growth rate is 20 per year when the population is 100, then the growth rate will be 40 per year when the population is 200, the growth rate will be 60 per year when the population is 300, and so on.) This assumption leads directly to the differential equation

$$\dot{x} = kx \quad (x \geq 0), \tag{1.1}$$

where k is a constant. If k is positive, then x is an increasing function of time, while if k is negative, then x is decreasing.

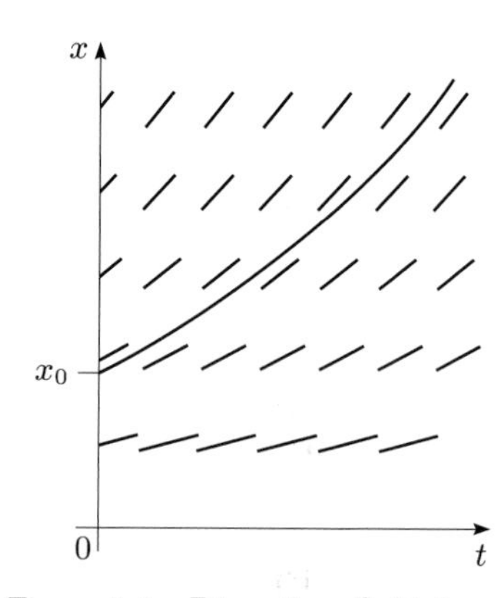

Figure 1.1 Direction field for Equation (1.1), with $k > 0$

Exercise 1.1

Under what circumstances is it reasonable to assume that the growth rate of a population is proportional to the current population?

In *Unit 2* you saw that a differential equation like Equation (1.1) can be described by a *direction field*. The graph of a solution is a curve whose tangent at any point has a slope that is equal to the value of the direction field at that point (see Figure 1.1). However, Equation (1.1) can be solved explicitly. Choosing a value for the population $x(t)$ at time $t = 0$, for example, $x(0) = x_0$, gives the solution

$$x(t) = x_0 e^{kt} \quad (x \geq 0), \tag{1.2}$$

which is an *exponential* function. If the constant k is positive, the population is increasing. If k is negative, the population is decreasing. This difference is demonstrated by comparing the graphs of the functions e^t and e^{-t}, for $t \geq 0$, as shown in Figure 1.2. We may describe the two situations as *exponential growth* and *exponential decay*, although we could say that the latter case is merely exhibiting 'negative growth'. For this reason we refer to Equation (1.1) as the **exponential differential equation**, or, when applied to a population, the **exponential model**.

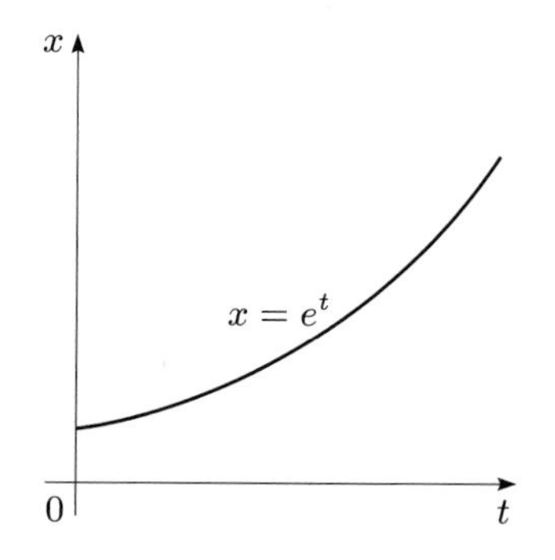

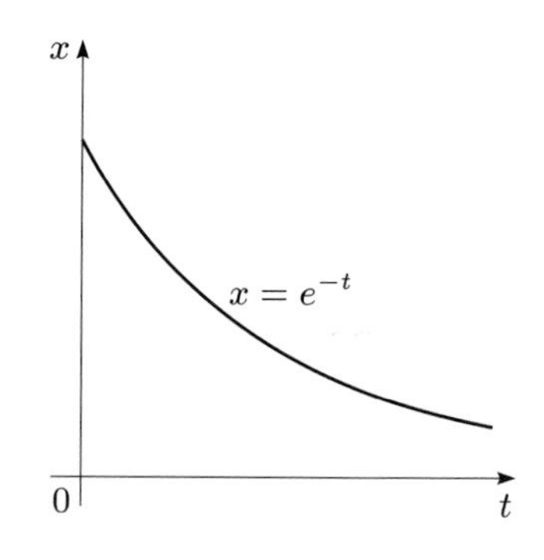

Figure 1.2

The **proportionate growth rate** $\dot{x}/x$ represents the rate of increase of the population per unit of the current population, and may be considered as the difference between the birth and death rates per head of population. It may be positive (for a growing population in which the birth rate exceeds the death rate), negative (for a declining population in which the death rate exceeds the birth rate) or zero (for a static population in which the birth and death rates are equal). In the case of the exponential model (1.1), we have $\dot{x}/x = k$, so the proportionate growth rate is constant. (We previously assumed that $x \geq 0$. While talking about proportionate growth rate, we exclude the possibility that x takes the value zero.)

Exercise 1.2

Can you suggest any reason why the assumption that the proportionate growth rate $\dot{x}/x$ is constant is unrealistic for real populations?

The exponential model is fairly accurate for many populations in a state of rapid increase, but it can be reasonable only over a restricted domain of validity. As a model of the behaviour of increasing populations over longer periods of time, the exponential model is clearly unsatisfactory because it predicts unbounded growth. However, in this unit we shall not revise our first (simple) model to give a more realistic description of the growth of a single population.

1.2 A first model for populations of rabbits and foxes

In the rest of this section we shall be concerned with developing models for populations of rabbits (the prey) and foxes (the predators). Our purpose is to determine how these populations evolve with time. At a particular time t, we suppose that these populations are $x(t)$ and $y(t)$, respectively. We represent this system by a point in the (x, y)-plane. The evolution of the two populations can be represented as a path, as shown in Figure 1.3, where the directions of the arrows on the path indicate the directions in which the point $(x(t), y(t))$ moves along the path with increasing time. However, this type of representation does not show how quickly or slowly the point moves along the path.

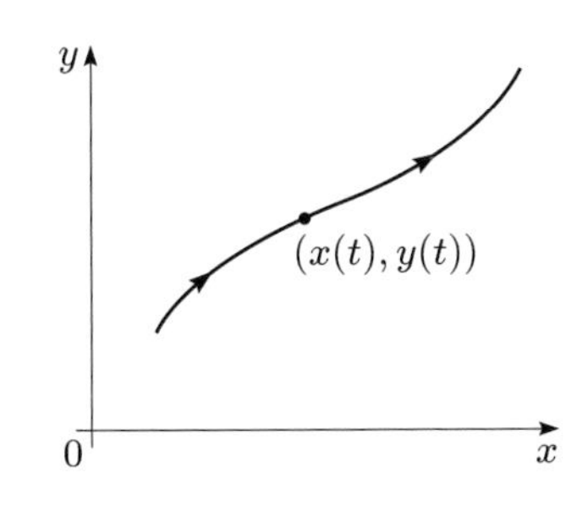

Figure 1.3

In our mathematical model we make the following assumptions.

- There is plenty of vegetation for the rabbits to eat.
- The rabbits are the only source of food for the foxes.
- An encounter between a fox and a rabbit contributes to the fox's larder, which leads directly to a decrease in the rabbit population and indirectly to an increase in the number of foxes.

We may, for convenience, measure the populations in hundreds or thousands, as appropriate, so that we are able to use quite small numbers in our models.

We begin by examining a very simple model which generalizes the exponential model that we used for a single population in the previous subsection. This simple case has the advantage that we can determine easily an algebraic solution, and we use it to investigate the geometric approach.

As a first model, we assume that the populations are evolving independently (perhaps on separate islands). Because there are *no interactions*, the populations may be modelled by the pair of equations

$$\begin{aligned} \dot{x} &= kx, \\ \dot{y} &= -hy \quad (x \geq 0,\ y \geq 0), \end{aligned} \tag{1.3}$$

Each of these equations has an exponential function as its general solution.

where k and h are positive constants. The condition $(x \geq 0, y \geq 0)$ applies here, as well as in similar situations throughout the unit, to the first equation $\dot{x} = kx$, as well as the second equation $\dot{y} = -hy$.

The first equation models a colony of rabbits not affected by the predation of foxes, growing exponentially according to a rule of the form

$$x(t) = Ce^{kt},$$

where C is a positive constant representing the initial rabbit population.

When $t = 0$, $x = C$.

*Exercise 1.3

Determine a formula for the population $y(t)$ of foxes. How would you interpret this solution for the population of foxes?

Equations (1.3) form a system of linear differential equations which you met in *Unit 11*. Using vector notation, the pair of populations may be represented by the vector $\mathbf{x} = [x \quad y]^T$. The system of equations (1.3) then becomes the vector equation

$$\dot{\mathbf{x}} = \begin{bmatrix} \dot{x} \\ \dot{y} \end{bmatrix} = \begin{bmatrix} kx \\ -hy \end{bmatrix}. \tag{1.4}$$

It is helpful now to introduce the notion of a *vector field*, which is similar to a direction field. In a plane, a direction field associates a direction

Vector fields are discussed in more detail in *Unit 23*.

$f(x, y)$ with each point (x, y), whereas a vector field associates a vector $\mathbf{u}(x, y)$ with each point (x, y). For example, if $\mathbf{u}(x, y) = [2x \quad 3y + 2]^T$, then $\mathbf{u}(1, 2) = [2 \quad 8]^T = 2\mathbf{i} + 8\mathbf{j}$. For our predator–prey model, we would associate with Equation (1.4) the vector field

$$\mathbf{u}(x, y) = \begin{bmatrix} kx \\ -hy \end{bmatrix}, \qquad (1.5)$$

so that Equation (1.4) becomes

$$\dot{\mathbf{x}} = \mathbf{u}(x, y).$$

Sometimes this will be written as $\dot{\mathbf{x}} = \mathbf{u}(\mathbf{x})$.

For a direction field, $f(x, y)$ represents the slope of a particular solution of the differential equation $dy/dx = f(x, y)$ at the point (x, y). Similarly, $\mathbf{u}(x, y)$ is the vector $\dot{x}\mathbf{i} + \dot{y}\mathbf{j}$ that is tangential to a particular solution of $\dot{\mathbf{x}} = \mathbf{u}(x, y)$ at the point (x, y), because the slope of the tangent is

$$\frac{dy}{dx} = \frac{(dy/dt)}{(dx/dt)} = \frac{\dot{y}}{\dot{x}}.$$

This suggests a geometric way of finding a particular solution to Equation (1.4): choose a particular starting point (x_0, y_0), then follow the directions of the tangent vectors. The essential difference between a direction field and a vector field is that the latter consists of directed line segments (which we indicate by arrows) whose lengths indicate the magnitude of $\mathbf{u}(x, y)$. However, since the magnitudes of $\mathbf{u}(x, y)$ may vary considerably and so make the diagram difficult to interpret, we often use arrows of a fixed length.

An exception, which we discuss later, occurs when $\dot{x} = \dot{y} = 0$ at (x_e, y_e), so $\mathbf{u}(x_e, y_e) = \mathbf{0}$ and there is no tangent vector to follow.

In many cases, it is the direction of $\mathbf{u}(x, y)$ that is our primary concern, rather than its magnitude.

We now widen the discussion and look at similar systems that do not arise from populations.

Example 1.1

(a) Using arrows of a fixed length, sketch the vector field given by

$$\mathbf{u}(x, y) = \begin{bmatrix} 0.2x \\ 0.3y \end{bmatrix}.$$

(b) Write down the system of differential equations $\dot{\mathbf{x}} = \mathbf{u}(\mathbf{x})$ corresponding to this vector field. Solve this system of equations, and hence find an equation in terms of x and y for each path in the (x, y)-plane represented by this solution.

(c) Sketch a sample of the paths in the (x, y)-plane which represent the solutions.

Solution

(a) We use values of $\mathbf{u}(x, y)$ to construct Figure 1.4. The arrows represent vectors of a fixed length parallel to $\mathbf{u}(x, y)$. Each arrow indicates the direction of a path through a given point.

For example, at the point $(1, 1)$, we have $\mathbf{u}(1, 1) = [0.2 \quad 0.3]^T$.

(b) We have

$$\mathbf{u}(x, y) = \begin{bmatrix} \dot{x} \\ \dot{y} \end{bmatrix} = \begin{bmatrix} 0.2x \\ 0.3y \end{bmatrix},$$

so the system of equations is

$$\dot{x} = 0.2x,$$
$$\dot{y} = 0.3y.$$

The general solution is

$$x(t) = Ce^{0.2t}, \quad y(t) = De^{0.3t}. \qquad (1.6)$$

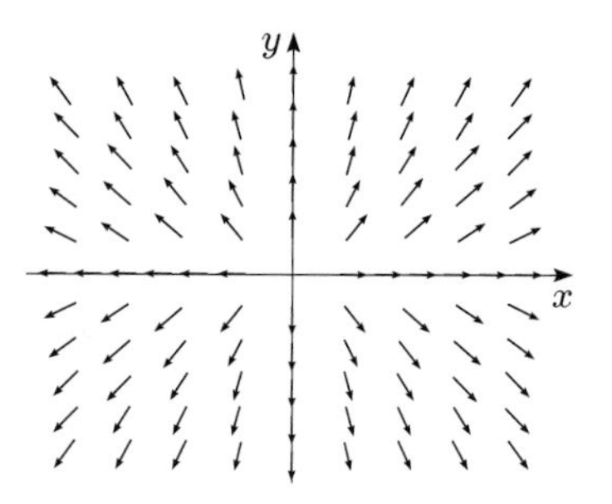

Figure 1.4

To obtain the equation for the paths in terms of x and y, we eliminate t from $x = Ce^{0.2t}$ and $y = De^{0.3t}$. Cubing the first equation and squaring the second gives $x^3 = C^3e^{0.6t}$ and $y^2 = D^2e^{0.6t}$, so $x^3/C^3 = y^2/D^2$. Hence the equations of the paths are of the form

$$y = K\,|x|^{3/2},$$

for some constant K.

The modulus signs around x ensure that we do not try to obtain the square root of a negative number. The arbitrariness of K ensures that the equation represents all possible cases.

(c) As we have been able to analytically find the equations of the paths in part (b), namely $y = K|x|^{3/2}$, we can use this to sketch the paths in the (x, y)-plane. These are shown in Figure 1.5. It remains to put the arrows on these paths to indicate the direction of increasing time. The first of the differential equations is $\dot{x} = 0.2x$. So for positive x, $\dot{x} > 0$ so x is an increasing function of time. Therefore in the right half-plane, the arrows on the paths point to the right. Similarly, for negative x, $\dot{x} < 0$ so x is a decreasing function of time. Hence the arrows on the paths point to the left in the left half-plane. These directions have been added to the paths in Figure 1.5. (Consideration of the second differential equation, $\dot{y} = 0.3y$, confirms the directions of the arrows on the paths.) The arrows on the paths along the positive and negative y-axes can be deduced from consideration of the differential equation $\dot{y} = 0.3y$. Note that the origin is also a path, corresponding to $K = 0$, but it has no time arrow associated with it.

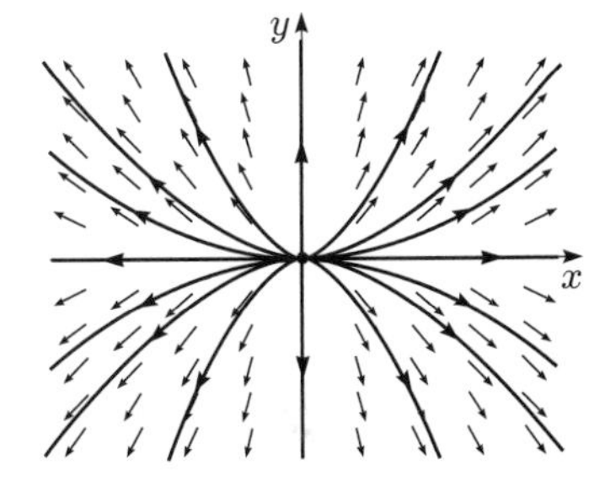

Figure 1.5

The direction of the time arrow on a path is the same as the direction of the vector field. This can be confirmed by looking at Figure 1.5.

Alternatively, we could have drawn the paths using the techniques we used for direction fields in *Unit 2*: the direction of the tangent to the path at any point (x, y) is the same as the vector field $\mathbf{u}(x, y)$ at that point. ■

A solution curve along which the coordinates x and y vary as t increases is called a **phase path** or orbit. The (x, y)-plane containing the solution curves is called the **phase plane**, and a diagram, such as Figure 1.5, showing the phase paths is called a **phase diagram**.

Before we leave Example 1.1, you may have noticed in Figure 1.5 that the paths radiate *outwards* from the origin in all directions. For this reason, we refer to the origin as a **source**.

A source can occur at a point other than the origin.

We now look at the phase paths for a similar system, for which

$$\mathbf{u}(x, y) = \begin{bmatrix} -0.2x \\ -0.3y \end{bmatrix}.$$

This system behaves in a similar fashion to the system in Example 1.1. The general solution is

$$x = Ce^{-0.2t}, \quad y = De^{-0.3t}.$$

Eliminating t gives

$$y = K\,|x|^{3/2},$$

as before. However, as t increases, there is a significant difference in the motion along the phase paths between this case and the case in Example 1.1. At any point (x, y), the vector field $\mathbf{u}(x, y) = [-0.2x \quad -0.3y]^T$ has the same magnitude but the opposite direction to the vector field $\mathbf{u}(x, y) = [0.2x \quad 0.3y]^T$. So in this case, the phase diagram would be identical to Figure 1.5 except that the directions would be pointing towards the origin.

Now the paths radiate inwards *towards* the origin and, for this reason, we refer to the origin as a **sink**.

A sink can occur at a point other than the origin.

*Exercise 1.4

Write down the system of differential equations $\dot{\mathbf{x}} = \mathbf{u}(x, y)$ given by the vector field

$$\mathbf{u}(x, y) = \begin{bmatrix} x \\ -y \end{bmatrix}.$$

Solve this system of equations, and hence find an equation in terms of x and y for the phase paths in the (x, y)-plane represented by this solution. Sketch some of these paths. Is there a path through the origin?

Apart from the restrictions $x \geq 0$, $y \geq 0$, this is the equation for our first model for the predator–prey populations (Equation (1.5)) with $k = 1$ and $h = 1$.

The phase diagram for the vector field examined in Exercise 1.4 is shown in Figure 1.6. You can see that the vast majority of paths do not radiate into or out of the origin. On these paths, a point initially travels towards the origin, but eventually travels away from it again. The only paths which actually radiate inwards towards or outwards from the origin are those along the x- and y-axes. In this case we call the origin a **saddle** (as you will understand from *Unit 12*).

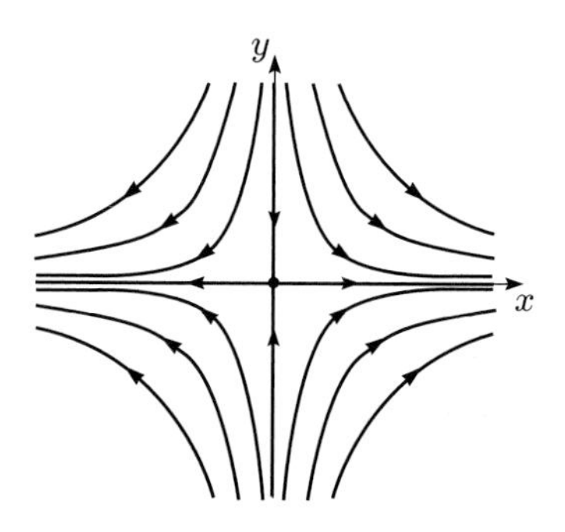

Figure 1.6

The behaviour of the populations of rabbits and foxes illustrated in the quadrant $x \geq 0$, $y \geq 0$ of Figure 1.6 is what we would expect from our first model. The population of rabbits increases without limit, as they are isolated from their predators. On the other hand, the population of foxes decreases to zero, as they have no access to their sole source of food.

1.3 A second model for populations of rabbits and foxes

In the previous subsection we looked at a model for rabbit and fox populations when there was no interaction between the two populations. This may be a reasonable model when both species inhabit the same environment but the populations are so low that the rabbits and foxes rarely meet. As we saw, for initial positive populations, this first model predicts that rabbits will increase without limit and foxes will die out. However, this is not what we expect for interacting populations, when encounters are unavoidable. We assume that the number of encounters between foxes and rabbits is proportional both to the population x of rabbits and to the population y of foxes.

In addition to our previous assumptions, stated in Subsection 1.2, our model assumes that

- the number of encounters between foxes and rabbits is proportional to the product xy.

In this subsection we look at a revised model, which allows for interaction based on this assumption.

For a population x of rabbits in a fox-free environment, our first model for population change is given by the equation $\dot{x} = kx$, where k is a positive constant. This represents exponential growth. However, if there is a population y of predator foxes, then you would expect the growth rate $\dot{x}$ of rabbits to be reduced. A simple assumption is that

- the growth rate $\dot{x}$ of rabbits decreases by a factor proportional to the number of encounters between rabbits and foxes, i.e. by a factor proportional to xy.

We revise our first model to include this extra term, so the differential equation that models the population x of rabbits is now

$$\dot{x} = kx - Axy,$$

for some positive constant A. As we shall see later, it is convenient to write $A = k/Y$, for some positive constant Y, giving

$$\dot{x} = kx\left(1 - \frac{y}{Y}\right). \qquad (1.7)$$

This is a non-linear equation, since the right-hand side contains an xy term.

This equation comes from the input–output principle, which was introduced in *Unit 2* Subsection 1.1. In a period of time δt, the change in the rabbit population is the number $kx\,\delta t$ of additional rabbits born, taking into account those dying from natural causes, less the number $Axy\,\delta t$ of rabbits eaten.

Similarly, for a population y of foxes in a rabbit-free environment, our first model for the population change is given by the equation $\dot{y} = -hy$, where h is a positive constant. This represents exponential decay. However, if there is a population x of rabbits for the foxes to eat, we should expect the growth rate $\dot{y}$ of foxes to increase. A simple assumption is that

- the growth rate $\dot{y}$ of foxes increases by a factor proportional to the number of encounters between foxes and rabbits, i.e. by a factor proportional to xy.

Our revised model for the foxes is given by

$$\dot{y} = -hy + Bxy$$

for some positive constant B. Again, it is convenient to write $B = h/X$, for some positive constant X, so that this equation becomes

$$\dot{y} = -hy\left(1 - \frac{x}{X}\right). \qquad (1.8)$$

Again, this equation is non-linear because of the xy term on the right-hand side.

Together, the differential equations (1.7) and (1.8) model the pair of interacting populations.

***Exercise 1.5**

Sketch the graph of the proportionate growth rate $\dot{x}/x$ of rabbits as a function of the population y of foxes, and the graph of the proportionate growth rate $\dot{y}/y$ of foxes as a function of the population x of rabbits. Interpret these graphs.

Lotka–Volterra equations

The evolution of two interacting populations x and y can be modelled by the **Lotka–Volterra equations**

$$\dot{x} = kx\left(1 - \frac{y}{Y}\right),$$
$$\dot{y} = -hy\left(1 - \frac{x}{X}\right) \quad (x \geq 0,\ y \geq 0), \qquad (1.9)$$

where x is the population of the prey and y is the population of the predators, and k, h, X and Y are positive constants.

This model was one of the first successful applications of mathematical models to biological systems. It was independently proposed in 1925 by the American biophysicist Alfred Lotka and in 1926 by the Italian mathematician Vito Volterra.

As in Equations (1.3), the condition $(x \geq 0, y \geq 0)$ applies to both differential equations.

The Lotka–Volterra equations can be written as

$$\dot{\mathbf{x}} = \mathbf{u}(x, y),$$

where $\dot{\mathbf{x}} = [\dot{x} \quad \dot{y}]^T$ and the vector field $\mathbf{u}(x, y)$ is given by

$$\mathbf{u}(x, y) = \begin{bmatrix} kx\left(1 - \frac{y}{Y}\right) \\ -hy\left(1 - \frac{x}{X}\right) \end{bmatrix}. \qquad (1.10)$$

Exercise 1.6

Suppose in Equations (1.9) that $k = 0.05$, $h = 0.1$, $X = 1000$ and $Y = 100$. Find the values of the corresponding vector field $\mathbf{u}(x, y)$ at the following points.

(a) $(0, 0)$ (b) $(0, 100)$ (c) $(500, 100)$ (d) $(1000, 0)$

(e) $(1000, 100)$ (f) $(1500, 100)$ (g) $(1000, 50)$ (h) $(1000, 150)$

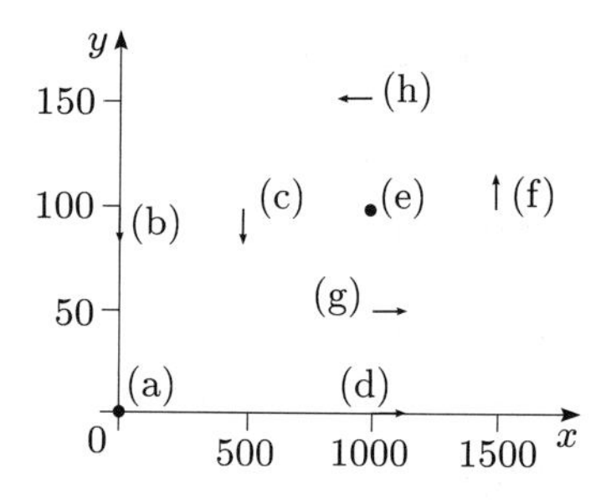

Figure 1.7

Previously, we were able to solve the pairs of differential equations that arose from our mathematical model, but, for Equations (1.9), no explicit formulae for $x(t)$ and $y(t)$ are available. However, using the given parameters and the values obtained in Exercise 1.6, we can begin to construct a vector field, as in Figure 1.7, where we have used arrows of fixed length. As we add more data to this figure, we shall be able to draw some phase paths, as in Figure 1.8. The path shown represents our guess at a solution to Equations (1.9) Although it may seem possible that the phase path forms a closed loop, this is far from certain.

In Figure 1.8 we have labelled a point A on the path, which can be taken as the initial value for a particular solution. Some other points have been marked to aid the following discussion. To interpret this guess at a solution, we think about what happens to the values of the populations as we follow the path.

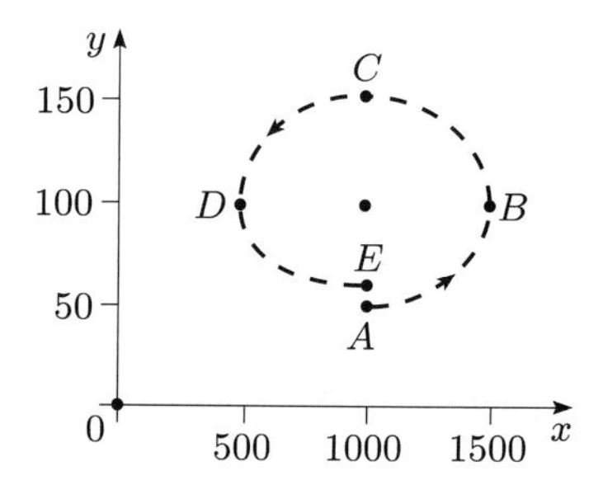

Figure 1.8

Initially, at the point A, there are 1000 rabbits and 50 foxes. As we follow the path, the rabbit population increases and so does the fox population until, at the point B, we have reached a maximum rabbit population. As the fox population continues to rise, the rabbit population goes into decline. At C the fox population has reached its maximum, while the rabbits decline further. After this point, there are not enough rabbits available to sustain the number of foxes, and the fox population also goes into decline. At D the declining fox population gives some relief to the rabbit population, which begins to pick up. Finally, at E, the decline of the fox population is halted as the rabbit population continues to increase. We may even return exactly to the point A, in which case the cycle will repeat indefinitely.

We have therefore modelled a system in which both the fox and rabbit populations repeatedly increase and decline, each in response to the other.

**Exercise 1.7*

Consider the system of differential equations defined in Exercise 1.6.

(a) For what values of x and y do the following hold?

(i) $\dot{x} = 0$ (ii) $\dot{x} > 0$ (iii) $\dot{x} < 0$

(b) For what values of x and y do the following hold?

(i) $\dot{y} = 0$ (ii) $\dot{y} > 0$ (iii) $\dot{y} < 0$

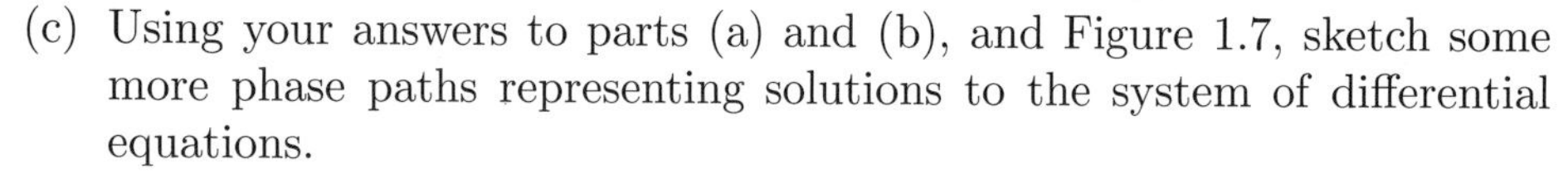

(c) Using your answers to parts (a) and (b), and Figure 1.7, sketch some more phase paths representing solutions to the system of differential equations.

Note that the differential equations are defined only in the quadrant $x \geq 0$, $y \geq 0$.

1.4 Equilibrium populations

Usually there is one and only one phase path through a point in the phase plane — this means that phase paths do not cross. One important exception to this is illustrated by the point $(0, 0)$ in Figure 1.6 and the point $(1000, 100)$ in Exercise 1.7. These points correspond to a constant solution $x(t) = C$, $y(t) = D$ of the system of differential equations, and are called the *equilibrium points* or *fixed points* of the system. These points generally represent important physical properties of the system being modelled. For example, the equilibrium point $(1000, 100)$ in Exercise 1.7 corresponds to the fact that a rabbit population of 1000 and a fox population of 100 can co-exist in equilibrium, not changing with time.

As you will see later, the point $(1000, 100)$ in Exercise 1.7 is an isolated point through which no phase path passes.

More generally, if $x(t) = C$, $y(t) = D$ is a constant solution of a system of differential equations, it follows that $\dot{x}(t) = 0$, $\dot{y}(t) = 0$, and we can use this property to find all the equilibrium points of the system.

> ***Definition***
>
> An **equilibrium point** of a system of differential equations
>
> $$\dot{\mathbf{x}} = \mathbf{u}(x, y)$$
>
> is a point (x_e, y_e) such that $x(t) = x_e$, $y(t) = y_e$ is a constant solution of the system of differential equations, i.e. (x_e, y_e) is a point at which $\dot{x}(t) = 0$ and $\dot{y}(t) = 0$.

> ***Procedure 1.1 Finding equilibrium points***
>
> To find the equilibrium points of the system of differential equations
>
> $$\dot{\mathbf{x}} = \mathbf{u}(x, y),$$
>
> for some vector field $\mathbf{u}$, solve the equation
>
> $$\mathbf{u}(x, y) = \mathbf{0}.$$

Solving $\mathbf{u}(x, y) = \mathbf{0}$ requires the solution of two simultaneous equations, generally non-linear, for the unknowns x and y. If the variables x and y represent populations, they must also satisfy the conditions $x \geq 0$ and $y \geq 0$.

Example 1.2

Find the equilibrium points for the Lotka–Volterra equations (1.9) for the rabbit and fox populations.

Solution

Using Procedure 1.1, we need to solve the equation $\mathbf{u}(x, y) = \mathbf{0}$, which becomes

$$\begin{bmatrix} kx\left(1 - \dfrac{y}{Y}\right) \\ -hy\left(1 - \dfrac{x}{X}\right) \end{bmatrix} = \begin{bmatrix} 0 \\ 0 \end{bmatrix}.$$

This gives the simultaneous equations

$$kx\left(1 - \frac{y}{Y}\right) = 0,$$
$$-hy\left(1 - \frac{x}{X}\right) = 0.$$

From the first equation, we deduce that either $x = 0$ or $y = Y$.

As stated earlier, h, k, X and Y are *positive* constants.

If $x = 0$, the second equation reduces to $-hy = 0$, so $y = 0$ and hence $(0, 0)$ is an equilibrium point.

If $y = Y$, the second equation becomes $-hY(1 - x/X) = 0$, so $x = X$ and hence (X, Y) is an equilibrium point.

Thus there are two possible equilibrium points for the pair of populations. The first has both the rabbit and fox populations zero, i.e. the equilibrium point is at $(0, 0)$; there are no births or deaths — nothing happens. However, the other equilibrium point occurs when there are X rabbits and Y foxes, i.e. the equilibrium point is at (X, Y), when the births and deaths exactly cancel out and both populations remain constant. ■

This explains our choice of constants X and Y in Subsection 1.3.

*Exercise 1.8

Suppose that the population x of a prey animal and the population y of a predator animal evolve according to the system of differential equations

$$\dot{x} = 0.1x - 0.005xy,$$
$$\dot{y} = -0.2y + 0.0004xy \quad (x \geq 0,\ y \geq 0).$$

Find the equilibrium points of the system. What does this tell you about the populations? Put these equations in the standard form of the Lotka–Volterra equations.

Exercise 1.9

Suppose that two interacting populations x and y evolve according to the system of differential equations

$$\dot{x} = x(20 - y),$$
$$\dot{y} = y(10 - y)(10 - x) \quad (x \geq 0,\ y \geq 0).$$

These are not Lotka–Volterra equations.

Find the equilibrium points of the system.

1.5 Stability of equilibrium points

In a real ecosystem it is unlikely that predator and prey populations are in perfect harmony. What if equilibrium is disturbed by a small deviation caused perhaps by a severe winter or hunting? If the number of rabbits is reduced, there would be a decreased food supply for the foxes, and the population of foxes could decrease to zero as a consequence. On the other hand, if the number of foxes is reduced, the birth rate for rabbits would then exceed their death rate, and the number of rabbits could increase without limit.

Our investigations in Exercise 1.7 suggest that these speculations are not correct.

If a small change or *perturbation* in the populations of rabbits and foxes from their equilibrium values, no matter what the cause, results in subsequent populations which remain close to their equilibrium values, we say that the equilibrium point is **stable**. On the other hand, if a perturbation results in a catastrophic change, with, for example, the population of foxes or rabbits collapsing to zero or increasing without limit, we say that the equilibrium point is **unstable**.

If you look at the phase diagram Figure 1.9, where the origin is a sink, you can see that any slight perturbation from the origin will result in a point that returns to the origin as time t increases. So the point $(0,0)$ is a *stable* equilibrium point. Similarly, the point $(1000, 100)$ in Exercise 1.7 (page 41) is a *stable* equilibrium point. In this case the perturbation from the equilibrium point does not result in a point which returns to the equilibrium point as t increases, but does result in a point which remains in the neighbourhood of the equilibrium point.

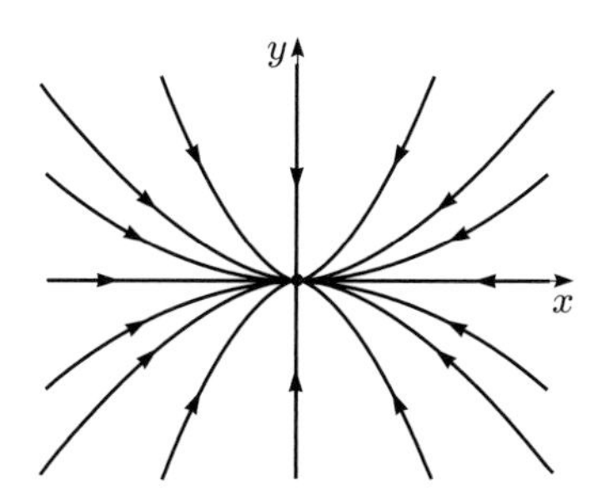

Figure 1.9

On the other hand, the origin in the phase diagram shown in Figure 1.5 (page 11) is an *unstable* equilibrium point. Any perturbation of the point (x, y) from the origin will result in the point travelling further and further away from the origin with time. Similarly, the origin in the phase diagram shown in Figure 1.6 (page 12) is an *unstable* equilibrium point. Apart from increases or decreases in y with x unchanged, any perturbation will result in a point which travels further and further away from the origin with time.

The stability of equilibrium points

Suppose that the system of differential equations

$$\dot{\mathbf{x}} = \mathbf{u}(x, y)$$

has an equilibrium point at $x = x_e$, $y = y_e$. The equilibrium point is said to be:

- **stable** when all points in the neighbourhood of the equilibrium point remain in the neighbourhood of the equilibrium point as time increases;
- **unstable** otherwise.

*Exercise 1.10

Classify the equilibrium points $(0,0)$ shown in the following phase diagrams as stable or unstable.

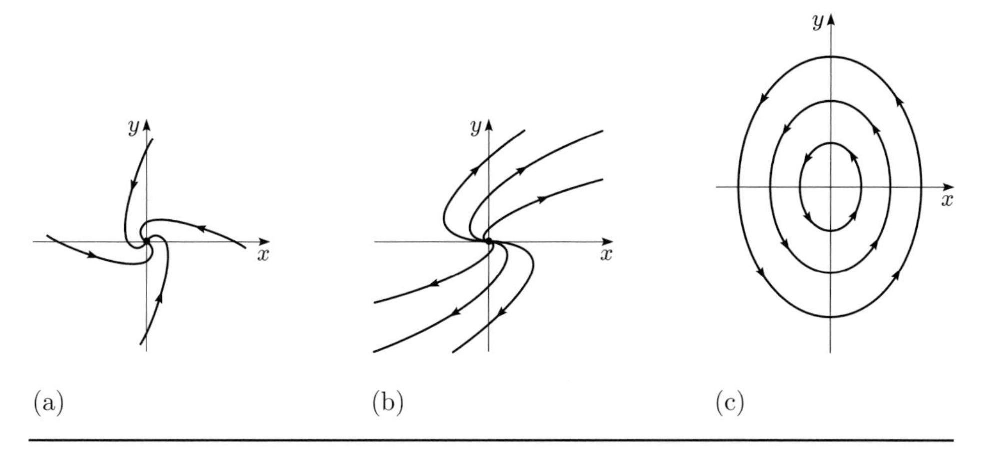

1.6 Populations close to equilibrium

The predator–prey model developed in Subsection 1.3 resulted in the Lotka–Volterra equations (1.9) which have equilibrium points at the origin $(0,0)$ and the point (X,Y). Our preliminary attempts at drawing a phase diagram, in Figure 1.8 and Exercise 1.7, indicate that the behaviour of the populations in the neighbourhood of the equilibrium point (X,Y) could be cyclical, but on the other hand could spiral outwards or inwards. To investigate the behaviour of a non-linear system in the neighbourhood of equilibrium points, we shall develop in this subsection *linear* approximations to the system which are applicable close to the equilibrium points.

If (x_e, y_e) is an equilibrium point, consider small perturbations p and q giving new populations x and y defined by

Although a population x or y cannot be negative, a perturbation p or q can (usually) be negative if the population is less than the equilibrium value.

$$x = x_e + p, \quad y = y_e + q. \tag{1.11}$$

We can find the time-development of the small perturbations p and q by linearizing the differential equation $\dot{\mathbf{x}} = \mathbf{u}(x,y)$. We shall make use of Taylor polynomials to achieve this.

In order to do so, we must write each component of the vector $\mathbf{u}(x,y)$ as a function of the two variables x and y:

$$\mathbf{u}(x,y) = \begin{bmatrix} u(x,y) \\ v(x,y) \end{bmatrix}.$$

At the equilibrium point (x_e, y_e), we have $\mathbf{u}(x_e, y_e) = \mathbf{0}$, i.e.

$$u(x_e, y_e) = 0 \quad \text{and} \quad v(x_e, y_e) = 0.$$

Now, for small perturbations p and q, we can use the linear Taylor polynomial for functions of two variables to approximate each of $u(x,y)$ and $v(x,y)$ near the equilibrium point (x_e, y_e):

Taylor polynomials were introduced in *Unit 12*.

$$\begin{aligned} u(x_e + p, y_e + q) &\simeq u(x_e, y_e) + p\frac{\partial u}{\partial x}(x_e, y_e) + q\frac{\partial u}{\partial y}(x_e, y_e) \\ &= p\frac{\partial u}{\partial x}(x_e, y_e) + q\frac{\partial u}{\partial y}(x_e, y_e), \end{aligned}$$

since $u(x_e, y_e) = 0$, and

$$\begin{aligned} v(x_e + p, y_e + q) &\simeq v(x_e, y_e) + p\frac{\partial v}{\partial x}(x_e, y_e) + q\frac{\partial v}{\partial y}(x_e, y_e) \\ &= p\frac{\partial v}{\partial x}(x_e, y_e) + q\frac{\partial v}{\partial y}(x_e, y_e), \end{aligned}$$

since $v(x_e, y_e) = 0$.

The above two equations appear rather unwieldy, but are much more succinctly represented in matrix form:

$$\begin{bmatrix} u(x,y) \\ v(x,y) \end{bmatrix} = \begin{bmatrix} \dfrac{\partial u}{\partial x}(x_e, y_e) & \dfrac{\partial u}{\partial y}(x_e, y_e) \\ \dfrac{\partial v}{\partial x}(x_e, y_e) & \dfrac{\partial v}{\partial y}(x_e, y_e) \end{bmatrix} \begin{bmatrix} p \\ q \end{bmatrix}.$$

Since $x(t) = x_e + p(t)$ and $y(t) = y_e + q(t)$, we also have

$$\dot{x} = \dot{p}, \quad \dot{y} = \dot{q}.$$

Putting the pieces together, substituting in $\dot{\mathbf{x}} = \mathbf{u}(x, y)$ gives a system of *linear* differential equations for the perturbations p and q:

$$\begin{bmatrix} \dot{p} \\ \dot{q} \end{bmatrix} = \begin{bmatrix} \dfrac{\partial u}{\partial x}(x_{\mathrm{e}}, y_{\mathrm{e}}) & \dfrac{\partial u}{\partial y}(x_{\mathrm{e}}, y_{\mathrm{e}}) \\ \dfrac{\partial v}{\partial x}(x_{\mathrm{e}}, y_{\mathrm{e}}) & \dfrac{\partial v}{\partial y}(x_{\mathrm{e}}, y_{\mathrm{e}}) \end{bmatrix} \begin{bmatrix} p \\ q \end{bmatrix}. \tag{1.12}$$

An example will help to make this clear.

Example 1.3

Transform the Lotka–Volterra equations (1.9) into a system of linear differential equations for the perturbations p and q from the equilibrium point (X, Y).

Solution

Here we have

$$u(x, y) = kx\left(1 - \frac{y}{Y}\right), \quad v(x, y) = -hy\left(1 - \frac{x}{X}\right).$$

First we compute the partial derivatives, obtaining

$$\frac{\partial u}{\partial x}(x, y) = k\left(1 - \frac{y}{Y}\right), \quad \frac{\partial u}{\partial y}(x, y) = -\frac{kx}{Y},$$
$$\frac{\partial v}{\partial x}(x, y) = \frac{hy}{X}, \quad \frac{\partial v}{\partial y}(x, y) = -h\left(1 - \frac{x}{X}\right).$$

Evaluating these at the point (X, Y) gives

$$\frac{\partial u}{\partial x}(X, Y) = 0, \quad \frac{\partial u}{\partial y}(X, Y) = -\frac{kX}{Y},$$
$$\frac{\partial v}{\partial x}(X, Y) = \frac{hY}{X}, \quad \frac{\partial v}{\partial y}(X, Y) = 0.$$

Thus the required system of linear differential equations is

$$\begin{bmatrix} \dot{p} \\ \dot{q} \end{bmatrix} = \begin{bmatrix} 0 & -kX/Y \\ hY/X & 0 \end{bmatrix} \begin{bmatrix} p \\ q \end{bmatrix}, \tag{1.13}$$

which can be written as the pair of equations

$$\dot{p} = -\frac{kX}{Y} q,$$
$$\dot{q} = \frac{hY}{X} p.$$

We have replaced a system of non-linear equations, for which we have no algebraic solution, with a pair of *linear* equations that we can solve. We should expect the solutions of Equation (1.13) to provide a good approximation to the original system only when p and q are small (i.e. when the system is close to equilibrium). ■

The matrix

$$\mathbf{J}(x, y) = \begin{bmatrix} \dfrac{\partial u}{\partial x}(x, y) & \dfrac{\partial u}{\partial y}(x, y) \\ \dfrac{\partial v}{\partial x}(x, y) & \dfrac{\partial v}{\partial y}(x, y) \end{bmatrix}$$

is called the **Jacobian matrix** of the vector field

$$\mathbf{u}(x, y) = [u(x, y) \quad v(x, y)]^T.$$

The 2×2 matrix on the right-hand side of Equation (1.12) is this Jacobian matrix evaluated at the equilibrium point (x_e, y_e), so Equation (1.12) can be written succinctly as

$$\dot{\mathbf{p}} = \mathbf{J}(x_e, y_e)\mathbf{p},$$

where $\mathbf{p} = [p \quad q]^T$ is the perturbation from the equilibrium point (x_e, y_e).

Procedure 1.2 Linearizing the system of differential equations $\dot{\mathbf{x}} = \mathbf{u}(\mathbf{x})$ near an equilibrium point

Suppose that the system of differential equations

$$\dot{\mathbf{x}} = \mathbf{u}(x, y) = \begin{bmatrix} u(x, y) \\ v(x, y) \end{bmatrix}$$

has an equilibrium point at $x = x_e$, $y = y_e$.

(a) Find the Jacobian matrix

$$\mathbf{J}(x, y) = \begin{bmatrix} \dfrac{\partial u}{\partial x}(x, y) & \dfrac{\partial u}{\partial y}(x, y) \\ \dfrac{\partial v}{\partial x}(x, y) & \dfrac{\partial v}{\partial y}(x, y) \end{bmatrix}.$$

(b) In the neighbourhood of the equilibrium point (x_e, y_e), the differential equations can be approximated by the linearized form

$$\begin{bmatrix} \dot{p} \\ \dot{q} \end{bmatrix} = \begin{bmatrix} \dfrac{\partial u}{\partial x}(x_e, y_e) & \dfrac{\partial u}{\partial y}(x_e, y_e) \\ \dfrac{\partial v}{\partial x}(x_e, y_e) & \dfrac{\partial v}{\partial y}(x_e, y_e) \end{bmatrix} \begin{bmatrix} p \\ q \end{bmatrix},$$

where $x(t) = x_e + p(t)$ and $y(t) = y_e + q(t)$.

This approximation does not hold if the matrix $\mathbf{J}(x_e, y_e)$ is non-invertible.

Exercise 1.11

Write down the linear approximations to the Lotka–Volterra equations (1.9) near the equilibrium point $(0, 0)$.

Exercise 1.12

Consider two populations modelled by the equations

See Exercise 1.9.

$$\dot{x} = x(20 - y),$$
$$\dot{y} = y(10 - y)(10 - x) \quad (x \geq 0,\ y \geq 0).$$

Find the linear approximations to these equations near the equilibrium point $(10, 20)$.

We have reduced the discussion of the behaviour of a system near an equilibrium point to an examination of the behaviour of a pair of linear differential equations. In the next section we shall use the techniques from *Unit 11* to solve these differential equations.

End-of-section Exercises

Exercise 1.13

Find the equilibrium point (x_e, y_e) of the system of differential equations

$$\dot{x} = 3x + 2y - 8,$$
$$\dot{y} = x + 4y - 6.$$

Find a system of linear differential equations satisfied by small perturbations p and q from the equilibrium point.

*Exercise 1.14

Suppose that the pair of populations x and y can be modelled by the system of differential equations

$$\dot{x} = 0.5x - 0.000\,05x^2,$$
$$\dot{y} = -0.1y + 0.0004xy - 0.01y^2 \quad (x \geq 0,\ y \geq 0).$$

(a) Find the three equilibrium points of the system.

(b) Find the Jacobian matrix of the system.

(c) For each of the three equilibrium points, find the linear differential equations which give the approximate behaviour of the system near the equilibrium point.

2 Classifying equilibrium points

In the previous section we have seen how a system of non-linear differential equations $\dot{\mathbf{x}} = \mathbf{u}(x, y)$ may be approximated near an equilibrium point by a linear system $\dot{\mathbf{p}} = \mathbf{A}\mathbf{p}$ by the use of the Jacobian matrix $\mathbf{A} = \mathbf{J}(x_e, y_e)$. In this section we develop an algebraic method of classification, based on the eigenvalues of the matrix of coefficients that arises from the linear approximations. The procedure for classifying an equilibrium point of a non-linear system will then be:

- near an equilibrium point, approximate the non-linear system by a linear system;
- find the eigenvalues of the matrix of coefficients for this linear approximation;
- classify the equilibrium point of the linear system using these eigenvalues;
- deduce the behaviour of the original system in the neighbourhood of the equilibrium point.

The linearized system of differential equations for the perturbation from the equilibrium point, which approximates the behaviour of the system in the neighbourhood of the equilibrium point, has the form

$$\dot{p} = ap + bq,$$
$$\dot{q} = cp + dq,$$

The perturbations p and q can usually take negative, as well as positive, values.

where a, b, c and d are constants. These equations can be written in matrix form as

$$\begin{bmatrix} \dot{p} \\ \dot{q} \end{bmatrix} = \begin{bmatrix} a & b \\ c & d \end{bmatrix} \begin{bmatrix} p \\ q \end{bmatrix}.$$

From *Unit 11*, we know that the general solutions of such equations are determined by the eigenvalues and eigenvectors of the matrix of coefficients. We shall illustrate various kinds of behaviour that can arise, by examining some examples. We begin by looking at matrices with two real distinct eigenvalues, then consider matrices with complex eigenvalues, and finally matrices with a repeated eigenvalue.

2.1 Matrices with two real distinct eigenvalues

Let us first consider the system of differential equations $\dot{\mathbf{p}} = \mathbf{A}\mathbf{p}$ where

$$\mathbf{A} = \begin{bmatrix} 2 & 0 \\ 0 & 3 \end{bmatrix}. \qquad (2.1)$$

This system is very similar to that considered in Example 1.1.

The matrix $\mathbf{A}$ is diagonal, so the eigenvalues are 2 and 3. The corresponding eigenvectors are $[1 \quad 0]^T$ and $[0 \quad 1]^T$, respectively. The general solution can be written as

$$\begin{bmatrix} p(t) \\ q(t) \end{bmatrix} = C \begin{bmatrix} 1 \\ 0 \end{bmatrix} e^{2t} + D \begin{bmatrix} 0 \\ 1 \end{bmatrix} e^{3t},$$

where C and D are constants, or as

$$p(t) = Ce^{2t}, \quad q(t) = De^{3t}.$$

We are interested in the behaviour of phase paths near the equilibrium point at $p = 0$, $q = 0$. Consider, for example, the paths with $D = 0$ (and $C \neq 0$). On these paths we have $p(t) = Ce^{2t}$ and $q(t) = 0$, so the point $(p(t), q(t))$ moves away from the origin along the p-axis as t increases.

On the other hand, consider the paths with $C = 0$ (and $D \neq 0$). On these paths we have $p(t) = 0$ and $q(t) = De^{3t}$, so the point $(p(t), q(t))$ moves away from the origin along the q-axis as t increases.

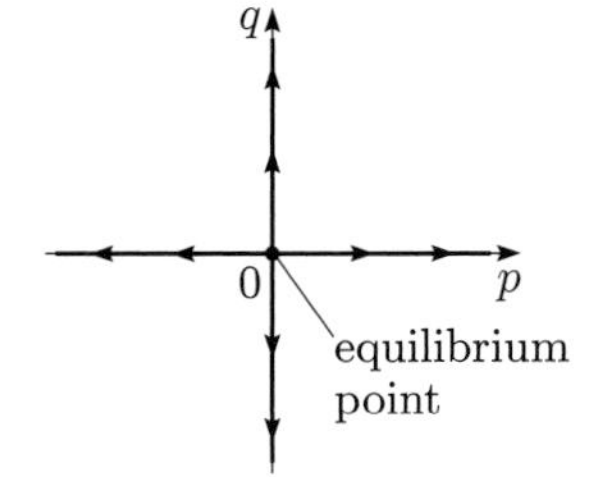

Figure 2.1

Hence we have seen that there are phase paths along the axes, corresponding to the eigenvectors $[1 \quad 0]^T$ and $[0 \quad 1]^T$. As t increases, a point on one of these axes moves away from the origin as shown in Figure 2.1.

For general values of C and D, where neither $C = 0$ nor $D = 0$, the point (Ce^{2t}, De^{3t}) still moves away from the origin as t increases, but not along a straight line. As t decreases, however, the exponential functions e^{2t} and e^{3t} decrease (and tend to zero as t tends to $-\infty$). So the point (Ce^{2t}, De^{3t}) approaches the origin as t decreases. As t increases, the point moves along a path which radiates outwards from the origin. This is illustrated in Figure 2.2, where we have incorporated the fact that the only straight-line paths are the two axes, which correspond to the eigenvectors of the matrix $\mathbf{A}$.

In this case, we can show that the paths are $q = K|p|^{3/2}$, as in Example 1.1, but in this section we are interested in the qualitative behaviour.

An equilibrium point with this type of qualitative behaviour in its neighbourhood is an (**unstable**) **source**. This occurs for any linear system $\dot{\mathbf{p}} = \mathbf{A}\mathbf{p}$ where the matrix of coefficients $\mathbf{A}$ has *positive distinct eigenvalues*. The only straight-line paths are in the directions of the eigenvectors of the matrix $\mathbf{A}$, although these will not, in general, be along the axes!

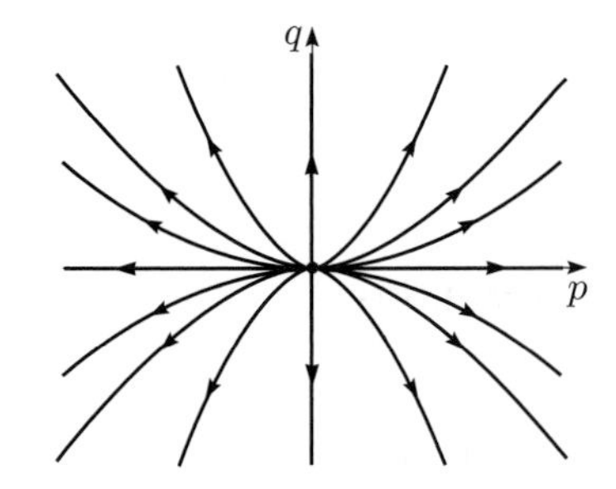

Figure 2.2 Unstable source

Exercise 2.1

Consider the linear system of differential equations

$$\begin{bmatrix} \dot{p} \\ \dot{q} \end{bmatrix} = \begin{bmatrix} 3 & 0 \\ 2 & 1 \end{bmatrix} \begin{bmatrix} p \\ q \end{bmatrix}.$$

(a) Find the eigenvalues of the matrix of coefficients.

(b) Classify the equilibrium point $p = 0$, $q = 0$ of the system.

Consider now the system of differential equations $\dot{\mathbf{p}} = \mathbf{A}\mathbf{p}$ where

$$\mathbf{A} = \begin{bmatrix} -2 & 0 \\ 0 & -3 \end{bmatrix}. \qquad (2.2)$$

The change in sign for matrix $\mathbf{A}$ from Equation (2.1) to Equation (2.2) changes the solution from one involving positive exponentials to one involving negative exponentials. You can think of this as replacing t by $-t$, so the solutions describe the same paths, but traversed in opposite directions. A change in the sign of both eigenvalues changes the direction of the arrows along the paths in Figure 2.2.

If the matrix of coefficients for a linear system has *negative distinct eigenvalues*, the equilibrium point is a (**stable**) **sink**. The only straight-line paths are along the directions of the eigenvectors of the matrix of coefficients.

Exercise 2.2

Consider the linear system of differential equations

$$\begin{bmatrix} \dot{p} \\ \dot{q} \end{bmatrix} = \begin{bmatrix} 0 & -1 \\ 2 & -3 \end{bmatrix} \begin{bmatrix} p \\ q \end{bmatrix}.$$

(a) Find the eigenvalues of the matrix of coefficients.

(b) Classify the equilibrium point $p = 0$, $q = 0$ of the system.

So far in this section we have considered the case where the matrix of coefficients has two distinct positive eigenvalues and the case where the matrix has two distinct negative eigenvalues. We now consider the case where the matrix has *one positive eigenvalue and one negative eigenvalue.* For example, consider the matrix

$$\mathbf{A} = \begin{bmatrix} 1 & 4 \\ 1 & -2 \end{bmatrix},$$

which has eigenvalues 2 and -3, and corresponding eigenvectors $[4 \quad 1]^T$ and $[1 \quad -1]^T$. The general solution of the linear system of differential equations $\dot{\mathbf{p}} = \mathbf{A}\mathbf{p}$ is

$$\begin{bmatrix} p \\ q \end{bmatrix} = C \begin{bmatrix} 4 \\ 1 \end{bmatrix} e^{2t} + D \begin{bmatrix} 1 \\ -1 \end{bmatrix} e^{-3t}. \qquad (2.3)$$

When $D = 0$ (and $C \neq 0$), we have $p(t) = 4Ce^{2t}$ and $q(t) = Ce^{2t}$, and the point $(p(t), q(t))$ moves away from the origin along the straight-line path $q = \frac{1}{4}p$ as t increases. On the other hand, when $C = 0$ (and $D \neq 0$), the solution is $p(t) = De^{-3t}$, $q(t) = -De^{-3t}$, so the point $(p(t), q(t))$ approaches the origin along the straight-line path $q = -p$ as t increases.

Hence we have seen that there are two straight-line paths. On the line $q = \frac{1}{4}p$ (which corresponds to the eigenvector $[4 \quad 1]^T$), the point moves away from the origin as t increases. However, on the line $q = -p$ (which corresponds to the eigenvector $[1 \quad -1]^T$), the point moves towards the origin as t increases. These two paths are shown in Figure 2.3.

Now we shall consider the behaviour of a general point $(p(t), q(t))$, where $p(t)$ and $q(t)$ are given by Equation (2.3), and neither C nor D is zero. For large positive values of t, the terms involving e^{2t} dominate, so $p(t) \simeq 4Ce^{2t}$ and $q(t) \simeq Ce^{2t}$. So, for large positive values of t, the general path approaches the line $q = \frac{1}{4}p$. On the other hand, for large negative values of t, the terms involving e^{-3t} dominate, so $p(t) \simeq De^{-3t}$ and $q(t) \simeq -De^{-3t}$. So, for large negative values of t, the general path approaches the line $q = -p$. Using this information we can complete Figure 2.3 to obtain Figure 2.4.

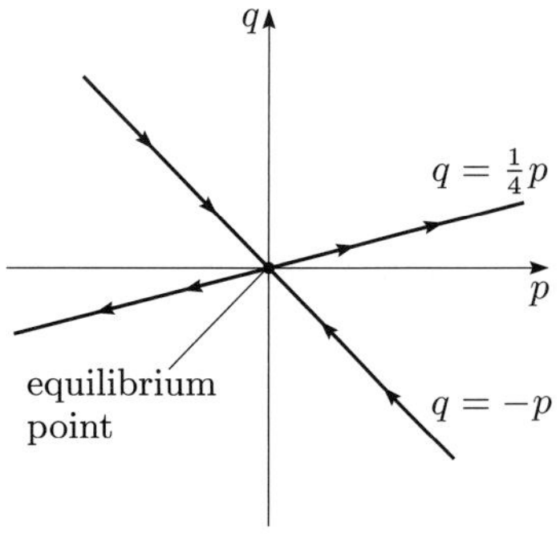

q
$q = \frac{1}{4}p$
p
equilibrium point
$q = -p$

Figure 2.3

We can see that the equilibrium point is an (**unstable**) **saddle**. The type of behaviour shown in Figure 2.4 occurs when the matrix of coefficients has *one positive eigenvalue and one negative eigenvalue.* Again, the two straight-line paths are in the directions of the eigenvectors of the matrix.

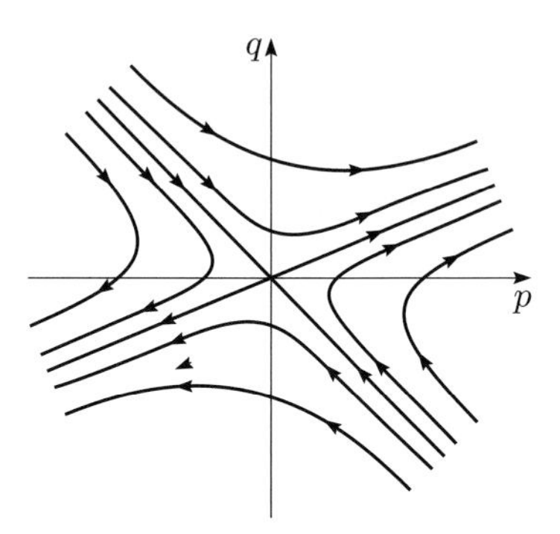

Figure 2.4 Unstable saddle

**Exercise 2.3*

Consider the linear system of differential equations

$$\begin{bmatrix} \dot{p} \\ \dot{q} \end{bmatrix} = \begin{bmatrix} 1 & 2 \\ 2 & -2 \end{bmatrix} \begin{bmatrix} p \\ q \end{bmatrix}.$$

(a) Find the eigenvalues and corresponding eigenvectors of the matrix of coefficients.

(b) Classify the equilibrium point $p = 0$, $q = 0$.

(c) Sketch the phase paths of the solutions of the differential equations.

2.2 Matrices with complex eigenvalues

In *Unit 10* you saw that some matrices have complex eigenvalues and eigenvectors. However, in *Unit 11* you saw that these complex quantities can be used to construct the *real* solutions of the corresponding system of linear differential equations. Our next example involves such a system.

Example 2.1

Consider the linear system of differential equations

$$\begin{bmatrix} \dot{p} \\ \dot{q} \end{bmatrix} = \begin{bmatrix} 0 & -1 \\ 4 & 0 \end{bmatrix} \begin{bmatrix} p \\ q \end{bmatrix}.$$

(a) Find the eigenvalues and corresponding eigenvectors of the matrix of coefficients.

(b) Hence write down the general solution of the system of differential equations.

(c) Show that the phase paths for these differential equations are the ellipses

$$p^2 + \tfrac{1}{4}q^2 = K,$$

where K is a positive constant.

Solution

(a) The matrix of coefficients has characteristic equation

$$\begin{vmatrix} -\lambda & -1 \\ 4 & -\lambda \end{vmatrix} = 0,$$

i.e. $\lambda^2 + 4 = 0$. So the eigenvalues are $\lambda = 2i$ and $\lambda = -2i$.

When $\lambda = 2i$, the eigenvector $[a \quad b]^T$ satisfies the equation

$$\begin{bmatrix} -2i & -1 \\ 4 & -2i \end{bmatrix} \begin{bmatrix} a \\ b \end{bmatrix} = \begin{bmatrix} 0 \\ 0 \end{bmatrix},$$

so an eigenvector corresponding to the eigenvalue $\lambda = 2i$ is $[1 \quad -2i]^T$.

Similarly, an eigenvector corresponding to the eigenvalue $\lambda = -2i$ is $[1 \quad 2i]^T$.

(b) Using the eigenvalues and corresponding eigenvectors from part (a), and Procedure 2.3 of *Unit 11*, the general solution of the differential equations is

$$\begin{bmatrix} p \\ q \end{bmatrix} = C \begin{bmatrix} \cos 2t \\ 2\sin 2t \end{bmatrix} + D \begin{bmatrix} \sin 2t \\ -2\cos 2t \end{bmatrix}.$$

(c) We have

$$p(t) = C\cos 2t + D\sin 2t,$$
$$q(t) = 2C\sin 2t - 2D\cos 2t,$$

so

$$\begin{aligned} p^2 + \tfrac{1}{4}q^2 &= (C\cos 2t + D\sin 2t)^2 + (C\sin 2t - D\cos 2t)^2 \\ &= (C^2\cos^2 2t + 2CD\cos 2t\sin 2t + D^2\sin^2 2t) \\ &\quad + (C^2\sin^2 2t - 2CD\cos 2t\sin 2t + D^2\cos^2 2t) \\ &= C^2(\cos^2 2t + \sin^2 2t) + D^2(\cos^2 2t + \sin^2 2t) \\ &= C^2 + D^2 = K, \end{aligned}$$

where $K = C^2 + D^2$.

So the phase paths are ellipses, as shown in Figure 2.5. The direction of the arrows indicated can be deduced from the original differential equations. For example, in the first quadrant $\dot{p} < 0$ and $\dot{q} > 0$. ∎

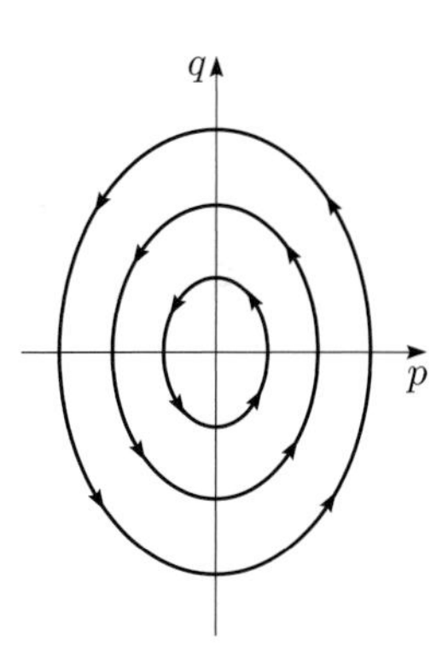

Figure 2.5 Stable centre

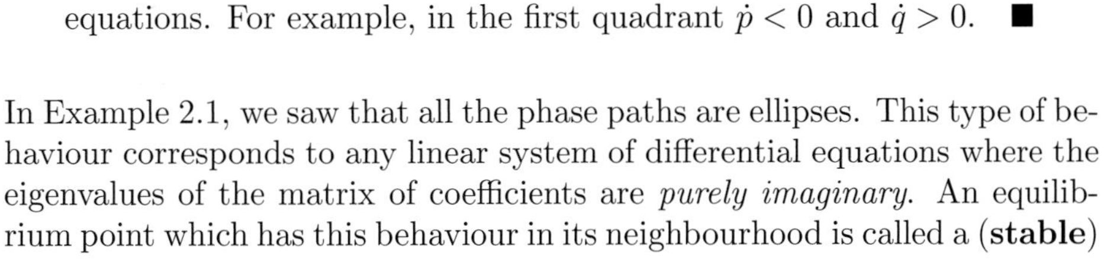

In Example 2.1, we saw that all the phase paths are ellipses. This type of behaviour corresponds to any linear system of differential equations where the eigenvalues of the matrix of coefficients are *purely imaginary*. An equilibrium point which has this behaviour in its neighbourhood is called a (**stable**) **centre**.

Exercise 2.4

Consider the linear system of differential equations

$$\begin{bmatrix} \dot{p} \\ \dot{q} \end{bmatrix} = \begin{bmatrix} 2 & -1 \\ 5 & -2 \end{bmatrix} \begin{bmatrix} p \\ q \end{bmatrix}.$$

(a) Find the eigenvalues of the matrix of coefficients.

(b) Classify the equilibrium point $p = 0$, $q = 0$.

In general, when the eigenvalues of a matrix are complex, they are not purely imaginary but also contain a real part. This has a significant effect on the solution of the corresponding system, as we shall see in the following example.

Example 2.2

Find the general solution of the system of equations $\dot{\mathbf{p}} = \mathbf{Ap}$, where $\mathbf{A} = \begin{bmatrix} -2 & -3 \\ 3 & -2 \end{bmatrix}$. Sketch some paths corresponding to the solutions of the system.

Solution

The characteristic equation of the matrix of coefficients is $(2+\lambda)^2 + 9 = 0$, so the eigenvalues are $-2+3i$ and $-2-3i$. Corresponding eigenvectors are $[1 \quad -i]^T$ and $[1 \quad i]^T$, respectively, so the general solution is given by

$$\begin{bmatrix} p \\ q \end{bmatrix} = Ce^{-2t}\begin{bmatrix} \cos 3t \\ \sin 3t \end{bmatrix} + De^{-2t}\begin{bmatrix} \sin 3t \\ -\cos 3t \end{bmatrix}.$$

If we neglect, for the time being, the e^{-2t} terms, the solution is

$$p = C\cos 3t + D\sin 3t,$$
$$q = C\sin 3t - D\cos 3t,$$

from which it follows that

$$p^2 + q^2 = C^2 + D^2.$$

So, in the absence of the e^{-2t} terms, the paths would be circles with centre at the origin. The effect of the e^{-2t} terms on these paths is to reduce the radius of the circles gradually. In other words, the paths spiral in towards the origin as t increases, as shown in Figure 2.6. ■

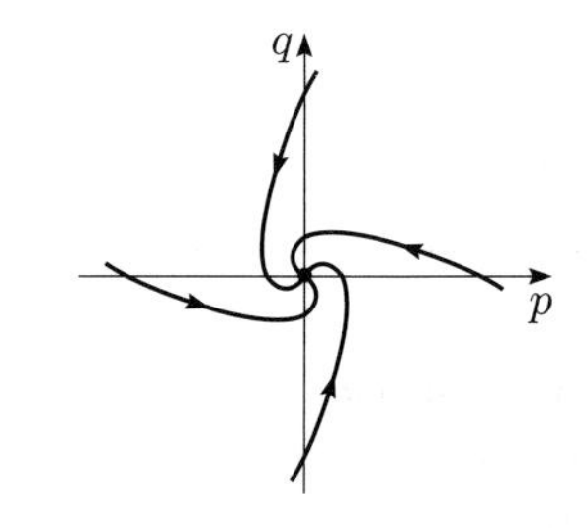

Figure 2.6 Stable spiral sink

In Example 2.2 the paths spiral in towards the origin, so the origin is a sink (which is called a **spiral sink**) and therefore is a *stable* equilibrium point. If the paths spiralled away from the origin, we should have a **spiral source** with the equilibrium point *unstable*. The stability is determined by the sign of the real part of the complex eigenvalues. To summarize, if the real part is positive, then the general solution involves e^{kt} terms (where k is positive) and the equilibrium point is an unstable spiral source; if the real part is negative, then the general solution involves e^{-kt} terms and the equilibrium point is a stable spiral sink.

*Exercise 2.5

Consider the linear system of differential equations

$$\begin{bmatrix} \dot{p} \\ \dot{q} \end{bmatrix} = \begin{bmatrix} 1 & 1 \\ -1 & 1 \end{bmatrix}\begin{bmatrix} p \\ q \end{bmatrix}.$$

(a) Find the eigenvalues of the matrix of coefficients.

(b) Classify the equilibrium point $p = 0$, $q = 0$.

2.3 Matrices with repeated eigenvalues

So far we have considered the cases where the matrix of coefficients for a linear system of differential equations has two real distinct eigenvalues or complex eigenvalues. In this subsection we consider a third possibility: the case where the matrix has a real repeated eigenvalue. In fact, there are two separate cases, depending on how many independent eigenvectors there are.

First, we consider the case where there are two linearly independent eigenvectors. In this case, the matrix must be diagonal and of the form

$$\mathbf{A} = \begin{bmatrix} \lambda & 0 \\ 0 & \lambda \end{bmatrix}$$

(see *Unit 10* Exercise 2.6(a)).

***Exercise 2.6**

Consider the linear system of differential equations

$$\begin{bmatrix} \dot{p} \\ \dot{q} \end{bmatrix} = \begin{bmatrix} 2 & 0 \\ 0 & 2 \end{bmatrix} \begin{bmatrix} p \\ q \end{bmatrix}.$$

(a) Find the general solution of the system of differential equations.

(b) By eliminating t, find the equations of the paths, and describe them.

(c) Is the equilibrium point $p = 0$, $q = 0$ stable or unstable?

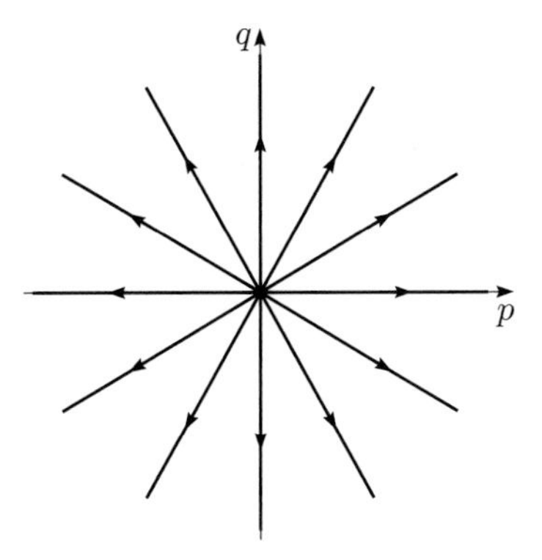

Figure 2.7 Unstable star source

In Exercise 2.6, we have seen that when the matrix of coefficients has two real *identical positive eigenvalues* and *two linearly independent eigenvectors*, all the paths are straight lines radiating away from the origin, as shown in Figure 2.7. The equilibrium point at $p = 0$, $q = 0$ is called an (**unstable**) **star source**. If the *two identical eigenvalues are negative* (but there are still *two independent eigenvectors*), the arrows on the paths in Figure 2.7 are reversed, and the equilibrium point at $p = 0$, $q = 0$ is called a (**stable**) **star sink**.

We turn finally to the case where there are two identical eigenvalues but only one independent eigenvector.

***Exercise 2.7**

(a) Find the eigenvalues and corresponding eigenvectors of the matrix

$$\mathbf{A} = \begin{bmatrix} 2 & 0 \\ 1 & 2 \end{bmatrix}.$$

(b) Find the general solution of the system of differential equations $\dot{\mathbf{p}} = \mathbf{Ap}$.

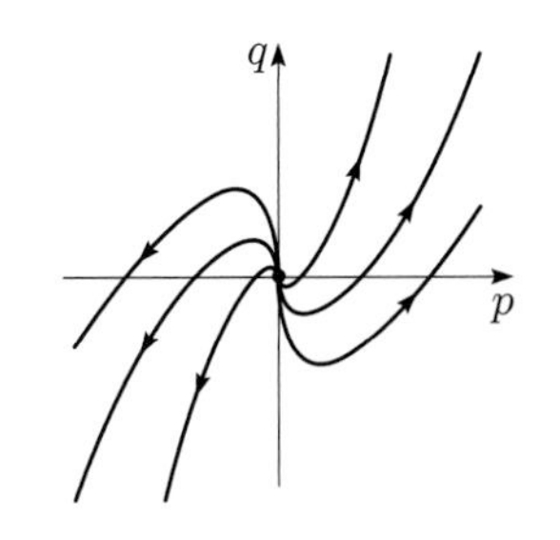

Figure 2.8 Unstable improper source

In Exercise 2.7 we have seen that the general solution of the system of linear differential equations

$$\begin{bmatrix} \dot{p} \\ \dot{q} \end{bmatrix} = \begin{bmatrix} 2 & 0 \\ 1 & 2 \end{bmatrix} \begin{bmatrix} p \\ q \end{bmatrix}$$

is

$$p(t) = Ce^{2t}, \quad q(t) = (Ct + D)e^{2t}.$$

Figure 2.8 shows some typical paths of this system, and we conclude that the equilibrium point at $p = 0$, $q = 0$ is unstable. It is called an (**unstable**) **improper source**. If the (repeated) eigenvalue is *negative*, then the phase paths are obtained by reversing the arrows in Figure 2.8 to obtain a (**stable**) **improper sink**.

This completes the discussion of our range of examples, which were chosen to illustrate most types of behaviour that one might meet.

2.4 Classifying the equilibrium point of a linear system of differential equations

In Procedure 2.1 we summarize the results of the previous three subsections.

Procedure 2.1 Classification of the equilibrium point of a linear system

Consider the linear system $\dot{\mathbf{p}} = \mathbf{A}\mathbf{p}$, for a 2×2 matrix $\mathbf{A}$. The nature of the equilibrium point at $p = 0$, $q = 0$ is determined by the eigenvalues and eigenvectors of $\mathbf{A}$.

If the eigenvalues are *real and distinct*, then:

- if both eigenvalues are positive, the equilibrium point is an *unstable source* (this type of behaviour is illustrated in Figure 2.2);
- if both eigenvalues are negative, the equilibrium point is a *stable sink* (this type of behaviour is illustrated in Figure 2.2 with the direction of the arrows reversed);
- if one of the eigenvalues is positive and the other is negative, the equilibrium point is an *unstable saddle* (this type of behaviour is illustrated in Figure 2.4).

If the eigenvalues are *real and equal*, and there are *two independent eigenvectors*, then:

- if the eigenvalues are positive, the equilibrium point is an *unstable star source* (this type of behaviour is illustrated in Figure 2.7);
- if the eigenvalues are negative, the equilibrium point is a *stable star sink* (this type of behaviour is illustrated in Figure 2.7 with the direction of the arrows reversed).

If the eigenvalues are *real and equal*, but there is only *one independent eigenvector*, then:

- if the eigenvalues are positive, the equilibrium point is an *unstable improper source* (this type of behaviour is illustrated in Figure 2.8);
- if the eigenvalues are negative, the equilibrium point is a *stable improper sink* (this type of behaviour is illustrated in Figure 2.8 with the direction of the arrows reversed).

If the eigenvalues are *complex*, then:

- if the eigenvalues are purely imaginary, the equilibrium point is a *stable centre* (this type of behaviour is illustrated in Figure 2.5);
- if the eigenvalues have a positive real component, the equilibrium point is an *unstable spiral source* (this type of behaviour is illustrated in Figure 2.6 with the direction of the arrows reversed);
- if the eigenvalues have a negative real component, the equilibrium point is a *stable spiral sink* (this type of behaviour is illustrated in Figure 2.6).

Procedure 2.1 is not exhaustive, and it does not include a number of special cases where one of the eigenvalues is zero.

Exercise 2.8

In Example 1.3 we saw that the Lotka–Volterra equations can be approximated by the system of linear differential equations

$$\begin{bmatrix} \dot{p} \\ \dot{q} \end{bmatrix} = \begin{bmatrix} 0 & -kX/Y \\ hY/X & 0 \end{bmatrix} \begin{bmatrix} p \\ q \end{bmatrix}$$

in the neighbourhood of the equilibrium point (X, Y). Find the eigenvalues of the matrix of coefficients, and hence classify the equilibrium point $p = 0$, $q = 0$.

Exercise 2.9

In Exercise 1.11 we saw that the Lotka–Volterra equations can be approximated by the system of linear differential equations

$$\begin{bmatrix} \dot{p} \\ \dot{q} \end{bmatrix} = \begin{bmatrix} k & 0 \\ 0 & -h \end{bmatrix} \begin{bmatrix} p \\ q \end{bmatrix}$$

in the neighbourhood of the equilibrium point $(0, 0)$. Find the eigenvalues of the matrix of coefficients, and hence classify the equilibrium point $p = 0$, $q = 0$.

2.5 Classifying the equilibrium points of non-linear systems

In Section 1 we saw how to find the equilibrium points of non-linear systems of differential equations $\dot{\mathbf{x}} = \mathbf{u}(\mathbf{x})$, and how to find the linear system $\dot{\mathbf{p}} = \mathbf{A}\mathbf{p}$ which approximates the system in the neighbourhood of the equilibrium point. In this section we have seen how to classify the equilibrium point of the linear system by finding the eigenvalues and eigenvectors of the matrix $\mathbf{A}$. But is the behaviour of the non-linear system near the equilibrium point the same as the behaviour of the linear system which approximates it? It can be shown that, not surprisingly, the answer is yes, *except* when the equilibrium point of the approximating linear system is a centre.

Near a centre, the paths are circular or elliptical. However, the paths of the original non-linear system may spiral towards or away from the equilibrium point. In such cases, we can say only that the paths are approximately circular or elliptical; we can say nothing about their actual behaviour without further examination. Thus, if the linear approximation has a centre, we cannot immediately deduce the nature of the equilibrium point of the original non-linear system: it may be a stable centre, a stable spiral sink or an unstable spiral source.

In the case of the Lotka–Volterra equations (1.9), in Exercise 2.9 we have seen that the linear system of differential equations which approximates the non-linear system in the neighbourhood of the equilibrium point $(0, 0)$ has an (*unstable*) *saddle* at the equilibrium point. So the (non-linear) Lotka–Volterra equations also have an (*unstable*) *saddle* at the equilibrium point $(0, 0)$, as you might expect from physical considerations.

On the other hand, we saw in Exercise 2.8 that the linear system of differential equations which approximates the Lotka–Volterra equations in the neighbourhood of the equilibrium point (X, Y) has a (*stable*) *centre* at the equilibrium point. This means that we cannot immediately say anything about the classification of this equilibrium point of the original (non-linear) system of differential equations — it could be a centre, a spiral source or a spiral sink. However, further investigation (which is beyond the scope of this course) shows that *every* phase path of the Lotka–Volterra equations is a closed path, with the exception of the equilibrium points and the coordinate axes. So the equilibrium point (X, Y) of the Lotka–Volterra equations *is* a (*stable*) *centre*, as shown in Figure 2.9.

These closed paths are not ellipses, however.

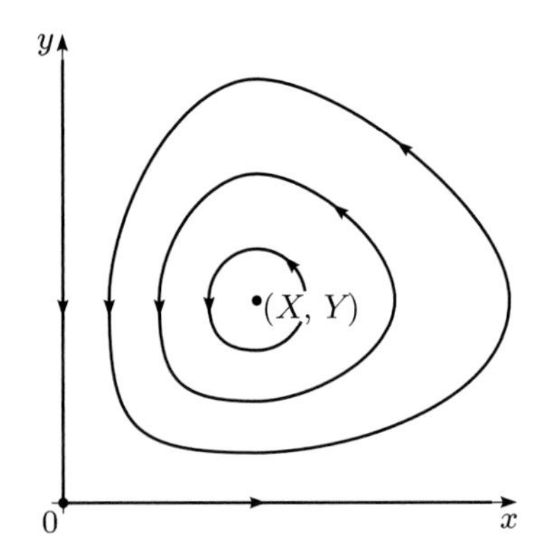

Figure 2.9 Phase diagram for the Lotka–Volterra equations

Procedure 2.2 Classification of an equilibrium point of a non-linear system

To classify the equilibrium points of the non-linear system of differential equations

$$\dot{\mathbf{x}} = \mathbf{u}(x, y),$$

do the following.

(a) Find the equilibrium points by using Procedure 1.1.

(b) Use Procedure 1.2 to find the linear system

$$\dot{\mathbf{p}} = \mathbf{A}\mathbf{p}$$

which approximates the original non-linear system in the neighbourhood of each equilibrium point.

(c) For each equilibrium point, use Procedure 2.1 to classify the linear system.

The behaviour of the original non-linear system near an equilibrium point is the same as that of the linear approximation, except when the linear system has a centre. If the linear system has a centre, the equilibrium point of the original non-linear system may be a stable centre, a stable spiral sink or an unstable spiral source.

Example 2.3

Consider the non-linear system of differential equations

$$\dot{x} = -4y + 2xy - 8,$$
$$\dot{y} = 4y^2 - x^2.$$

(a) Find the equilibrium points of the system.

(b) Compute the Jacobian matrix of the system.

(c) In the neighbourhood of each equilibrium point:

- linearize the system of differential equations;
- classify the equilibrium point of the linearized system.

(d) What can you say about the classification of the equilibrium points of the original (non-linear) system of differential equations?

Solution

(a) The equilibrium points are given by

$$-4y + 2xy - 8 = 0,$$
$$4y^2 - x^2 = 0.$$

The second equation gives

$$x = \pm 2y.$$

When $x = 2y$, substitution into the first equation gives

$$-4y + 4y^2 - 8 = 0,$$

or $y^2 - y - 2 = 0$, which factorizes to give

$$(y-2)(y+1) = 0.$$

Hence

$$y = 2 \quad \text{or} \quad y = -1.$$

When $y = 2$, $x = 2y = 4$. When $y = -1$, $x = 2y = -2$. So we have found two equilibrium points, namely $(4, 2)$ and $(-2, -1)$.

When $x = -2y$, substitution into the first equation gives

$$-4y - 4y^2 - 8 = 0,$$

or $y^2 + y + 2 = 0$. This quadratic equation has no real solutions, so there are no more equilibrium points.

(b) With the usual notation,

$$u(x, y) = -4y + 2xy - 8,$$
$$v(x, y) = 4y^2 - x^2.$$

So the Jacobian matrix is

$$\begin{bmatrix} \dfrac{\partial u}{\partial x} & \dfrac{\partial u}{\partial y} \\ \dfrac{\partial v}{\partial x} & \dfrac{\partial v}{\partial y} \end{bmatrix} = \begin{bmatrix} 2y & 2x - 4 \\ -2x & 8y \end{bmatrix}.$$

(c) At the equilibrium point $(4, 2)$, the Jacobian matrix is

$$\begin{bmatrix} 4 & 4 \\ -8 & 16 \end{bmatrix},$$

so the linearized system is

$$\begin{bmatrix} \dot{p} \\ \dot{q} \end{bmatrix} = \begin{bmatrix} 4 & 4 \\ -8 & 16 \end{bmatrix} \begin{bmatrix} p \\ q \end{bmatrix}.$$

The characteristic equation of the matrix of coefficients is

$$(4 - \lambda)(16 - \lambda) + 32 = 0,$$

or $\lambda^2 - 20\lambda + 96 = 0$, which factorizes to give

$$(\lambda - 8)(\lambda - 12) = 0,$$

so the eigenvalues are

$$\lambda = 8 \quad \text{and} \quad \lambda = 12.$$

The two eigenvalues are positive and distinct, so the equilibrium point $p = 0$, $q = 0$ is an *unstable source*.

At the equilibrium point $(-2, -1)$, the Jacobian matrix is

$$\begin{bmatrix} -2 & -8 \\ 4 & -8 \end{bmatrix},$$

so the linearized system is

$$\begin{bmatrix} \dot{p} \\ \dot{q} \end{bmatrix} = \begin{bmatrix} -2 & -8 \\ 4 & -8 \end{bmatrix} \begin{bmatrix} p \\ q \end{bmatrix}.$$

The characteristic equation of the matrix of coefficients is

$$(-2 - \lambda)(-8 - \lambda) + 32 = 0,$$

which simplifies to

$$\lambda^2 + 10\lambda + 48 = 0.$$

The roots of this quadratic equation are

$$\lambda = -5 \pm i\sqrt{23},$$

so the eigenvalues are complex with negative real part. Hence the equilibrium point $p = 0$, $q = 0$ is a *stable spiral sink*.

(d) As neither of the equilibrium points found in part (c) is a centre, the non-linear system has an equilibrium point $(4, 2)$ which is an unstable source, and an equilibrium point $(-2, -1)$ which is a stable spiral sink. ■

End-of-section Exercises

*Exercise 2.10

Find the eigenvalues and eigenvectors of the matrix $\mathbf{A} = \begin{bmatrix} 2 & -3 \\ 3 & 2 \end{bmatrix}$, and hence find the general solution of the system $\dot{\mathbf{p}} = \mathbf{A}\mathbf{p}$. Classify the equilibrium point $p = 0$, $q = 0$.

If this system is the linear approximation to a non-linear system $\dot{\mathbf{x}} = \mathbf{u}(x, y)$ in the neighbourhood of an equilibrium point, what can you say about this equilibrium point of the non-linear system?

***Exercise 2.11**

Consider the non-linear system of differential equations

$$\dot{x} = (1 + x - 2y)x,$$
$$\dot{y} = (x - 1)y.$$

(a) Find the equilibrium points of the system.

(b) Find the Jacobian matrix of the system.

(c) In the neighbourhood of each equilibrium point:

- find the linear system of differential equations which gives the approximate behaviour of the system near the equilibrium point;
- find the eigenvalues of the matrix of coefficients;
- use the eigenvalues to classify the equilibrium point of the linearized system.

(d) What can you say about the classification of the equilibrium points of the original non-linear system of differential equations?

3 Modelling a pendulum

In this section we discuss the motion of a pendulum which is oscillating, or revolving, in a plane. You may recall that we introduced a mathematical model of the pendulum in *Unit 8* that is satisfactory only for small oscillations. Here the oscillations may be large and the pendulum bob may revolve about the pivot.

3.1 Pendulum equations

We shall examine the motion of a pendulum consisting of a heavy bob, modelled as a particle of mass m (kg) attached to one end of a light rigid rod, modelled as a light model rod of length l (metres). The other end of the rod is pivoted at a fixed point O, as shown in Figure 3.1, with θ (radians) being the angular displacement from the downward vertical in an anticlockwise direction. In this model, the time t is measured in seconds.

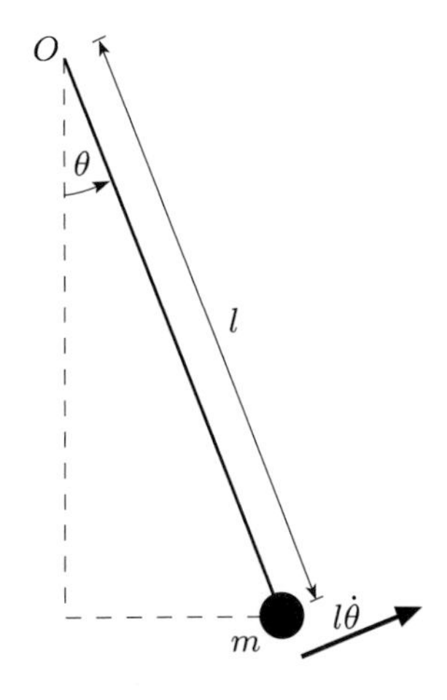

Figure 3.1

The bob is moving with speed $l\dot{\theta}$, so its kinetic energy is $\frac{1}{2}m(l\dot{\theta})^2$. The bob is a vertical distance $l\cos\theta$ below O, so, using the point O as datum, its potential energy is $-mgl\cos\theta$. Thus the total mechanical energy E of this system is

$$\begin{aligned} E &= \text{kinetic energy} + \text{potential energy} \\ &= \tfrac{1}{2}m(l\dot{\theta})^2 - mgl\cos\theta. \end{aligned} \tag{3.1}$$

Differentiating Equation (3.1) with respect to t, we obtain

$$\dot{E} = ml^2\dot{\theta}\,\ddot{\theta} + mgl\dot{\theta}\sin\theta. \tag{3.2}$$

If there are no friction forces (so no energy is transferred from the system), then E is constant, giving $\dot{E} = 0$, and we obtain the **undamped pendulum equation**

$$\ddot{\theta} = -\omega^2\sin\theta, \tag{3.3}$$

where $\omega^2 = g/l$. We can obtain the same result by using Newton's second law, by assuming that the only forces acting on the bob are its weight and the tension in the rod.

For small values of θ, the first-order Taylor approximation for $\sin\theta$ is $\sin\theta \simeq \theta$. Using this approximation in Equation (3.3), we obtain the **simple pendulum equation**

$$\ddot{\theta} = -\omega^2\theta. \tag{3.4}$$

This equation has the advantage that it is linear, but the disadvantage that it is a good approximation only for small oscillations.

There is another circumstance that we wish to investigate, namely the case when energy is being transferred from the system because of friction. We assume that $\dot{E}$ is proportional to $\dot{\theta}^2$, so the energy transfer is large when the pendulum is moving quickly. It simplifies the resulting equation if we assume that the constant of proportionality is of the form $-\varepsilon ml^2$, where ε is a positive constant. Now we may write

The negative sign is necessary because the mechanical energy of the system is decreasing as the pendulum moves.

$$\dot{E} = -\varepsilon ml^2\dot{\theta}^2,$$

and, when we substitute this expression for $\dot{E}$ into Equation (3.2), we obtain

$$-\varepsilon ml^2\dot{\theta}^2 = ml^2\dot{\theta}\ddot{\theta} + mgl\dot{\theta}\sin\theta,$$

which simplifies to become the **damped pendulum equation**

$$\ddot{\theta} = -\omega^2\sin\theta - \varepsilon\dot{\theta}, \tag{3.5}$$

where, again, $\omega^2 = g/l$. The same result can be obtained by using Newton's second law, by assuming that there is an additional force acting on the bob, namely linear damping which might be due to air resistance or other frictional effects.

3.2 The phase plane for a pendulum

Although the differential equations in the previous subsection (Equation (3.3), (3.4) and (3.5)) are of second order, we can rewrite each of them as a *pair* of first-order differential equations; this will enable us to use the techniques from earlier in the unit. More precisely, we shall replace θ by x and $\dot{\theta}$ by y, so that

$$y = \dot{x} = \dot{\theta}$$

and

$$\dot{y} = \ddot{x} = \ddot{\theta}.$$

So, for example, Equation (3.3) can be rewritten as the system of first-order differential equations

$$\begin{aligned} \dot{x} &= y, \\ \dot{y} &= -\omega^2\sin x. \end{aligned} \tag{3.6}$$

Equations (3.6) can be rewritten in terms of a vector field as $\dot{\mathbf{x}} = \mathbf{u}(x, y)$, where

$$\mathbf{u}(x, y) = [y \quad -\omega^2\sin x]^T.$$

*Exercise 3.1

Using the technique employed above, rewrite Equation (3.5) as a system of first-order differential equations.

So the two models introduced in Subsection 3.1 for the motion of a pendulum when the oscillations are not small give rise to two pairs of first-order differential equations.

The pendulum equations

(1) For large oscillations and no friction, we have

$$\dot{x} = y,\quad \dot{y} = -\omega^2 \sin x, \tag{3.6}$$

arising from the *undamped pendulum equation.*

(2) For large oscillations and a frictional force, we have

$$\dot{x} = y,\quad \dot{y} = -\omega^2 \sin x - \varepsilon y, \tag{3.7}$$

arising from the *damped pendulum equation.*

These are the equations you derived in Exercise 3.1.

The analogy with our previous discussion of two interacting populations should be immediately obvious, but here the variables x and y are even more closely related than before, since one is the derivative of the other. A path representing a solution of Equations (3.6) or (3.7) would tell us not only the position of the pendulum bob, but also its velocity.

For a pendulum, the variable $x = \theta$ represents an angle measured in radians, so the points $(x + 2\pi, y)$ and (x, y) represent the same state of the system. We could restrict the range of x to $-\pi < x \leq \pi$, although we could use any interval of length 2π, such as $0 \leq x < 2\pi$, for example.

Although we can solve the simple pendulum equation (3.4), we cannot find analytical solutions of the undamped and damped pendulum equations (3.3) and (3.5). However, we can use the techniques developed in Sections 1 and 2 of this unit to investigate the behaviour of the solutions of these equations.

Exercise 3.2

(a) Find the equilibrium points of the system described by Equations (3.6), i.e.

$$\dot{x} = y,\quad \dot{y} = -\omega^2 \sin x \quad (-\pi < x \leq \pi),$$

which is the system of differential equations arising from the undamped pendulum equation.

(b) Describe physically the two equilibrium points you found in part (a). Would you expect these equilibrium points to be stable or unstable?

Exercise 3.3

(a) Find the equilibrium points of the system described by Equations (3.7), i.e.

$$\dot{x} = y,$$
$$\dot{y} = -\omega^2 \sin x - \varepsilon y \quad (-\pi < x \leq \pi),$$

which is the system of differential equations arising from the damped pendulum equation.

(b) Describe physically the two equilibrium points you found in part (a), and indicate whether you expect these equilibrium points to be stable or unstable.

In Exercise 3.2, you showed that the undamped pendulum has two equilibrium points. The first equilibrium point is the origin $x = 0$, $y = 0$, which corresponds to the pendulum hanging vertically downwards at rest, and physically we expect this equilibrium point to be stable. The second equilibrium point is $x = \pi$, $y = 0$, which corresponds to a stationary pendulum pointing vertically upwards, which we would not expect to be stable! In the next exercise we shall confirm that this is indeed the case for the undamped pendulum.

*Exercise 3.4

Consider the non-linear system of differential equations

$$\dot{x} = y,$$
$$\dot{y} = -\omega^2 \sin x,$$

which is the system of differential equations arising from the undamped pendulum equation.

(a) Find the Jacobian matrix of the system.

(b) In the neighbourhood of each of the equilibrium points $(0, 0)$ and $(\pi, 0)$:

- find the linear system of differential equations which gives the approximate behaviour of the non-linear system near the equilibrium point;
- find the eigenvalues of the matrix of coefficients;
- use the eigenvalues to classify the equilibrium point of the linearized system.

In the previous exercise we have seen that the equilibrium point $x = 0$, $y = 0$, which corresponds to a stationary pendulum hanging vertically downwards, is a *stable centre*. So the paths in the neighbourhood of this point correspond to (small) oscillations of the pendulum. Our conclusion that this equilibrium point is a centre applies only to the linearized system, and may not be applicable to the non-linear system. However, we can show that the origin *is* a centre of the non-linear system — this follows from the conservation of mechanical energy.

The second equilibrium point, $x = \pi$, $y = 0$, corresponds to a stationary pendulum pointing vertically upwards. We have seen that this equilibrium point is an *unstable saddle*. This means that if we disturb the stationary pendulum slightly, the pendulum will move further away from the equilibrium point.

So far we have investigated the motion of the pendulum in the neighbourhood of the equilibrium points. But what about the motions which are not close to the equilibrium points? In order to investigate these, we need to use the *vector field*, which is shown in Figure 3.2 along with the associated phase paths. We can see that the pendulum has two distinct types of behaviour. First, there are paths like $ABCD$, which represent oscillations of the pendulum without it ever reaching the upwards vertical. Secondly, there are paths like $EFGH$, which represent the pendulum continuously circling the support in an anticlockwise direction, with the value of x increasing. The path $IJKL$ represents a similar motion, but in a clockwise direction.

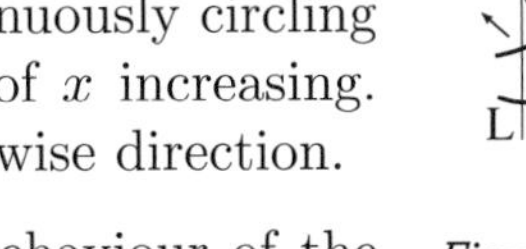

Figure 3.2

In the End-of-Section Exercises, we shall investigate the behaviour of the damped pendulum.

If you have time, now would be a suitable time to work through the optional multimedia package "Pendulums and phase planes".

End-of-section Exercises

Exercise 3.5

Consider the non-linear system of differential equations

$$\dot{x} = y,$$
$$\dot{y} = -\omega^2 \sin x - \varepsilon y,$$

arising from the damped pendulum equation.

(a) Find the Jacobian matrix of the system.

(b) In the neighbourhood of each of the equilibrium points $(0, 0)$ and $(\pi, 0)$:

- find the linear system of differential equations which gives the approximate behaviour of the system near the equilibrium point;
- find the eigenvalues of the matrix of coefficients;
- use the eigenvalues to classify the equilibrium point of the linearized system.

Note: For the equilibrium point $(0, 0)$, you will need to treat the cases $0 < \varepsilon < 2\omega$, $\varepsilon = 2\omega$ and $\varepsilon > 2\omega$ separately.

**Exercise 3.6*

Figure 3.3 shows the vector field for Equations (3.7), which arise from the damped pendulum equation for $0 < \varepsilon < 2\omega$. Describe the behaviour of the pendulum as it follows the path $ABCD$.

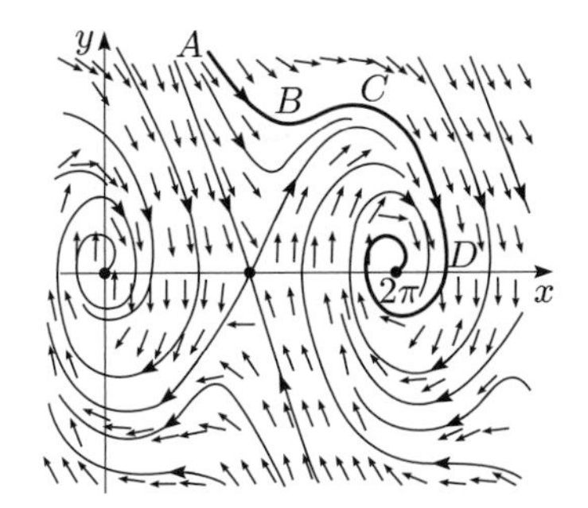

Figure 3.3

4 Computer activities

In this section you will carry out activities to show that the theoretical results based on linearization give a reasonable approximation to the solution close to the equilibrium points of a system modelled more accurately by non-linear differential equations.

Use your computer to complete the following activities.

PC

*Activity 4.1

Consider the two populations modelled by the equations

$$\frac{dx}{dt} = 0.5x - 0.000\,05x^2,$$

$$\frac{dy}{dt} = -0.1y + 0.0004xy - 0.01y^2 \quad (x \geq 0,\ y \geq 0).$$

The vector field for this pair of differential equations is given by

$$\mathbf{u}(x, y) = \begin{bmatrix} 0.5x - 0.000\,05x^2 \\ -0.1y + 0.0004xy - 0.01y^2 \end{bmatrix}.$$

(a) Construct the vector field plot for this equation over the ranges $0 \leq x \leq 20\,000$ and $0 \leq y \leq 600$, using 20 steps in each direction. Find all the equilibrium points in this region, and determine, as far as you can, the nature of each.

(b) To investigate further the nature of the equilibrium points, calculate and display numerical solutions for the initial conditions $(100, 500)$, $(15\,000, 100)$, $(0, 500)$ and $(15\,000, 0)$ over the time interval $0 \leq t \leq 20$.

(c) Interpret the behaviour of the two interacting populations.

*Activity 4.2

Consider the motion of a pendulum, modelled for large oscillations and *quadratic damping* by the second-order differential equation

$$\frac{d^2x}{dt^2} = -g \sin x - \frac{0.017D^2}{m} \frac{dx}{dt} \left| \frac{dx}{dt} \right|,$$

where $m = 1\,\mathrm{kg}$ is the mass of the pendulum bob, $D = 0.1\,\mathrm{m}$ is its diameter, and $g = 9.81\,\mathrm{m\,s^{-2}}$ is the acceleration due to gravity. The variable x is the angular displacement of the bob from the downward vertical in an anticlockwise direction. The vector field that gives rise to the phase plane for this differential equation is given by

$$\mathbf{u}(x, y) = \begin{bmatrix} y \\ -g \sin x - \dfrac{0.017D^2}{m} y\,|y| \end{bmatrix},$$

where $y = dx/dt$.

(a) Construct the phase plane for this equation, and confirm that there are equilibrium points at $(-2\pi, 0)$, $(-\pi, 0)$, $(0, 0)$, $(\pi, 0)$ and $(2\pi, 0)$. Determine the nature of each of these equilibrium points. Use the ranges $-2\pi \leq x \leq 2\pi$ and $-6 \leq y \leq 6$, with 20 steps in each direction.

(b) To investigate further the nature of the equilibrium points at $(-\pi, 0)$, $(0, 0)$ and $(\pi, 0)$, calculate and display numerical solutions for the initial conditions $(-\pi, 0.3)$, $(\pi, -0.3)$, $(1, 0)$ and $(3, 0)$ over the time interval $0 \leq t \leq 80$.

What can you deduce about the nature of these equilibrium points?

(c) Interpret the behaviour of the pendulum for the four given initial conditions. Compare this behaviour with that described in Exercise 3.6.

Outcomes

After studying this unit you should be able to:

- use a vector field to describe a pair of first-order non-linear differential equations, and use paths in the phase plane to represent the solutions;
- derive the Lotka–Volterra equations modelling the populations of predators and prey, and interpret their solution using paths in the phase plane;
- find the equilibrium points for a system of non-linear differential equations;
- find linear equations that approximate the behaviour of a system of non-linear differential equations near an equilibrium point, and determine whether this equilibrium point is stable or unstable by sketching paths near it;
- use the eigenvalues and eigenvectors of the matrix of coefficients that arises from the linear approximation near an equilibrium point to classify an equilibrium point as a source, a sink, a star source, a star sink, an improper source, an improper sink, a spiral source, a spiral sink, a saddle, or a centre;
- interpret points and paths in the phase plane;
- describe, using vector fields and paths in the plane, the qualitative behaviour of the undamped pendulum and the damped pendulum.

Solutions to the exercises

Section 1

1.1 The growth rate is proportional to the current population when every individual has an equal opportunity to survive and breed, and there are no external factors, such as a shortage of food, that might limit growth. This is generally true when the population is relatively small.

1.2 Assuming a constant proportionate growth rate means that no matter how large the population becomes, the proportionate birth rate exceeds the proportionate death rate by the same amount. The population goes on increasing in the same way. This can never be completely realistic for animals in the wild: for example, at some point the food supply that sustains the population must begin to be exhausted. The difference between the proportionate birth and death rates must then fall.

1.3 The solution of the differential equation $\dot{y} = -hy$ is $y = De^{-ht}$, where D represents the initial fox population, so the number of foxes is declining exponentially.

This equation represents a declining population of foxes, which is what we would expect as the foxes have no access to their assumed sole source of food, namely rabbits.

1.4 The system of differential equations is

$$\dot{x} = x,$$
$$\dot{y} = -y.$$

The general solution is

$$x(t) = Ce^t, \quad y(t) = De^{-t}.$$

Eliminating t gives

$$xy = A,$$

for some constant A. Some paths corresponding to these hyperbolae are shown in Figure 1.6.

There *is* a path through the origin. It is obtained by taking $C = D = 0$ and $x = y = 0$ for all t. The 'path' consists of just the point at the origin.

1.5 Rearranging Equation (1.7), we obtain

$$\frac{\dot{x}}{x} = k - \frac{k}{Y}y,$$

which is the equation of a straight line, as shown below.

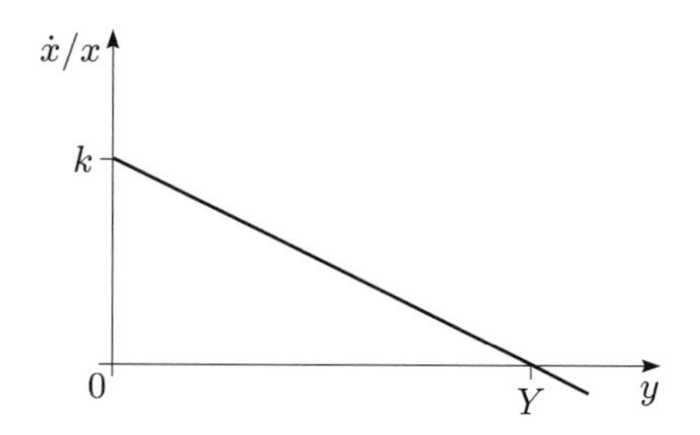

The proportionate growth rate $\dot{x}/x$ of rabbits decreases as the population y of foxes increases, becoming zero when $y = Y$. The population x of rabbits will increase if the population y of foxes is less than Y, but will decline if $y > Y$.

Similarly, we have the graph of $\dot{y}/y$ as a function of x.

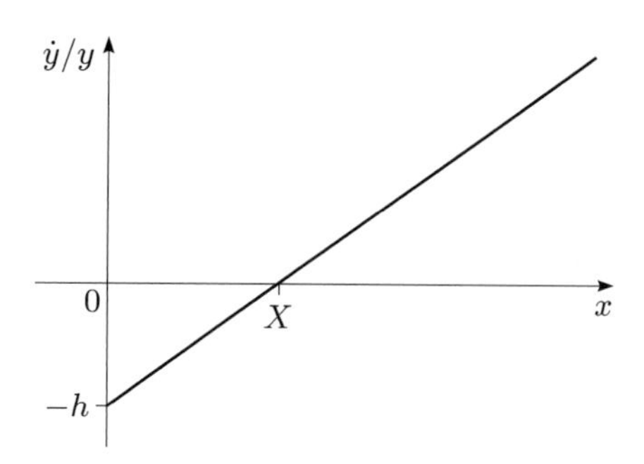

The proportionate growth rate $\dot{y}/y$ of foxes increases linearly as the population x of rabbits increases. The fox population y will decrease if the population x of rabbits is less than X, but it will increase if x is greater than X.

1.6 **(a)** $[0 \quad 0]^T$ **(b)** $[0 \quad -10]^T$ **(c)** $[0 \quad -5]^T$
(d) $[50 \quad 0]^T$ **(e)** $[0 \quad 0]^T$ **(f)** $[0 \quad 5]^T$
(g) $[25 \quad 0]^T$ **(h)** $[-25 \quad 0]^T$
Note that $\mathbf{u}(x, y) = \mathbf{0}$ for (a) and (e).

1.7 The differential equations under consideration are

$$\dot{x} = 0.05x\left(1 - \frac{y}{100}\right),$$
$$\dot{y} = 0.1y\left(1 - \frac{x}{1000}\right).$$

(a) **(i)** $\dot{x} = 0$ when $x = 0$ and when $y = 100$.

(ii) $\dot{x} > 0$ when $x > 0$, $0 \leq y < 100$.

(iii) $\dot{x} < 0$ when $x > 0$, $y > 100$.

(b) **(i)** $\dot{y} = 0$ when $y = 0$ and when $x = 1000$.

(ii) $\dot{y} > 0$ when $x > 1000$, $y > 0$.

(iii) $\dot{y} < 0$ when $0 \leq x < 1000$, $y > 0$.

(c) The information from parts (a) and (b) is summarized in the next diagram.

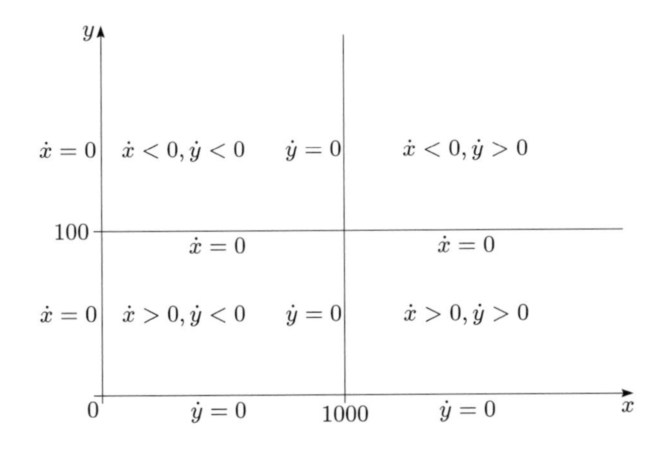

Using this information and Figure 1.7, typical paths representing solutions are shown below.

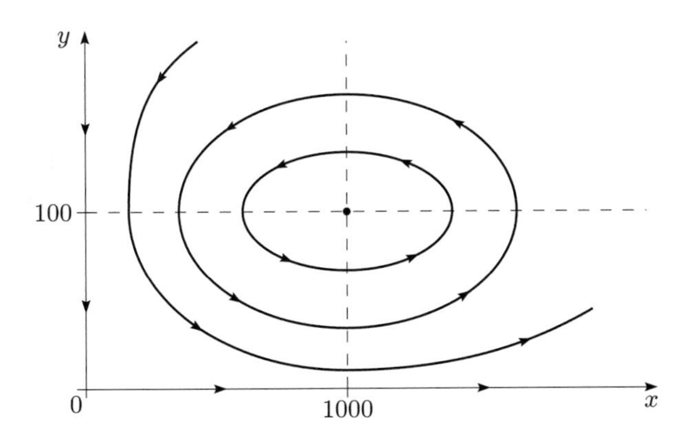

This shows a path down the positive y-axis, a path to the right along the positive x-axis, and various cycles about the point $(1000, 100)$. The path down the y-axis describes a population of foxes decreasing to zero in the absence of rabbits. The path to the right along the x-axis describes a population of rabbits increasing without limit in the absence of foxes. The cycles, which may not be closed (as shown in the diagram), indicate populations evolving as described in the paragraph preceding this exercise.

1.8 Using Procedure 1.1, we have to solve the pair of simultaneous equations

$$0.1x - 0.005xy = 0,$$
$$-0.2y + 0.0004xy = 0.$$

Factorizing these equations gives

$$0.1x(1 - 0.05y) = 0,$$
$$-0.2y(1 - 0.002x) = 0.$$

From the first equation, either $x = 0$ or $y = 20$.

If $x = 0$, the second equation gives $y = 0$, hence $(0, 0)$ is an equilibrium point. If $y = 20$, the second equation gives $x = 500$, so $(500, 20)$ is another equilibrium point.

Therefore the only equilibrium points are when there are no animals or when there is a balance between 500 prey and 20 predators. Using the values for this second equilibrium point, the equations can be put in the standard form

$$\dot{x} = 0.1x\left(1 - \frac{y}{20}\right),$$
$$\dot{y} = -0.2y\left(1 - \frac{x}{500}\right).$$

1.9 Procedure 1.1 leads to the pair of simultaneous equations

$$x(20 - y) = 0,$$
$$y(10 - y)(10 - x) = 0.$$

From the first equation, either $x = 0$ or $y = 20$.

If $x = 0$, the second equation gives $y = 0$ or $y = 10$. If $y = 20$, the second equation gives $x = 10$. Hence the equilibrium points are $(0, 0)$, $(0, 10)$ and $(10, 20)$.

1.10 **(a)** Stable **(b)** Unstable **(c)** Stable

1.11 We evaluate the various partial derivatives given in the solution to Example 1.3. At the equilibrium point $(0, 0)$, we obtain

$$\frac{\partial u}{\partial x}(0,0) = k, \quad \frac{\partial u}{\partial y}(0,0) = 0,$$
$$\frac{\partial v}{\partial x}(0,0) = 0, \quad \frac{\partial v}{\partial y}(0,0) = -h.$$

Thus the required linear approximation is

$$\begin{bmatrix} \dot{p} \\ \dot{q} \end{bmatrix} = \begin{bmatrix} k & 0 \\ 0 & -h \end{bmatrix} \begin{bmatrix} p \\ q \end{bmatrix},$$

giving the pair of equations

$$\dot{p} = kp,$$
$$\dot{q} = -hq.$$

(These are the equations studied in Subsection 1.2.)

1.12 Here we have

$$u(x, y) = x(20 - y), \quad v(x, y) = y(10 - y)(10 - x),$$

giving partial derivatives

$$\frac{\partial u}{\partial x}(x, y) = 20 - y,$$
$$\frac{\partial u}{\partial y}(x, y) = -x,$$
$$\frac{\partial v}{\partial x}(x, y) = -y(10 - y),$$
$$\frac{\partial v}{\partial y}(x, y) = 2(5 - y)(10 - x).$$

So the Jacobian matrix of the vector field $\mathbf{u}(x, y)$ is

$$\mathbf{J}(x, y) = \begin{bmatrix} 20 - y & -x \\ -y(10 - y) & 2(5 - y)(10 - x) \end{bmatrix}.$$

At the equilibrium point $(10, 20)$ we have

$$\mathbf{J}(10, 20) = \begin{bmatrix} 0 & -10 \\ 200 & 0 \end{bmatrix},$$

so the linear approximation is

$$\begin{bmatrix} \dot{p} \\ \dot{q} \end{bmatrix} = \begin{bmatrix} 0 & -10 \\ 200 & 0 \end{bmatrix} \begin{bmatrix} p \\ q \end{bmatrix},$$

giving the pair of equations

$$\dot{p} = -10q,$$
$$\dot{q} = 200p.$$

1.13 Solving the equations $3x + 2y - 8 = 0$ and $x + 4y - 6 = 0$, we obtain the equilibrium point $x_e = 2$, $y_e = 1$.

Putting $x = 2 + p$ and $y = 1 + q$, we obtain the matrix equation

$$\begin{bmatrix} \dot{p} \\ \dot{q} \end{bmatrix} = \begin{bmatrix} 3 & 2 \\ 1 & 4 \end{bmatrix} \begin{bmatrix} p \\ q \end{bmatrix}.$$

1.14 **(a)** To find the equilibrium points, we solve the simultaneous equations

$$0.5x - 0.000\,05x^2 = 0,$$
$$-0.1y + 0.0004xy - 0.01y^2 = 0.$$

Factorizing these equations gives

$$0.5x(1 - 0.0001x) = 0,$$
$$-0.1y(1 - 0.004x + 0.1y) = 0.$$

The first equation gives

$$x = 0 \quad \text{or} \quad x = 10\,000.$$

If $x = 0$, the second equation is

$$-0.1y(1 + 0.1y) = 0,$$

which gives $y = 0$ or $y = -10$. As $y \geq 0$, only the first solution is possible. This leads to the equilibrium point $(0, 0)$.

If $x = 10\,000$, the second equation is

$$-0.1y(-39 + 0.1y) = 0,$$

which gives $y = 0$ or $y = 390$. So we have found two more equilibrium points, namely $(10\,000, 0)$ and $(10\,000, 390)$.

(b) We have

$$u(x, y) = 0.5x - 0.000\,05x^2,$$
$$v(x, y) = -0.1y + 0.0004xy - 0.01y^2.$$

So the Jacobian matrix is

$$\mathbf{J}(x, y) = \begin{bmatrix} 0.5 - 0.0001x & 0 \\ 0.0004y & -0.1 + 0.0004x - 0.02y \end{bmatrix}.$$

(c) At the equilibrium point $(0, 0)$,

$$\mathbf{J}(0, 0) = \begin{bmatrix} 0.5 & 0 \\ 0 & -0.1 \end{bmatrix}$$

and the differential equations in the neighbourhood of this equilibrium point are approximated by

$$\begin{bmatrix} \dot{p} \\ \dot{q} \end{bmatrix} = \begin{bmatrix} 0.5 & 0 \\ 0 & -0.1 \end{bmatrix} \begin{bmatrix} p \\ q \end{bmatrix}.$$

At the equilibrium point $(10\,000, 0)$,

$$\mathbf{J}(10\,000, 0) = \begin{bmatrix} -0.5 & 0 \\ 0 & 3.9 \end{bmatrix},$$

and the linearized approximations to the differential equations near this equilibrium point are

$$\begin{bmatrix} \dot{p} \\ \dot{q} \end{bmatrix} = \begin{bmatrix} -0.5 & 0 \\ 0 & 3.9 \end{bmatrix} \begin{bmatrix} p \\ q \end{bmatrix}.$$

Finally, at the equilibrium point $(10\,000, 390)$,

$$\mathbf{J}(10\,000, 390) = \begin{bmatrix} -0.5 & 0 \\ 0.156 & -3.9 \end{bmatrix},$$

and the differential equations near the equilibrium point are

$$\begin{bmatrix} \dot{p} \\ \dot{q} \end{bmatrix} = \begin{bmatrix} -0.5 & 0 \\ 0.156 & -3.9 \end{bmatrix} \begin{bmatrix} p \\ q \end{bmatrix}.$$

Section 2

2.1 **(a)** The characteristic equation of the matrix of coefficients is

$$(3 - \lambda)(1 - \lambda) = 0,$$

so the eigenvalues are $\lambda = 1$ and $\lambda = 3$.

(b) As the eigenvalues are positive and distinct, the equilibrium point is an *unstable source.*

2.2 **(a)** The characteristic equation of the matrix of coefficients is

$$-\lambda(-3 - \lambda) + 2 = 0,$$

i.e. $\lambda^2 + 3\lambda + 2 = 0$, which factorizes to give

$$(\lambda + 1)(\lambda + 2) = 0,$$

so the eigenvalues are $\lambda = -1$ and $\lambda = -2$.

(b) As the eigenvalues are negative and distinct, the equilibrium point is a *stable sink.*

2.3 **(a)** The characteristic equation of the matrix of coefficients is

$$(1 - \lambda)(-2 - \lambda) - 4 = 0,$$

i.e. $\lambda^2 + \lambda - 6 = 0$, which factorizes to give

$$(\lambda - 2)(\lambda + 3) = 0,$$

so the eigenvalues are $\lambda = 2$ and $\lambda = -3$.

The eigenvectors $[a \quad b]^T$ corresponding to $\lambda = 2$ satisfy the equations

$$-a + 2b = 0,$$
$$2a - 4b = 0.$$

So an eigenvector corresponding to the positive eigenvalue $\lambda = 2$ is $[2 \quad 1]^T$, and all the eigenvectors are along the line $q = \frac{1}{2}p$.

The eigenvectors $[a \quad b]^T$ corresponding to $\lambda = -3$ satisfy the equations

$$4a + 2b = 0,$$
$$2a + b = 0.$$

So an eigenvector corresponding to the negative eigenvalue is $[1 \quad -2]^T$, and all the eigenvectors are along the line $q = -2p$.

(b) The matrix of coefficients has a positive and a negative eigenvalue, so the equilibrium point is an *unstable saddle.*

(c) There are two straight-line paths, namely $q = \frac{1}{2}p$ and $q = -2p$. On the line $q = \frac{1}{2}p$, the point $(p(t), q(t))$ moves away from the origin as t increases, because the corresponding eigenvalue is *positive*. On the line $q = -2p$, the point approaches the origin as t increases, because the corresponding eigenvalue is *negative*. This information, together with the knowledge that the equilibrium point is a saddle, allows us to sketch the phase diagram (see below).

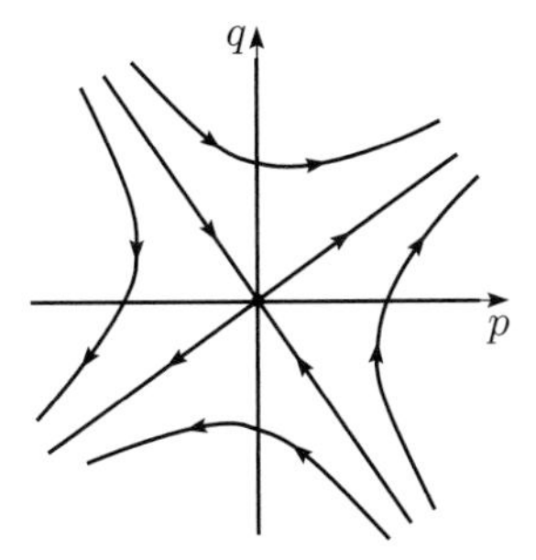

2.4 **(a)** The characteristic equation of the matrix of coefficients is

$$(2-\lambda)(-2-\lambda)+5=0,$$

i.e. $\lambda^2+1=0$, so the eigenvalues are $\lambda = i$ and $\lambda = -i$.

(b) As the eigenvalues are imaginary, the equilibrium point is a *stable centre*.

2.5 **(a)** The characteristic equation of the matrix of coefficients is

$$(1-\lambda)^2+1=0,$$

i.e. $\lambda^2-2\lambda+2=0$, which has complex roots $\lambda = 1+i$ and $\lambda = 1-i$.

(b) As the eigenvalues are complex with positive real part, the equilibrium point is an *unstable spiral source*.

2.6 **(a)** The differential equations are

$$\dot{p} = 2p,$$
$$\dot{q} = 2q,$$

which have general solution

$$p(t) = Ce^{2t}, \quad q(t) = De^{2t},$$

where C and D are arbitrary constants.

(b) Eliminating t from the general solution, the equations of the paths are

$$q = \frac{D}{C}p = Kp,$$

where $K = D/C$ is also an arbitrary constant. So the paths are all straight lines passing through the origin.

The above analysis has neglected the possibility $C = 0$. In this case the path is $p = 0$, which is also a straight line passing through the origin, namely the q-axis.

(c) Both $p(t)$ and $q(t)$ are increasing functions of time, so the point $(p(t), q(t))$ moves away from the origin as t increases. So the equilibrium point is *unstable*.

2.7 **(a)** The characteristic equation is

$$(2-\lambda)^2=0,$$

so the matrix has the *repeated* eigenvalue $\lambda = 2$.

The eigenvectors $[a \quad b]^T$ corresponding to this repeated eigenvalue satisfy the equations

$$0 = 0,$$
$$a = 0,$$

so all the eigenvectors take the form $[0 \quad k]^T$, where k is a (non-zero) constant. There is only one independent eigenvector, an obvious choice being $\mathbf{v} = [0 \quad 1]^T$.

(b) Using the solution to part (a) and Procedure 2.2 of *Unit 11*, we need to find the vector $\mathbf{b} = [c \quad d]^T$ which satisfies the equation

$$\begin{bmatrix} 0 & 0 \\ 1 & 0 \end{bmatrix}\begin{bmatrix} c \\ d \end{bmatrix} = \begin{bmatrix} 0 \\ 1 \end{bmatrix},$$

i.e. $0 = 0$, $c = 1$.

So $\mathbf{b} = [1 \quad 0]^T$, and the general solution of the system of differential equations is

$$\begin{bmatrix} p \\ q \end{bmatrix} = C\left(\begin{bmatrix} 0 \\ 1 \end{bmatrix}t + \begin{bmatrix} 1 \\ 0 \end{bmatrix}\right)e^{2t} + D\begin{bmatrix} 0 \\ 1 \end{bmatrix}e^{2t},$$

i.e.

$$p(t) = Ce^{2t}, \quad q(t) = Cte^{2t} + De^{2t}.$$

2.8 The characteristic equation of the matrix of coefficients is

$$\lambda^2 + hk = 0.$$

The eigenvalues are $\lambda = \pm i\sqrt{hk}$, so the equilibrium point is a *stable centre*.

2.9 The eigenvalues of the matrix of coefficients are $\lambda = k$ and $\lambda = -h$. So the equilibrium point is an *unstable saddle*. (In fact, in this case we have to restrict p and q to non-negative values, but this does not affect our conclusion.)

2.10 **(a)** The characteristic equation is

$$\lambda^2 - 4\lambda + 13 = 0,$$

so the eigenvalues are $2+3i$ and $2-3i$, corresponding to the eigenvectors $[1 \quad -i]^T$ and $[1 \quad i]^T$, respectively. The general solution is

$$\begin{bmatrix} p \\ q \end{bmatrix} = C\begin{bmatrix} \cos 3t \\ \sin 3t \end{bmatrix}e^{2t} + D\begin{bmatrix} \sin 3t \\ -\cos 3t \end{bmatrix}e^{2t}.$$

As the eigenvalues are complex with a positive real component, the equilibrium point $p = 0$, $q = 0$ is an *unstable spiral source*. The paths are similar to those of Figure 2.6, but with the arrows pointing away from the origin.

As the equilibrium point of the linear approximation is not a centre, the corresponding equilibrium point of the non-linear system is also an unstable spiral source.

2.11 **(a)** The equilibrium points are given by

$$(1 + x - 2y)x = 0,$$
$$(x - 1)y = 0.$$

The second equation gives

$$x = 1 \quad \text{or} \quad y = 0.$$

When $x = 1$, substituting into the first equation gives

$$2 - 2y = 0,$$

which leads to $y = 1$. So $(1, 1)$ is an equilibrium point.

When $y = 0$, substituting into the first equation gives

$$(1 + x)x = 0,$$

hence $x = 0$ or $x = -1$. So we have found two further equilibrium points, namely $(0, 0)$ and $(-1, 0)$.

(b) With the usual notation,

$$u(x, y) = (1 + x - 2y)x = x + x^2 - 2xy,$$
$$v(x, y) = (x - 1)y = xy - y.$$

So the Jacobian matrix is

$$\begin{bmatrix} \frac{\partial u}{\partial x} & \frac{\partial u}{\partial y} \\ \frac{\partial v}{\partial x} & \frac{\partial v}{\partial y} \end{bmatrix} = \begin{bmatrix} 1 + 2x - 2y & -2x \\ y & x - 1 \end{bmatrix}.$$

(c) At the point $(0, 0)$, the Jacobian matrix is

$$\begin{bmatrix} 1 & 0 \\ 0 & -1 \end{bmatrix},$$

so the linearized system is

$$\begin{bmatrix} \dot{p} \\ \dot{q} \end{bmatrix} = \begin{bmatrix} 1 & 0 \\ 0 & -1 \end{bmatrix} \begin{bmatrix} p \\ q \end{bmatrix}.$$

The eigenvalues of the matrix of coefficients are $\lambda = 1$ and $\lambda = -1$. As one of the eigenvalues is positive and the other is negative, the equilibrium point of the linearized system is an *unstable saddle*.

At the point $(-1, 0)$, the Jacobian matrix is

$$\begin{bmatrix} -1 & 2 \\ 0 & -2 \end{bmatrix},$$

so the linearized system is

$$\begin{bmatrix} \dot{p} \\ \dot{q} \end{bmatrix} = \begin{bmatrix} -1 & 2 \\ 0 & -2 \end{bmatrix} \begin{bmatrix} p \\ q \end{bmatrix}.$$

The eigenvalues of the matrix of coefficients are $\lambda = -1$ and $\lambda = -2$. As the eigenvalues are negative and distinct, the equilibrium point of the linearized system is a *stable sink*.

At the point $(1, 1)$, the Jacobian matrix is

$$\begin{bmatrix} 1 & -2 \\ 1 & 0 \end{bmatrix},$$

so the linearized system is

$$\begin{bmatrix} \dot{p} \\ \dot{q} \end{bmatrix} = \begin{bmatrix} 1 & -2 \\ 1 & 0 \end{bmatrix} \begin{bmatrix} p \\ q \end{bmatrix}.$$

The characteristic equation of the matrix of coefficients is

$$\lambda^2 - \lambda + 2 = 0.$$

The roots of this quadratic equation are

$$\lambda = \tfrac{1}{2}(1 \pm i\sqrt{7}),$$

so the eigenvalues are complex with a positive real component. Hence the equilibrium point of the linearized system is an *unstable spiral source.*

(d) As none of the equilibrium points of the linearized systems found in part (c) are centres, the behaviour of the original non-linear system near the equilibrium points is the same as that of the linear approximations. In other words,

$(0, 0)$ is an *unstable saddle*,
$(-1, 0)$ is a *stable sink*,
$(1, 1)$ is an *unstable spiral source.*

Section 3

3.1 If we replace θ by x and let $y = \dot{x} = \dot{\theta}$, we have

$$\dot{y} = \ddot{x} = \ddot{\theta} = -\omega^2 \sin\theta - \varepsilon\dot{\theta}$$
$$= -\omega^2 \sin x - \varepsilon y.$$

So the system of first-order differential equations which is equivalent to Equation (3.5) is

$$\dot{x} = y,$$
$$\dot{y} = -\omega^2 \sin x - \varepsilon y.$$

The associated vector field is

$$\mathbf{u}(x, y) = [y \quad -\omega^2 \sin x - \varepsilon y]^T.$$

3.2 **(a)** To find the equilibrium points, we use Procedure 1.1 and put $\mathbf{u}(x, y) = \mathbf{0}$:

$$y = 0,$$
$$-\omega^2 \sin x = 0.$$

So there are two equilibrium points in the range $-\pi < x \leq \pi$, namely $(0, 0)$ and $(\pi, 0)$.

(b) The equilibrium point $(0, 0)$ corresponds to $\theta = 0$, $\dot{\theta} = 0$. Physically, this corresponds to a stationary pendulum hanging vertically downwards. A small disturbance from this equilibrium point will result in small oscillations about the downwards vertical. So we would expect this equilibrium point to be *stable.*

The equilibrium point $(\pi, 0)$ corresponds to $\theta = \pi$, $\dot{\theta} = 0$, which is a pendulum pointing vertically upwards at rest. (Not easy to achieve in practice!) A small disturbance from this equilibrium point will result in the pendulum moving away from the upwards vertical and speeding up until it is vertically downwards. It will move through its lowest position and continue to move in the same direction. It will then slow down and head towards the highest point again. So we would expect this equilibrium point to be *unstable.*

3.3 **(a)** As in Solution 3.2, to find the equilibrium points we need to find the solutions of

$$y = 0,$$
$$-\omega^2 x - \varepsilon y = 0.$$

Substituting $y = 0$ from the first equation into the second equation leads to $x = 0$ or $x = \pi$. So there are two equilibrium points in the range $-\pi < x \leq \pi$, namely $(0, 0)$ and $(\pi, 0)$.

(b) Using reasoning similar to that used in Solution 3.2(b), the equilibrium point $(0, 0)$ corresponds to a pendulum hanging vertically downwards at rest. We expect this equilibrium point to be stable. The equilibrium point $(\pi, 0)$ corresponds to a stationary pendulum pointing vertically upwards. We expect this equilibrium point to be unstable.

3.4 **(a)** Using the usual notation,

$$u(x, y) = y,$$
$$v(x, y) = -\omega^2 \sin x.$$

So the Jacobian matrix is

$$\mathbf{J} = \begin{bmatrix} \dfrac{\partial u}{\partial x} & \dfrac{\partial u}{\partial y} \\ \dfrac{\partial v}{\partial x} & \dfrac{\partial v}{\partial y} \end{bmatrix} = \begin{bmatrix} 0 & 1 \\ -\omega^2 \cos x & 0 \end{bmatrix}.$$

(b) Using Procedure 2.2, in the neighbourhood of the equilibrium point $(0, 0)$, the linear system of differential equations which approximates the non-linear system is

$$\begin{bmatrix} \dot{p} \\ \dot{q} \end{bmatrix} = \begin{bmatrix} 0 & 1 \\ -\omega^2 & 0 \end{bmatrix} \begin{bmatrix} p \\ q \end{bmatrix}.$$

The characteristic equation of the matrix of coefficients is

$$\lambda^2 + \omega^2 = 0,$$

so the eigenvalues are $\lambda = \pm i\omega$.

Hence the equilibrium point $(0, 0)$ is a *stable centre.*

The approximating linear system of differential equations in the neighbourhood of the equilibrium point $(\pi, 0)$ is

$$\begin{bmatrix} \dot{p} \\ \dot{q} \end{bmatrix} = \begin{bmatrix} 0 & 1 \\ \omega^2 & 0 \end{bmatrix} \begin{bmatrix} p \\ q \end{bmatrix}.$$

The eigenvalues of the matrix of coefficients are $\lambda = \pm\omega$.

Hence the equilibrium point $(\pi, 0)$ is an *unstable saddle.*

3.5 **(a)** Using the usual notation,

$$u(x, y) = y,$$
$$v(x, y) = -\omega^2 \sin x - \varepsilon y.$$

So the Jacobian matrix is

$$\mathbf{J} = \begin{bmatrix} 0 & 1 \\ -\omega^2 \cos x & -\varepsilon \end{bmatrix}.$$

(b) The linear system of differential equations which approximates the system near the equilibrium point $(0, 0)$ is

$$\begin{bmatrix} \dot{p} \\ \dot{q} \end{bmatrix} = \begin{bmatrix} 0 & 1 \\ -\omega^2 & -\varepsilon \end{bmatrix} \begin{bmatrix} p \\ q \end{bmatrix}.$$

The characteristic equation of the matrix of coefficients is

$$\lambda^2 + \varepsilon\lambda + \omega^2 = 0.$$

For $0 < \varepsilon < 2\omega$, the eigenvalues are

$$\lambda = \tfrac{1}{2}(-\varepsilon \pm i\sqrt{4\omega^2 - \varepsilon^2}),$$

so the equilibrium point is a *stable spiral sink.*

For $\varepsilon = 2\omega$, the eigenvalues are real, negative and equal. There is only one independent eigenvector, so $(0, 0)$ is a *stable improper sink.*

For $\varepsilon > 2\omega$, the eigenvalues are

$$\lambda = \tfrac{1}{2}(-\varepsilon \pm \sqrt{\varepsilon^2 - 4\omega}).$$

Both the eigenvalues are negative, so $(0, 0)$ is a *stable sink.*

The approximating linear system of differential equations in the neighbourhood of the equilibrium point $(\pi, 0)$ is

$$\begin{bmatrix} \dot{p} \\ \dot{q} \end{bmatrix} = \begin{bmatrix} 0 & 1 \\ \omega^2 & -\varepsilon \end{bmatrix} \begin{bmatrix} p \\ q \end{bmatrix}.$$

The characteristic equation of the matrix of coefficients is

$$\lambda^2 + \varepsilon\lambda - \omega^2 = 0,$$

so the eigenvalues are $\lambda = \frac{1}{2}(-\varepsilon \pm \sqrt{\varepsilon^2 + 4\omega^2})$. One of these eigenvalues is positive, whereas the other is negative, so the equilibrium point $(\pi, 0)$ is an *unstable saddle.*

3.6 At A the pendulum is moving in an anticlockwise direction and approaching its highest point. It slows down as it passes through this point, and continues to slow down until a little after the highest point at B. It then continues to move in an anticlockwise direction, and speeds up until it reaches C. It moves through its lowest position, still moving anticlockwise, and heads towards its highest point again — but does not reach it. At D it stops, then falls back and oscillates about its lowest point with ever-decreasing amplitude.

UNIT 14 Modelling motion in two and three dimensions

Study guide for Unit 14

This unit is about motion and forces in more than one dimension. It draws on ideas about vectors (*Unit 4*), forces and components of forces (*Unit 5*), and fundamental ideas about the mechanics of particles, in particular Newton's second law (*Unit 6*). There is also mention of kinetic energy and potential energy (*Unit 8*).

You should study Sections 2 and 3 in the order in which they appear. From the point of view of later units, the material in Section 2 is more important than that in Sections 1 and 3. You will need your computer when studying Section 3.

You should expect Section 2 to take about twice as long as each of the other sections. You may wish to treat Subsections 2.1 and 2.2 as one study session, and Subsections 2.3 and 2.4 as a second study session.

There are two short video sequences in Section 2, each showing an example of the types of motion discussed. However, it is *not* essential that you view these video sequences at exactly the point where the associated exercises occur, though you should ensure that you have watched the appropriate sequence before trying the associated exercise.

Introduction

In *Units 6*, *7* and *8* you saw models of the motion of an object in one dimension. In this unit, we turn to motion in more than one dimension. In *Unit 4* you met vectors — quantities with magnitude and direction. In modelling one-dimensional motion, we noted that many quantities of interest in mechanics are vectors: for example, force, velocity and acceleration all have both magnitude and direction. In modelling motion in more than one dimension the role of vectors is more crucial, as it was in *Unit 5* when modelling forces in equilibrium in two and three dimensions.

The first type of motion we consider here involves objects constrained to follow some particular path in two or three dimensions. This might be a vehicle cornering, or a car on a funfair ride following a complicated path determined by its track. In Section 1 we consider such constrained motions, with particular consideration devoted to calculations relating to passenger sensations of forces on amusement park rides and in cars driving over hump-backed bridges.

A thrown object, such as a basketball (see Figure 0.1) or a shot, from the point of release until it hits the ground, is subject only to the force of gravity and to any force exerted on it by the air (broadly referred to as air resistance). Such objects are examples of **projectiles** and form the second type of example whose motion we shall consider, where we know the forces acting on the object and want to deduce the path of the object through space. Of course, such thrown objects may happen to execute motion that is purely vertical (straight up and straight down), but our interest here is in cases where the motion is horizontal as well as vertical. Athletic and sporting activities provide a wide variety of examples of projectile motion. As well as the throwing or striking of objects such as basketballs or golf balls, sports may involve humans themselves acting as projectiles, as in diving, long-jumping and ski-jumping.

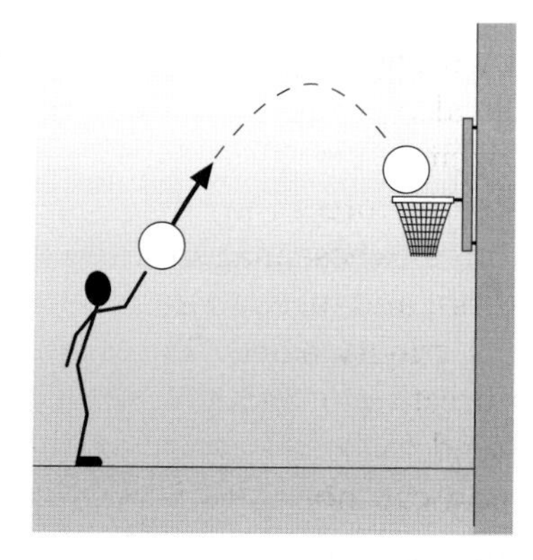

Figure 0.1

Here we shall deal mainly, though not exclusively, with models of projectiles without air resistance. Section 2 examines a variety of aspects of such motion, including energy considerations. In Section 3 we look briefly at how air resistance may be introduced into models of projectile motion. There you will use your computer to investigate the magnitude of air resistance effects on the 'range' of a projectile. There are a number of interesting aspects of projectile motion that we are not able to cover. These include 'lift' forces, which affect the flight of ski-jumpers for example, and forces on spinning balls, leading to 'swing' for a cricket ball for example.

Conservation of mechanical energy was introduced in *Unit 8*.

In many of the examples considered in this unit, the size of the moving object is of significance. For example, a motorcycle when cornering must have its centre of mass positioned appropriately to avoid falling over. We shall not consider such aspects of motion here, though. In this unit we shall consider only objects modelled as particles.

Throughout this unit we shall make use of Newton's second law of motion in vector form, given by

$$\mathbf{F} = m\mathbf{a}, \tag{0.1}$$

where the total force $\mathbf{F}$ and the acceleration $\mathbf{a}$ are vectors. In *Unit 6* this law was used almost exclusively in one dimension. Here we shall be concerned with its use in more than one dimension. As you saw in *Unit 6*, if the position vector of a particle is known as a function of time, we can obtain its velocity and acceleration vectors by differentiation. To differentiate the position vector function $\mathbf{r}(t)$ with respect to t, we differentiate separately each of the functions giving its $\mathbf{i}$-, $\mathbf{j}$- and $\mathbf{k}$-components. We shall usually employ the notation $\dot{\mathbf{r}}(t)$ (or just $\dot{\mathbf{r}}$) for the velocity $\mathbf{v} = d(\mathbf{r}(t))/dt$. Similarly, we shall usually write $\ddot{\mathbf{r}}(t)$ (or just $\ddot{\mathbf{r}}$) for the second derivative of $\mathbf{r}(t)$ that gives the acceleration $\mathbf{a}$.

Throughout this unit we shall use SI units. In numerical calculations, in Examples and Exercises, we shall work to the full accuracy of the calculator throughout, but quote intermediate results and the final answer to 4 significant figures.

1 Bumpy rides

A designer of a rollercoaster ride wants to make it as exciting as possible. It also needs to be safe. High speeds alone are not sufficient to provide the excitement. The experience of passengers on the ride is largely determined by the forces they experience from their seats. The designer will incorporate forces whose magnitude is close to zero, creating a feeling of near weightlessness, and, in contrast, forces whose magnitude is greater than those provided by gravity alone. The forces have components not only vertically and in the direction of motion, but also sideways, although the sideways components tend to be of lesser magnitude, since they are less welcomed by passengers and can pose problems in the engineering of the supporting structures.

Suppose that the designer of a ride can specify both the shape of the track and the speeds at which it will be traversed, and so, in effect, can specify the position in space of a car on the ride as a function of time. Now, if the car's position vector $\mathbf{r}$ is known as a function of time, we can deduce its velocity and acceleration by differentiation of $\mathbf{r}$ and can then use Newton's second law to find the total force on the car. Such knowledge will provide information about the likely experiences of a passenger on the ride and also about the safety of its design.

In this section we shall investigate the forces on passengers in a variety of situations. We start with cars accelerating on straight tracks inclined to the horizontal. In Subsection 1.2 we consider a vehicle going over a hump of known shape, while in Subsection 1.3 we look at some examples that do not fall into either of these categories.

1.1 Acceleration on slopes

We shall start our consideration of motion in two and three dimensions by looking at a one-dimensional situation, namely the forces involved when a vehicle is accelerating on a slope. In *Unit 6* we considered an object sliding down a slope under gravity. Here we consider a vehicle accelerating under its own power on a sloping track.

Example 1.1

A car is accelerating up a slope of angle θ to the horizontal with an acceleration of magnitude a. Assuming that a passenger follows the motion of the car exactly, what is the magnitude of the force exerted by the seat on a passenger of mass m?

Solution

The forces on the passenger are the passenger's weight $\mathbf{W}$, which has direction vertically downwards and magnitude $|\mathbf{W}| = mg$, and the force $\mathbf{R}$ exerted by the seat (see Figure 1.1). Suppose that $\mathbf{R}$ makes an angle α with the slope as shown in the diagram. We know the component (magnitude a) of the acceleration up the slope and the component (magnitude 0) of the acceleration normal to the slope. So it is convenient to choose axes in these directions. Choosing the unit vector $\mathbf{i}$ to be up the slope and the unit vector $\mathbf{j}$ to be normal to the slope, as shown in Figure 1.1, we have

We assume that the car is closed, so there is no force due to air resistance acting on the passenger.

$$\mathbf{W} = -mg\sin\theta\,\mathbf{i} - mg\cos\theta\,\mathbf{j},$$
$$\mathbf{R} = |\mathbf{R}|\cos\alpha\,\mathbf{i} + |\mathbf{R}|\sin\alpha\,\mathbf{j}$$

and

$$\ddot{\mathbf{r}} = a\mathbf{i}.$$

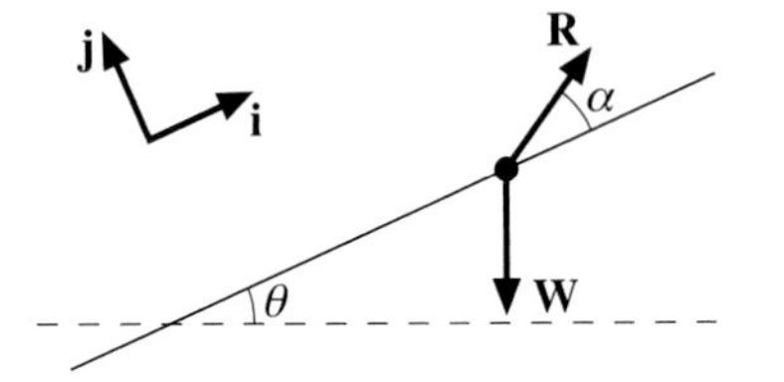

Figure 1.1

Newton's second law gives

$$\mathbf{R} + \mathbf{W} = m\ddot{\mathbf{r}},$$

i.e. $(|\mathbf{R}|\cos\alpha\,\mathbf{i} + |\mathbf{R}|\sin\alpha\,\mathbf{j}) + (-mg\sin\theta\,\mathbf{i} - mg\cos\theta\,\mathbf{j}) = ma\mathbf{i}$.

Equating the $\mathbf{i}$- and $\mathbf{j}$-components on both sides of this equation, we obtain

$$|\mathbf{R}|\cos\alpha - mg\sin\theta = ma$$

and

$$|\mathbf{R}|\sin\alpha - mg\cos\theta = 0.$$

We are asked for $|\mathbf{R}|$. We have

$$|\mathbf{R}|\cos\alpha = mg\sin\theta + ma = m(a + g\sin\theta)$$

and

$$|\mathbf{R}|\sin\alpha = mg\cos\theta.$$

We wish to eliminate α. If we square each of these equations and then add them, we obtain

$$\begin{aligned}|\mathbf{R}|^2 &= m^2(a + g\sin\theta)^2 + m^2g^2\cos^2\theta \\ &= m^2(a^2 + 2ag\sin\theta + g^2\sin^2\theta + g^2\cos^2\theta) \\ &= m^2(a^2 + 2ag\sin\theta + g^2).\end{aligned}$$

$\cos^2\theta + \sin^2\theta = 1$

Hence $|\mathbf{R}| = m\sqrt{a^2 + 2ag\sin\theta + g^2}$. ■

**Exercise 1.1*

A car accelerates down a slope inclined at $\frac{1}{6}\pi$ to the horizontal with an acceleration of magnitude $\frac{1}{2}g$. What are the magnitude and direction of the force exerted by the seat on a passenger of mass m?

1.2 Crossing a hump-backed bridge

You may be familiar with the rather curious sensation associated with driving at speed over a hump-backed bridge. During such a manoeuvre, the force from the seat seems to vary. At the top of the bridge your stomach seems to rise and there is a tendency to leave the seat. The situation causes the force exerted by the seat on a passenger to vary with the car's position.

Consider a bridge that appears straight when viewed from above. (That is, the road does not bend sideways as it goes over the bridge.) The motion of a car going over such a bridge will be confined to two dimensions, i.e. to the vertical plane containing the bridge. (We are modelling the car as a particle and ignoring the width of the road.) Suppose that a car is driven over the bridge in such a way that it has a velocity with a constant horizontal component. A constant speed might seem to you to be more likely. We choose to look at a constant horizontal component because the mathematics is then less complicated.

Although we are considering a road bridge, the same approach can be applied to other situations, such as a fairground ride of similar geometry.

We shall consider the forces on a passenger (of mass m) riding in the car. Assume that this passenger follows exactly the same path as the car as a whole. Now the forces on the passenger are those exerted by the seat, $\mathbf{R}$ say, and the passenger's weight $\mathbf{W}$. In general, $\mathbf{R}$ will have non-zero components in both the horizontal and vertical directions. If we choose $\mathbf{i}$ to be the horizontal unit vector and $\mathbf{j}$ to be the vertical unit vector, as shown in Figure 1.2, then $\mathbf{W} = -mg\mathbf{j}$ and $\mathbf{R} = R_1\mathbf{i} + R_2\mathbf{j}$, where R_1 and R_2 are the horizontal and vertical components of the reaction $\mathbf{R}$. Newton's second law applied to the passenger gives

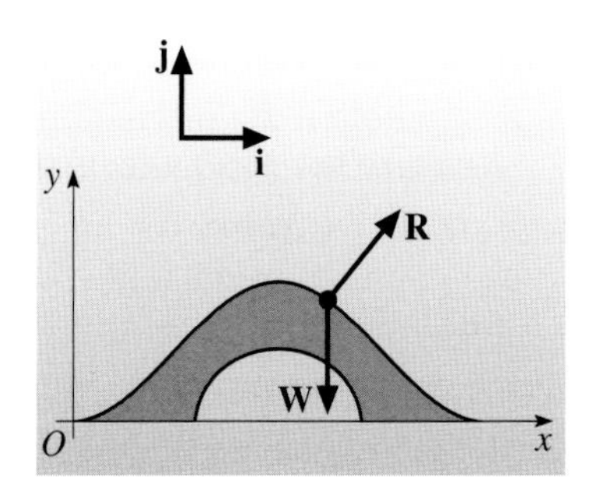

Figure 1.2

$$\mathbf{R} + \mathbf{W} = m\ddot{\mathbf{r}},$$

or

$$(R_1\mathbf{i} + R_2\mathbf{j}) - mg\mathbf{j} = m\ddot{\mathbf{r}} = m(\ddot{x}\mathbf{i} + \ddot{y}\mathbf{j}),$$

where y is the height of the bridge at a horizontal position x. Equating the components in the $\mathbf{i}$- and $\mathbf{j}$-directions on both sides of this equation, we obtain

$$R_1 = m\ddot{x},$$
$$R_2 - mg = m\ddot{y}. \tag{1.1}$$

The horizontal component $\dot{x}$ of the velocity is constant, so $\ddot{x} = 0$ and $R_1 = 0$. So, in this case, the force exerted on the passenger by the seat acts vertically upwards. To find R_2, we need to know the profile of the bridge. We shall consider a hump-backed bridge with a profile in the vertical plane given by

$$y = \frac{h}{2}\left(1 - \cos\left(\frac{2\pi x}{L}\right)\right) \quad (0 \le x \le L). \tag{1.2}$$

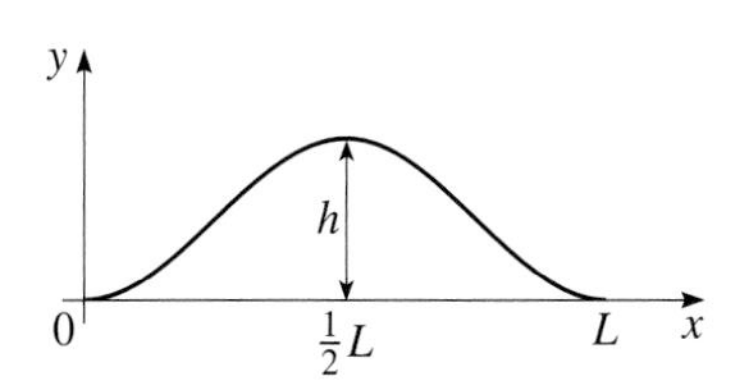

Figure 1.3 Graph of Equation (1.2)

Such a bridge has length L and maximum height h, as indicated in Figure 1.3. Suppose that the constant component of the velocity of the car in the x-direction is u, i.e. $\dot{x} = u$, where u is positive if the car is moving in the positive x-direction. If t is measured from the instant when the car is at the beginning, $x = 0$, of the bridge, then its horizontal position after time t will be $x = ut$. Consequently the y-coordinate can be written in terms of t rather than x, as

$$y = \frac{h}{2}\left(1 - \cos\left(\frac{2\pi ut}{L}\right)\right) \quad \left(0 \le t \le \frac{L}{u}\right). \tag{1.3}$$

To obtain an expression for R_2 from Equation (1.1), we need $\ddot{y}$, which we obtain by differentiating Equation (1.3) twice with respect to t. We obtain

$$\dot{y} = \frac{h}{2}\left(\frac{2\pi u}{L}\sin\left(\frac{2\pi ut}{L}\right)\right) = \frac{\pi hu}{L}\sin\left(\frac{2\pi ut}{L}\right),$$

$$\ddot{y} = \frac{\pi hu}{L}\frac{2\pi u}{L}\cos\left(\frac{2\pi ut}{L}\right) = \frac{2\pi^2 hu^2}{L^2}\cos\left(\frac{2\pi ut}{L}\right).$$

Now, from Equation (1.1),

$$R_2 = m(g + \ddot{y}), \tag{1.4}$$

so

$$R_2 = m\left(g + \frac{2\pi^2 hu^2}{L^2}\cos\left(\frac{2\pi ut}{L}\right)\right) \quad \left(0 \le t \le \frac{L}{u}\right). \tag{1.5}$$

The quantity $2\pi^2 hu^2/L^2$ is a constant, say A, that depends on the constant horizontal component of the velocity and on the profile of the bridge. When $x = 0$, we have $t = 0$ and $R_2 = m(g + A)$. When $x = L$ we have $ut = L$ and $R_2 = m(g + A)$ again. When $x = \frac{1}{2}L$, we have $ut = \frac{1}{2}L$ and $R_2 = m(g - A)$ (we assume here that $g \ge A$). This means that the force exerted by the seat on the passenger is greatest at the start and at the end of the bridge, and least in the middle. The passenger's weight is mg. The passenger feels lighter than this in the middle of the bridge and heavier at the ends of the bridge.

You may notice that the force exerted by the seat on the passenger changes from mg to $m(g + A)$ 'instantaneously' as the car starts up the bridge. This sudden change in acceleration results from a discontinuity at $x = 0$ in the second derivative of the function giving the road profile. This is not a good bridge design!

If $g < A$, then the above calculation yields values of R_2 that are negative at times. This cannot happen in practice, however. The seat cannot pull the passenger *downwards* — at least, not unless they are strapped into it by a seat belt. What is more, exactly the same analysis can be applied to the car as a whole (except that m then needs to be replaced by the total mass of the car and the occupants). The road certainly cannot pull the car downwards! A negative value for R_2 in Equation (1.5) means that it is impossible for the car to remain following the profile of the bridge at the given horizontal speed u. At the point when R_2 first becomes zero, the force exerted by the road on the car's wheels becomes zero and the car leaves the ground. From then on, the car no longer follows the profile of the road, but instead becomes a projectile, until it impacts onto the road once more.

The motion of projectiles will be discussed in the next section of this unit.

We can generalize this to any object moving across a surface but not attached to the surface. A normal reaction force exerted by the surface on the object must act *away* from the surface. Suppose that a model of the motion implies a reaction force whose component normal to and away from the surface is negative. In this situation, the object is likely to leave the surface (and become a projectile) at the instant at which the calculated normal reaction becomes zero. This gives a useful test for determining when the object leaves the surface.

Exercise 1.2

A hump-backed bridge has a profile that is given by Equation (1.2) with $h = 4$ metres and $L = 30$ metres. A car crossing this bridge contains a passenger of mass 90 kilograms.

(a) Suppose that the car crosses the bridge at a velocity with a constant horizontal component of $10\,\mathrm{m\,s^{-1}}$. Calculate the greatest and least magnitudes of the force exerted by the seat on the passenger as the bridge is crossed.

(b) What are the greatest and least magnitudes of the force from the seat if the horizontal component of the car's velocity is increased to $15\,\mathrm{m\,s^{-1}}$?

(c) What is the greatest horizontal speed at which the car can travel without leaving the ground as it crosses the bridge?

*Exercise 1.3

A climbing section of track on a rollercoaster ride appears straight when viewed from above. Viewed from the side, the track has the profile

$$y = \tfrac{1}{160}(30x^2 - x^3) \quad (0 \le x \le 20) \tag{1.6}$$

(see Figure 1.4), where the origin is taken at the start of this section of the track and y is its height at a horizontal position x (both measured in metres). Suppose that a car traverses this section of the track with a constant positive horizontal component u of velocity (measured in $\mathrm{m\,s^{-1}}$).

What value of u should be chosen to give a passenger a momentary feeling of near weightlessness at the end of this section of the track?

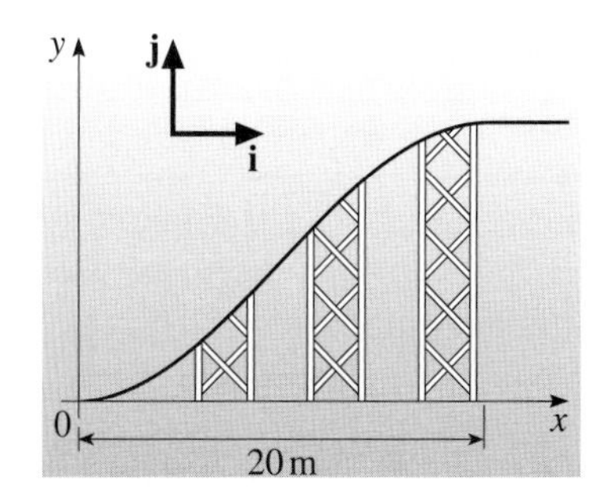

Figure 1.4

1.3 Complicated paths

In Subsections 1.1 and 1.2 we considered cars travelling with known acceleration on a slope and over a hump-backed bridge respectively, and calculated the force exerted by the seat on a passenger. Indeed, however complicated its path, if we know the position of a particle as a function of time, then we can find its velocity and acceleration by differentiation, and hence the total force on it from Newton's second law.

Example 1.2

A rollercoaster ride starts with a horizontal bend. Working in SI units, the position of a car during the first five seconds of the ride is given by

$$\mathbf{r} = \left(10 - 10\cos\tfrac{1}{2}t\right)\mathbf{i} + 20\sin\tfrac{1}{2}t\,\mathbf{j} \quad (0 \le t \le 5),$$

This path forms part of an ellipse.

where $\mathbf{i}$ and $\mathbf{j}$ are Cartesian unit vectors in the horizontal plane.

(a) Find expressions for the velocity and acceleration vectors at time t.

(b) Deduce the magnitude of the velocity and of the acceleration at $t = 0$. Show that the velocity and acceleration vectors are mutually perpendicular at this time. Are the velocity and acceleration vectors perpendicular at $t = 1$?

(c) Show that the magnitude of the acceleration of the car at time t is

$$|\ddot{\mathbf{r}}| = 2.5\sqrt{1 + 3\sin^2\tfrac{1}{2}t} \quad (0 \le t \le 5).$$

Hence show that the magnitude of the acceleration of the car is greatest when $t = \pi$.

(d) Ignoring any forces due to air resistance, what is the largest magnitude of the force from the seat to which a passenger of mass m in the car is subjected while the bend is traversed?

Solution

(a) The velocity vector is obtained by differentiating $\mathbf{r}$ with respect to t:

$$\dot{\mathbf{r}} = 5\sin\tfrac{1}{2}t\,\mathbf{i} + 10\cos\tfrac{1}{2}t\,\mathbf{j}.$$

The acceleration vector is obtained by differentiating $\dot{\mathbf{r}}$:

$$\ddot{\mathbf{r}} = 2.5\cos\tfrac{1}{2}t\,\mathbf{i} - 5\sin\tfrac{1}{2}t\,\mathbf{j}. \tag{1.7}$$

(b) At $t = 0$, the velocity is $10\mathbf{j}$ and the acceleration is $2.5\mathbf{i}$. So the velocity has magnitude 10 and the acceleration has magnitude 2.5. The $\mathbf{i}$- and $\mathbf{j}$-directions are mutually perpendicular, so the velocity and acceleration are mutually perpendicular at $t = 0$.

At $t = 1$, the velocity is $\dot{\mathbf{r}}(1) = 5\sin\frac{1}{2}\,\mathbf{i} + 10\cos\frac{1}{2}\,\mathbf{j}$ and the acceleration is $\ddot{\mathbf{r}}(1) = 2.5\cos\frac{1}{2}\,\mathbf{i} - 5\sin\frac{1}{2}\,\mathbf{j}$. The dot product of these vectors is

$$\begin{aligned}\dot{\mathbf{r}}(1)\cdot\ddot{\mathbf{r}}(1) &= 12.5\sin\tfrac{1}{2}\cos\tfrac{1}{2} - 50\sin\tfrac{1}{2}\cos\tfrac{1}{2}\\ &= -37.5\sin\tfrac{1}{2}\cos\tfrac{1}{2} \quad (= -15.78),\end{aligned}$$

which is not 0. So these vectors are not perpendicular when $t = 1$.

In fact, the only other time when the velocity and acceleration are perpendicular is $t = \pi$.

(c) The magnitude of the acceleration found in part (a) is

$$\begin{aligned}|\ddot{\mathbf{r}}| &= \sqrt{2.5^2\cos^2\tfrac{1}{2}t + 5^2\sin^2\tfrac{1}{2}t}\\ &= 2.5\sqrt{\cos^2\tfrac{1}{2}t + 4\sin^2\tfrac{1}{2}t}\\ &= 2.5\sqrt{1 + 3\sin^2\tfrac{1}{2}t},\end{aligned}$$

using the identity $\cos^2\frac{1}{2}t + \sin^2\frac{1}{2}t = 1$. This expression will be a maximum when $\sin^2\frac{1}{2}t$ takes its maximum value of 1. This occurs when $t = \pm\pi, \pm3\pi, \pm5\pi, \ldots$, but the only value that occurs in the range $0 \le t \le 5$ is $t = \pi$. In other words, the magnitude of the acceleration is greatest when $t = \pi$, and this maximum magnitude is $2.5\sqrt{1+3} = 5$.

(d) The seat exerts a force $\mathbf{R}$ such that, by Newton's second law,

$$\mathbf{R} + \mathbf{W} = m\ddot{\mathbf{r}},$$

where $\mathbf{W}$, the passenger's weight, has magnitude mg and acts vertically downwards, and $\ddot{\mathbf{r}}$ is the acceleration calculated in part (a), whose magnitude was found in part (c). We have $\mathbf{R} = m\ddot{\mathbf{r}} - \mathbf{W}$. Since $\ddot{\mathbf{r}}$ is always horizontal and $\mathbf{W}$ is vertical, these vectors are mutually perpendicular, so

$$|\mathbf{R}| = \sqrt{m^2|\ddot{\mathbf{r}}|^2 + |\mathbf{W}|^2} = \sqrt{m^2|\ddot{\mathbf{r}}|^2 + m^2g^2} = m\sqrt{|\ddot{\mathbf{r}}|^2 + g^2}.$$

Since g is a constant, this expression for $|\mathbf{R}|$ is greatest when $|\ddot{\mathbf{r}}|$ has its greatest value. From part (c) this occurs at $t = \pi$, and this maximum magnitude is $|\ddot{\mathbf{r}}| = 5$. So the maximum value of the magnitude of the force from the seat is

$$m\sqrt{5^2 + 9.81^2} \simeq 11.01m,$$

which is about 12% greater than the weight of the passenger. ■

Differentiating functions representing motion in three dimensions is no harder than for two dimensions.

Visualizing the geometry of the situations may be difficult, though!

Example 1.3

A climbing section of a spiral rollercoaster track has the same profile in the vertical direction as that considered in Exercise 1.3, but looks like part of a circle of radius 30 metres when viewed from above. A car following this section of track has position vector $\mathbf{r}$. In SI units,

$$\mathbf{r} = 30\cos\left(\tfrac{1}{30}ut\right)\mathbf{i} + 30\sin\left(\tfrac{1}{30}ut\right)\mathbf{j} + \tfrac{1}{160}(30u^2t^2 - u^3t^3)\mathbf{k},$$

for $0 \le t \le 20/u$, where u is a constant. Here $\mathbf{i}$, $\mathbf{j}$ and $\mathbf{k}$ are Cartesian unit vectors, with $\mathbf{k}$ vertically upwards (see Figure 1.5).

(a) Find expressions for the velocity and acceleration of the car.

(b) Find the speed of the car when $t = 10/u$.

(c) If $u = \sqrt{8g/3}$, what is the direction of the force exerted by a seat on a passenger at $t = 20/u$?

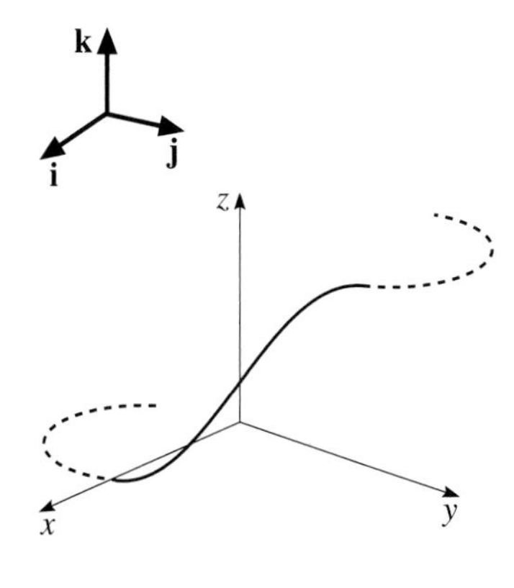

Figure 1.5

Solution

(a) Differentiating $\mathbf{r}$ with respect to t, we obtain

$$\begin{aligned}\dot{\mathbf{r}} &= -30\left(\tfrac{1}{30}u\right)\sin\left(\tfrac{1}{30}ut\right)\mathbf{i} + 30\left(\tfrac{1}{30}u\right)\cos\left(\tfrac{1}{30}ut\right)\mathbf{j} \\ &\quad + \tfrac{1}{160}\left(60u^2t - 3u^3t^2\right)\mathbf{k} \\ &= -u\sin\left(\tfrac{1}{30}ut\right)\mathbf{i} + u\cos\left(\tfrac{1}{30}ut\right)\mathbf{j} + \tfrac{1}{160}\left(60u^2t - 3u^3t^2\right)\mathbf{k}\end{aligned}$$

and

$$\begin{aligned}\ddot{\mathbf{r}} &= -\tfrac{1}{30}u^2\cos\left(\tfrac{1}{30}ut\right)\mathbf{i} - \tfrac{1}{30}u^2\sin\left(\tfrac{1}{30}ut\right)\mathbf{j} + \tfrac{1}{160}\left(60u^2 - 6u^3t\right)\mathbf{k} \\ &= -\tfrac{1}{30}u^2\cos\left(\tfrac{1}{30}ut\right)\mathbf{i} - \tfrac{1}{30}u^2\sin\left(\tfrac{1}{30}ut\right)\mathbf{j} + \tfrac{1}{80}\left(30u^2 - 3u^3t\right)\mathbf{k}.\end{aligned}$$

(b) When $t = 10/u$, the velocity of the car is

$$\begin{aligned}\dot{\mathbf{r}}\,(10/u) &= -u\sin\tfrac{1}{3}\,\mathbf{i} + u\cos\tfrac{1}{3}\,\mathbf{j} + \tfrac{1}{160}(600u - 300u)\,\mathbf{k} \\ &= -u\sin\tfrac{1}{3}\,\mathbf{i} + u\cos\tfrac{1}{3}\,\mathbf{j} + \tfrac{15}{8}u\,\mathbf{k}.\end{aligned}$$

The car's speed is the magnitude of this vector, which is

$$\sqrt{u^2\sin^2\tfrac{1}{3} + u^2\cos^2\tfrac{1}{3} + (\tfrac{15}{8})^2u^2} = u\sqrt{1 + (\tfrac{15}{8})^2} = \tfrac{17}{8}u.$$

(c) Suppose that the passenger has mass m; the passenger's weight is thus $\mathbf{W} = -mg\mathbf{k}$. Suppose that $\mathbf{R}$ is the force exerted by the seat on the passenger. Newton's second law applied to the passenger gives

$$\mathbf{R} + \mathbf{W} = m\ddot{\mathbf{r}},$$

so

$$\mathbf{R} = m(\ddot{\mathbf{r}} + g\mathbf{k}).$$

At $t = 20/u$, using $\ddot{\mathbf{r}}$ as calculated in part (a), we obtain

$$\begin{aligned}\mathbf{R} &= m\left(-\tfrac{1}{30}u^2\cos\tfrac{2}{3}\,\mathbf{i} - \tfrac{1}{30}u^2\sin\tfrac{2}{3}\,\mathbf{j} + \left(\tfrac{1}{80}(30u^2 - 60u^2) + g\right)\mathbf{k}\right) \\ &= m\left(-\tfrac{1}{30}u^2\cos\tfrac{2}{3}\,\mathbf{i} - \tfrac{1}{30}u^2\sin\tfrac{2}{3}\,\mathbf{j} + \left(g - \tfrac{3}{8}u^2\right)\mathbf{k}\right).\end{aligned}$$

The $\mathbf{k}$-component of $\mathbf{R}$ is $m(g - \tfrac{3}{8}u^2)$. With $u = \sqrt{8g/3}$ this is zero, so the force from the seat experienced by the passenger at $t = 20/u$ is

$$m\left(-\tfrac{1}{30}u^2\cos\tfrac{2}{3}\,\mathbf{i} - \tfrac{1}{30}u^2\sin\tfrac{2}{3}\,\mathbf{j}\right) = -\tfrac{8}{90}mg\left(\cos\tfrac{2}{3}\,\mathbf{i} + \sin\tfrac{2}{3}\,\mathbf{j}\right).$$

This is a horizontal force (of magnitude $8mg/90$) acting radially towards the axis of the spiral rollercoaster track. ■

***Exercise 1.4**

In an amusement park ride, the position of a car at time t has coordinates (in SI units)

$$x = 3t,\ y = 4t^2,\ z = 0 \quad (0 \leq t \leq 3),$$

where the x- and y-axes lie in the horizontal plane and the z-axis is vertically upwards.

(a) At what angle to the horizontal is the force exerted on the car by the track?

(b) What is the magnitude of the force exerted by the car's seat on a passenger of mass 100 kilograms?

End-of-section Exercise

Exercise 1.5

A rollercoaster car of mass m descending a spiral section of track has position

$$\mathbf{r} = a\cos bt\,\mathbf{i} + a\sin bt\,\mathbf{j} + (h - \tfrac{1}{4}gt^2)\,\mathbf{k}$$

at time t, where a, b and h are constants, and $\mathbf{i}$, $\mathbf{j}$ and $\mathbf{k}$ are Cartesian unit vectors, with $\mathbf{k}$ vertically upwards.

(a) Find the velocity and acceleration of the car at time t.

(b) What is the force exerted by the track on the car at time t?

(c) Show that the force exerted by the track on the car has constant magnitude $m\sqrt{a^2b^4 + \frac{1}{4}g^2}$.

2 Projectiles without air resistance

In the previous section we discussed problems where we knew the position of a particle as a function of time and wished to find the force acting on the particle. In this section we are concerned with the inverse of this problem: we know the force acting on the particle and wish to find the position of the particle as a function of time. In particular we shall discuss the motion of projectiles modelled as particles. We shall use the following terminology in our discussion. During the period that the projectile is off the ground and subject only to the force of gravity (and possibly air resistance), it is said to be *in flight*. The start of the flight is the *launch*, and the initial velocity is the *launch velocity*. The flight ends with an *impact* (often hitting the ground again, but possibly hitting some other target). The *time of flight* is the time between the moment of launch and the moment of impact. The path of the projectile while in flight is its **trajectory**.

Whenever we mention a projectile in this section, it will be modelled as a particle.

Here, we consider only models in which the effect of air resistance is assumed to be negligible. All the models in this section make the assumption of no air resistance. We revisit projectiles in the next section, and there we consider the effect of taking air resistance into account.

In ignoring air resistance, we also ignore effects such as the swerve that may occur when a football is kicked with spin, or when a golf ball is sliced.

In Subsection 2.1, we set up the basic methodology and consider horizontal launches. Then, in Subsection 2.2, we go on to more general launch conditions. In Subsection 2.3, we look at the trajectory of a projectile and consider a variety of examples. Subsection 2.4 looks at energy conservation.

2.1 Horizontal launch

We start by considering a projectile launched in a horizontal direction. This might be an object thrown horizontally from the top of a cliff or bridge. The only force acting on the projectile while it is in flight is that due to gravity — we are assuming that air resistance is negligible and can be ignored. So the subsequent motion is in two dimensions, i.e. in the vertical plane determined by the direction of the launch velocity. Figure 2.1 shows a coordinate system in this plane. We have chosen the origin to be at the point of launch, the x-axis to be in the direction of the launch velocity and the y-axis to be vertically upwards.

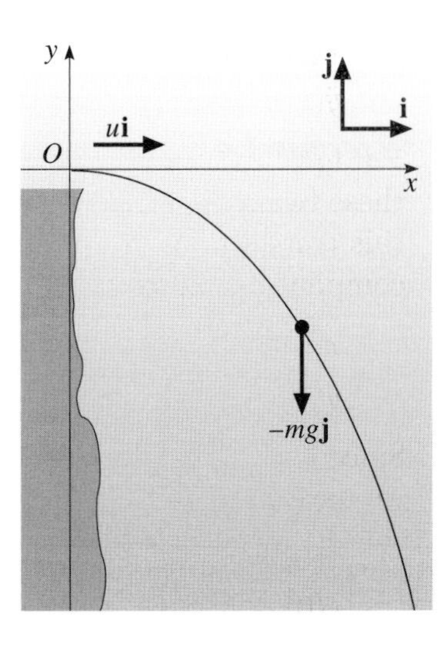

Figure 2.1 An object thrown from the top of a cliff

The force due to gravity has magnitude mg, where m is the mass of the projectile, and acts vertically downwards, and therefore is $-mg\mathbf{j}$. Putting this into Newton's second law gives the equation of motion

$$m\ddot{\mathbf{r}} = -mg\mathbf{j}. \tag{2.1}$$

Dividing by m gives

$$\ddot{\mathbf{r}}(t) = -g\mathbf{j}. \tag{2.2}$$

As well as this equation of motion, we also have information about how the projectile was launched. Take $t = 0$ to be the moment of launch. Then, since the object is launched from the origin O, we have

$$\mathbf{r}(0) = \mathbf{0}.$$

The zero vector (in two dimensions) is $\mathbf{0} = 0\mathbf{i} + 0\mathbf{j}$.

The launch velocity is horizontal, in the direction of $\mathbf{i}$. Suppose that the magnitude of the launch velocity (or the launch speed) is u (and that this is known). Then

$$\dot{\mathbf{r}}(0) = u\mathbf{i}.$$

The differential equation (2.2), together with the initial conditions $\mathbf{r}(0) = \mathbf{0}$ and $\dot{\mathbf{r}}(0) = u\mathbf{i}$, constitute a 'mathematical problem', whose solution will give the subsequent position $\mathbf{r}(t)$ of the projectile in terms of t. We shall look at two ways of solving this mathematical problem. The second method works directly in terms of vectors. First, however, we shall deal with the x- and y-coordinates separately.

'Uncoupled' approach

The position vector at time t is

$$\mathbf{r}(t) = x(t)\mathbf{i} + y(t)\mathbf{j}.$$

The velocity is

$$\dot{\mathbf{r}}(t) = \dot{x}(t)\mathbf{i} + \dot{y}(t)\mathbf{j},$$

and the acceleration is

$$\ddot{\mathbf{r}}(t) = \ddot{x}(t)\mathbf{i} + \ddot{y}(t)\mathbf{j}. \tag{2.3}$$

Substituting this expression for $\ddot{\mathbf{r}}(t)$ in Equation (2.2) gives

$$\ddot{x}(t)\mathbf{i} + \ddot{y}(t)\mathbf{j} = -g\mathbf{j} \quad (t \geq 0).$$

For this equation between vectors to hold, the $\mathbf{i}$- and $\mathbf{j}$-components on both sides of the equation must be equal. Hence we must have

$$\ddot{x}(t) = 0, \tag{2.4}$$
$$\ddot{y}(t) = -g. \tag{2.5}$$

We have, in effect, 'uncoupled' the horizontal and vertical motions, since these two differential equations can be solved separately for x and y. Before this can be done, we also need to separate the initial conditions into their components. Since $\mathbf{r}(0) = x(0)\mathbf{i} + y(0)\mathbf{j} = \mathbf{0}$, we have

$$x(0) = 0,$$
$$y(0) = 0.$$

Since $\dot{\mathbf{r}}(0) = \dot{x}(0)\mathbf{i} + \dot{y}(0)\mathbf{j} = u\mathbf{i}$, equating the $\mathbf{i}$- and $\mathbf{j}$-components separately, we have

$$\dot{x}(0) = u,$$
$$\dot{y}(0) = 0.$$

We first solve Equation (2.4) for the horizontal component of the motion with the initial conditions $x(0) = 0$, $\dot{x}(0) = u$. Integrating once, we obtain

$$\dot{x}(t) = C,$$

where C is a constant. We have $\dot{x}(0) = u$, the (horizontal) launch speed, so putting $t = 0$ gives $C = u$, thus

$$\dot{x}(t) = u. \tag{2.6}$$

A second integration then gives

$$x(t) = ut + D,$$

where D is a constant. Since $x(0) = 0$, putting $t = 0$ gives $D = 0$, so

$$x(t) = ut. \tag{2.7}$$

Consider now the vertical motion given by Equation (2.5). Integrating once,

$$\dot{y}(t) = -gt + E,$$

where E is a constant. Since $\dot{y}(0) = 0$, putting $t = 0$ gives $E = 0$, and therefore

$$\dot{y}(t) = -gt. \tag{2.8}$$

Integrating again gives

$$y(t) = -\tfrac{1}{2}gt^2 + F,$$

where F is a constant. Since $y(0) = 0$, putting $t = 0$ gives $F = 0$, so

$$y(t) = -\tfrac{1}{2}gt^2. \tag{2.9}$$

We can recombine Equations (2.7) and (2.9) to obtain an expression for the position vector $\mathbf{r}$ of the projectile in terms of time t, as

$$\begin{aligned}\mathbf{r}(t) &= x(t)\mathbf{i} + y(t)\mathbf{j}\\ &= ut\mathbf{i} - \tfrac{1}{2}gt^2\mathbf{j}.\end{aligned} \tag{2.10}$$

In a similar way, combining Equations (2.6) and (2.8) gives

$$\mathbf{v}(t) = \dot{\mathbf{r}}(t) = u\mathbf{i} - gt\mathbf{j}$$

as the vector combination of the results for the components of the velocity.

Alternatively, we could differentiate Equation (2.10) with respect to t.

Equations (2.7) and (2.9), i.e. $x(t) = ut$ and $y(t) = -\frac{1}{2}gt^2$, are sufficient in themselves to enable us to plot the trajectory of the projectile, by plotting $y(t)$ against $x(t)$ for various values of t. An example calculation of the path during the first 3.5 seconds of the descent of an object thrown horizontally with a launch speed of $10\,\mathrm{m\,s^{-1}}$ is shown in Figure 2.2.

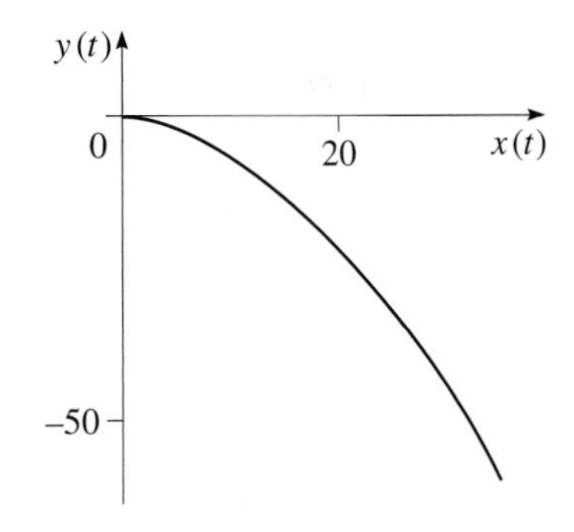

Figure 2.2

However, we can readily obtain an equation giving y directly in terms of x. We have $t = x/u$ from Equation (2.7), and substituting this into Equation (2.9) gives a formula for the trajectory:

$$y = -\frac{g}{2}\left(\frac{x}{u}\right)^2 = -\frac{g}{2u^2}x^2 \quad (x \geq 0). \tag{2.11}$$

This has the form $y = Ax^2$, where $A = -g/(2u^2)$ is a negative constant, so the trajectory is part of a parabola 'opening downwards'.

Example 2.1

Suppose that a marble is thrown horizontally at $10\,\mathrm{m\,s^{-1}}$ from the Clifton Suspension Bridge. How far will it travel horizontally before it splashes into the River Avon, 77 metres below the point of launch?

We considered the motion of a marble *dropped* from the bridge in *Unit 6*.

Solution

We use a coordinate system as in the preceding discussion (see Figure 2.3) and concentrate first on the vertical motion. The strategy is to use the vertical motion to calculate the time it takes the marble to fall to the water surface and then to use this time to find the horizontal distance moved. We can use Equation (2.9) to find the time needed to fall 77 metres. The required value of t will correspond to $y = -77$ metres, that is,

$$-\tfrac{1}{2}gt^2 = -77.$$

This gives

$$t = \sqrt{154/9.81} \simeq 3.962 \text{ seconds.}$$

During this time, according to Equation (2.7), the marble will have moved a horizontal distance ut. Since $u = 10$, the horizontal distance moved is about 39.62 metres. The coordinates (in metres) of the point of splashdown are $(39.62, -77)$. ■

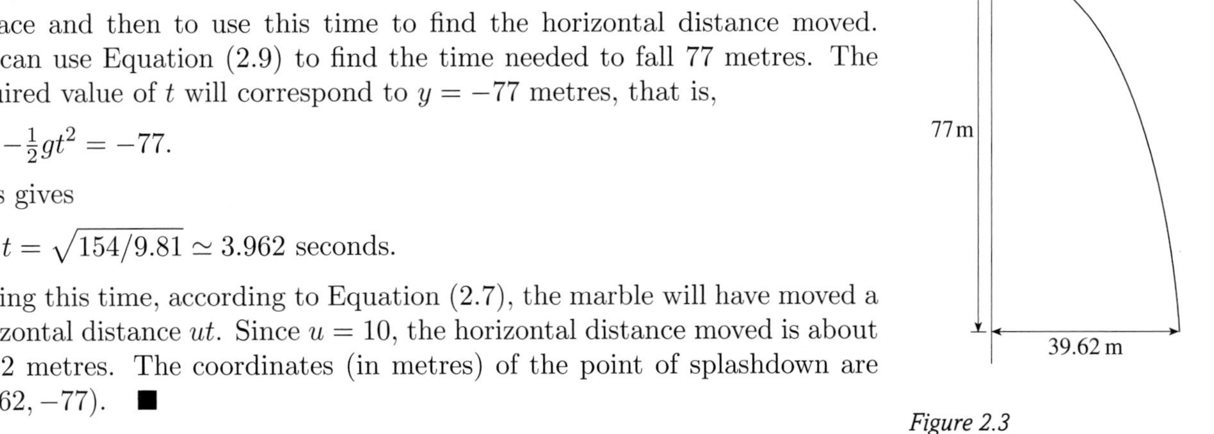

Figure 2.3

In our general analysis of a horizontally launched projectile, we used the components of the equation of motion, $\ddot{y} = -g$ and $\ddot{x} = 0$. In particular, integrating $\ddot{x} = 0$ gave $\dot{x} = C$, where C is a constant. This result, which is independent of the initial conditions and applies to any projectile, however it is launched, shows an important feature of projectile motion in the absence of air resistance: the *horizontal* behaviour is *constant (horizontal) speed*.

Vector approach

An alternative approach is to integrate the vector equation (2.2), $\ddot{\mathbf{r}}(t) = -g\mathbf{j}$, directly, to produce vector expressions for the velocity and then for the position, without first splitting the equation into components. To do this, we first need to think about what it means to integrate a vector.

Suppose that we know the velocity of some object moving in two dimensions as a function of time:

$$\mathbf{v}(t) = f(t)\mathbf{i} + g(t)\mathbf{j}.$$

Since $\mathbf{v}(t) = \dot{\mathbf{r}}(t) = \dot{x}(t)\mathbf{i} + \dot{y}(t)\mathbf{j}$, we have $\dot{x}(t) = f(t)$ and $\dot{y}(t) = g(t)$. Then $x(t) = \int f(t)\,dt$ and $y(t) = \int g(t)\,dt$; that is,

$$\mathbf{r}(t) = x(t)\mathbf{i} + y(t)\mathbf{j} = \left(\int f(t)\,dt\right)\mathbf{i} + \left(\int g(t)\,dt\right)\mathbf{j}.$$

Alternatively, we can write

$$\mathbf{r}(t) = \int \mathbf{v}(t)\,dt = \int (f(t)\mathbf{i} + g(t)\mathbf{j})\,dt.$$

Comparing the last two equations, we see that the integral of the vector function $\mathbf{v}(t)$ is obtained by integrating each scalar component function separately. That is,

$$\int (f(t)\mathbf{i} + g(t)\mathbf{j})\,dt = \left(\int f(t)\,dt\right)\mathbf{i} + \left(\int g(t)\,dt\right)\mathbf{j}.$$

This provides a definition of the integral of a two-dimensional vector function.

We can extend this definition to a vector function in three dimensions.

Integrating a vector

If $\mathbf{i}$, $\mathbf{j}$ and $\mathbf{k}$ are Cartesian unit vectors, then

$$\int \left(f(t)\mathbf{i} + g(t)\mathbf{j} + h(t)\mathbf{k}\right) dt$$
$$= \left(\int f(t)\,dt\right)\mathbf{i} + \left(\int g(t)\,dt\right)\mathbf{j} + \left(\int h(t)\,dt\right)\mathbf{k}.$$

Example 2.2

Find $\int (2t\mathbf{i} + 3\mathbf{j})\,dt$.

Solution

Using the definition for the integration of a two-dimensional vector function, we have

$$\begin{aligned}\int (2t\mathbf{i} + 3\mathbf{j})\,dt &= \left(\int 2t\,dt\right)\mathbf{i} + \left(\int 3\,dt\right)\mathbf{j} \\ &= (t^2 + a)\mathbf{i} + (3t + b)\mathbf{j} \\ &= t^2\mathbf{i} + 3t\mathbf{j} + \mathbf{c},\end{aligned}$$

where a and b are arbitrary constants, and $\mathbf{c}$ (where $\mathbf{c} = a\mathbf{i} + b\mathbf{j}$) is an arbitrary *vector* constant. ■

*Exercise 2.1

If $\mathbf{c}$ is the constant vector $c_1\mathbf{i} + c_2\mathbf{j}$, show that $\int \mathbf{c}\,dt = \mathbf{c}t + \mathbf{d}$, where $\mathbf{d}$ is an arbitrary constant vector.

Let us now see how we can solve the vector differential equation (2.2), $\ddot{\mathbf{r}}(t) = -g\mathbf{j}$, together with the initial conditions $\mathbf{r}(0) = \mathbf{0}$ and $\dot{\mathbf{r}}(0) = u\mathbf{i}$, without explicit division of the differential equation into components. Integrating this equation we obtain

$$\dot{\mathbf{r}}(t) = \int \ddot{\mathbf{r}}(t)\,dt = \int -g\mathbf{j}\,dt = -gt\mathbf{j} + \mathbf{c},$$

where $\mathbf{c}$ is an arbitrary constant vector. Since $\dot{\mathbf{r}}(0) = u\mathbf{i}$, putting $t = 0$ gives

$$u\mathbf{i} = \dot{\mathbf{r}}(0) = \mathbf{c}.$$

So we have

$$\dot{\mathbf{r}}(t) = -gt\mathbf{j} + u\mathbf{i}.$$

Integrating again gives

$$\mathbf{r}(t) = \int \dot{\mathbf{r}}(t)\,dt = \int (-gt\mathbf{j} + u\mathbf{i})\,dt = -\tfrac{1}{2}gt^2\mathbf{j} + ut\mathbf{i} + \mathbf{d},$$

where $\mathbf{d}$ is an arbitrary constant vector. Putting $t = 0$ and using the initial condition $\mathbf{r}(0) = \mathbf{0}$, we have $\mathbf{0} = \mathbf{r}(0) = \mathbf{d}$. So the solution of the differential equation (2.2) satisfying the required initial conditions is

$$\mathbf{r}(t) = ut\mathbf{i} - \tfrac{1}{2}gt^2\mathbf{j}.$$

We obtained this solution before as Equation (2.10). On the whole, working with vectors in this case is more compact and convenient.

Example 2.3

Consider two identical ramps, as shown in Figure 2.4. Identical ball-bearings are released at the top of each ramp in identical ways and at the same time. Consequently, each ball-bearing reaches the end of its ramp at the same time and with the same speed, say u. Ignore all resistive forces both for the upper ball-bearing moving through the air and for the lower ball-bearing rolling along the ground.

This 'projectile demonstrator' is shown in Part 1 of the video associated with this unit. A good moment to watch this video sequence is just after you have studied Example 2.3. However, it is not essential for you to watch the video at exactly that moment — it can be viewed whenever you find it convenient.

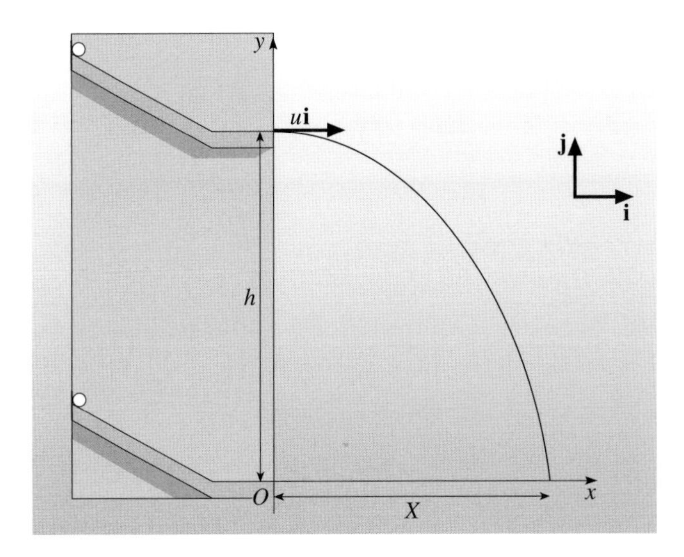

Figure 2.4 Projectile demonstrator

(a) What will be the relative positions of the ball-bearings when the ball-bearing from the upper ramp hits the ground?

(b) Suppose that the upper ramp is at a vertical height h above the lower ramp, and that the ball-bearing from the upper ramp hits the ground at a horizontal distance X from the end of the lower ramp. Find an expression giving X in terms of h and u.

Solution

(a) If resistive forces are negligible, each ball-bearing travels with constant speed in the x-direction. Since the ball-bearings leave their ramps at the same time with the same horizontal speed and the same horizontal position, we can see that their positions must have the same x-component at all times. So this applies when the upper ball-bearing hits the ground. At that instant, the two ball-bearings will (be trying to) occupy the same point in space. So if resistive forces are negligible, they should hit each other.

(b) We need to model the projectile motion of the upper ball-bearing from the time it leaves the ramp to when it hits the ground. We shall choose axes as shown in Figure 2.4, and choose $t = 0$ to be the instant when the upper ball-bearing leaves the ramp. The velocity as it leaves the ramp will be horizontal, with magnitude u, so we have the initial condition

$$\dot{\mathbf{r}}(0) = u\mathbf{i}.$$

The position at $t = 0$ is $x = 0$, $y = h$, so the initial position vector is

$$\mathbf{r}(0) = h\mathbf{j}.$$

The position at $t = 0$ is not the origin, as it was in previous examples.

To find the solution of Equation (2.2), $\ddot{\mathbf{r}}(t) = -g\mathbf{j}$, that satisfies these initial conditions, we need to integrate twice. Integrating once gives

$$\dot{\mathbf{r}}(t) = -gt\mathbf{j} + \mathbf{c},$$

where $\mathbf{c}$ is a constant vector. Since $\dot{\mathbf{r}}(0) = u\mathbf{i}$, putting $t = 0$ gives $\mathbf{c} = u\mathbf{i}$, so

$$\dot{\mathbf{r}}(t) = u\mathbf{i} - gt\mathbf{j}.$$

Integrating again gives

$$\mathbf{r}(t) = ut\mathbf{i} - \tfrac{1}{2}gt^2\mathbf{j} + \mathbf{d},$$

where $\mathbf{d}$ is a constant vector. Since $\mathbf{r}(0) = h\mathbf{j}$, putting $t = 0$ gives $\mathbf{d} = h\mathbf{j}$. Hence

$$\begin{aligned}\mathbf{r}(t) &= ut\mathbf{i} - \tfrac{1}{2}gt^2\mathbf{j} + h\mathbf{j} \\ &= ut\mathbf{i} + (h - \tfrac{1}{2}gt^2)\mathbf{j}.\end{aligned} \tag{2.12}$$

We can separate this vector solution into components, to obtain

$$x = ut,$$
$$y = h - \tfrac{1}{2}gt^2.$$

Alternatively, you could obtain these equations by uncoupling the equation of motion and solving for the x- and y-components separately.

When the upper ball-bearing hits the ground, $y = 0$. This occurs when

$$t = \pm\sqrt{\frac{2h}{g}}.$$

We are interested only in $t > 0$ (i.e. after the ball-bearing leaves the ramp), so we can reject the negative square root. At this time, the x-component is X, so, using $x = ut$, we have

$$X = u\sqrt{\frac{2h}{g}}. \quad \blacksquare$$

Now would be a good time to watch Part 1 of the video for this unit.

At the same time you may wish to watch Part 2 of the video, which is associated with Exercise 2.5.

In different runs of the projectile demonstrator in the video, u remains the same while the height h is varied and the distance X is measured. We expect X to be proportional to $\sqrt{h}$.

Exercise 2.2

Using the notation in Example 2.3, the experiment in the video produced the following data.

h (metres)	0.44	0.22	0.11
X (metres)	0.215	0.150	0.107

Are these data points consistent with the deduction in Example 2.3 that X is proportional to $\sqrt{h}$? What do the data points suggest for the value of u?

*Exercise 2.3

After a road accident, a crashed car is found on a sandy beach at the base of a cliff. The cliff is vertical and is 18 metres high. The investigating police officer finds that the marks in the sand resulting from the car's impact on the beach start 8 metres from the base of the cliff, and that the point of impact is at roughly the same horizontal level as the cliff base. The car appears to have been travelling at right angles to the cliff when it went over. Assuming that the car was travelling in a horizontal direction when it left the cliff, estimate the speed with which it went over.

Exercise 2.4

Figure 2.5 shows a side-on view of a ski-jump course. The jumper starts at A, skis down the slope AO, leaves the ground at O, and lands again at B. Assume that the jumper's velocity just after leaving the ground is horizontal, and ignore resistive forces.

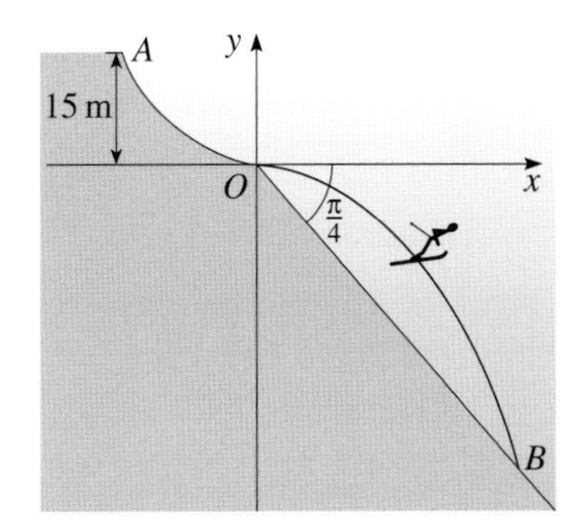

Figure 2.5

(a) Point A is 15 metres higher than O. Assume that there is no significant loss of mechanical energy as the jumper skis from A to O, and that the jumper's initial speed leaving A is zero. What is the jumper's speed just after leaving O?

Recall from *Unit 8* that mechanical energy is kinetic energy + potential energy.

(b) With axes as shown in Figure 2.5, use Equation (2.11), $y = -gx^2/(2u^2)$, to give the equation of the jumper's trajectory while the jumper is in the air.

(c) Assume that the slope OB is a straight line at an angle of $\frac{1}{4}\pi$ to the horizontal. What is the equation of the line OB?

(d) Use your answers to parts (b) and (c) to find the coordinates of point B and hence the distance OB.

(e) Suggest some factors not taken into account in this model of a ski-jump. In each case, indicate whether you think the factor would lead to a longer or shorter ski-jump (measured by the distance OB) being achieved.

Part 2 of the video for this unit shows an example of the type of motion that can be modelled using methods discussed in this subsection as well as those in Section 1. We suggest that you now watch this part of the video and try Exercise 2.5, which is associated with the situation shown in the video. This exercise provides further practice using methods that you have already met. The video has the advantage that you can see the situation being discussed, rather than having to visualize it on the basis of printed descriptions!

Watch Part 2 of the video for this unit now, before trying Exercise 2.5.

*Exercise 2.5

The video showed a buggy drive up a ramp, which was in a vertical plane, take off from the top of the ramp, and then land again (see Figure 2.6).

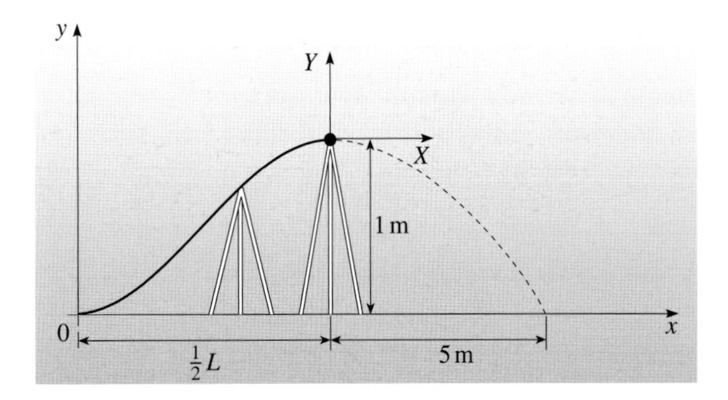

This diagram is not drawn to scale.

Figure 2.6

Model the buggy as a particle. Suppose that the vertical cross-section of the ramp can be modelled by an equation of the form

$$y = \frac{h}{2}\left(1 - \cos\left(\frac{2\pi x}{L}\right)\right) \quad (0 \leq x \leq 0.5L),$$

The notation is chosen to be consistent with that used in Subsection 1.2.

with $h = 1$ metre, where the origin is taken at the start of the ramp and y is the vertical height of the ramp at a horizontal distance x from the start (both measured in metres).

Suppose that the buggy drives up the ramp in such a way that the horizontal component of its velocity is constant. It takes off from the highest point of the ramp, travelling horizontally, and lands a horizontal distance of 5 metres from the take off point.

(a) Treating the buggy during its flight as a projectile, and assuming that air resistance is negligible, calculate the speed of the buggy at take off. (We suggest that you use the (X, Y)-axes shown in Figure 2.6 for this part.)

(b) If the vertical component of the force exerted by the ramp on the buggy at take off is zero, calculate the horizontal length $0.5L$ of the ramp.

2.2 Launches at an angle

Many examples of projectile motion involve launches at angles other than the horizontal; Figure 2.7 shows two such examples. Also, it is sometimes convenient to choose an origin that is not the point of projection, as we did in Example 2.3; Figure 2.7(b) provides another illustration. Furthermore, it may be convenient to take $t = 0$ at some time other than the moment of projection. All these complications will change the initial conditions of the projectile motion. None changes the fundamental equation of motion, however. So long as we choose the y-axis (and the unit vector $\mathbf{j}$) to be vertically upwards, and ignore air resistance, the only force on a projectile of mass m is that due to gravity, $-mg\mathbf{j}$, and Newton's second law gives $m\ddot{\mathbf{r}}(t) = -mg\mathbf{j}$, that is,

$$\ddot{\mathbf{r}}(t) = -g\mathbf{j}, \qquad (2.2)$$

as before. Different initial conditions will, however, change the constants that enter as we integrate this equation to obtain $\mathbf{r}(t)$.

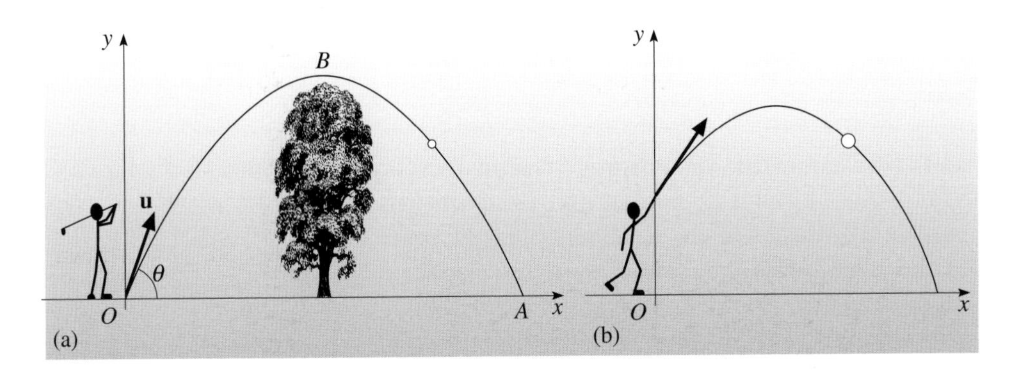

Figure 2.7 (a) Golf shot (b) Shot put

In this subsection we look first at projectile motion of the type illustrated in Figure 2.7(a), where the launch point and the impact point are in the same horizontal plane. Assume that the projectile is launched with speed u, at an angle θ above the horizontal. We shall derive expressions in terms of u and θ for the 'range' of the projectile's flight (OA in Figure 2.7(a)), and for the coordinates of the highest point of its trajectory (B in Figure 2.7(a)).

We refer to θ as the **launch angle**.

To solve the differential equation (2.2) we can integrate it twice. We shall work in the vector form. Integrating once gives

$$\dot{\mathbf{r}}(t) = -gt\mathbf{j} + \mathbf{c}, \tag{2.13}$$

where $\mathbf{c}$ is a constant vector. Integrating Equation (2.13) gives

$$\mathbf{r}(t) = -\tfrac{1}{2}gt^2\mathbf{j} + \mathbf{c}t + \mathbf{d}, \tag{2.14}$$

where $\mathbf{d}$ is a constant vector. We shall take $t = 0$ to be the moment of launch and the origin to be the point of launch. Then we have the initial condition

$$\mathbf{r}(0) = \mathbf{0}.$$

Substituting this into Equation (2.14) gives $\mathbf{d} = \mathbf{0}$, so we have

$$\mathbf{r}(t) = -\tfrac{1}{2}gt^2\mathbf{j} + \mathbf{c}t.$$

The constant vector $\mathbf{c}$ can be determined from a knowledge of the initial launch velocity. Suppose that the launch velocity is $\mathbf{u}$. Substituting $t = 0$ in Equation (2.13) gives $\dot{\mathbf{r}}(0) = \mathbf{u} = \mathbf{c}$, so

$$\mathbf{r}(t) = -\tfrac{1}{2}gt^2\mathbf{j} + \mathbf{u}t.$$

From this equation, we can see that the motion of the projectile is in the vertical plane which contains the launch velocity $\mathbf{u}$, as you might expect. We choose the horizontal x-axis to lie in this plane, as shown in Figures 2.7 and 2.8.

To express the launch velocity $\mathbf{u}$ in terms of the unit vectors $\mathbf{i}$ and $\mathbf{j}$, recall from *Unit 4* that we can resolve the vector $\mathbf{u}$ into its $\mathbf{i}$-component vector $(|\mathbf{u}|\cos\theta)\,\mathbf{i}$ and its $\mathbf{j}$-component vector $(|\mathbf{u}|\sin\theta)\,\mathbf{j}$ (see Figure 2.8). Since the launch speed is u, we have $|\mathbf{u}| = u$, so $\mathbf{u} = (u\cos\theta)\,\mathbf{i} + (u\sin\theta)\,\mathbf{j}$. So the solution of Equation (2.2) satisfying these initial conditions is

$$\begin{aligned}\mathbf{r}(t) &= -\tfrac{1}{2}gt^2\mathbf{j} + (u\cos\theta\,\mathbf{i} + u\sin\theta\,\mathbf{j})t \\ &= (ut\cos\theta)\mathbf{i} + (ut\sin\theta - \tfrac{1}{2}gt^2)\mathbf{j}.\end{aligned} \tag{2.15}$$

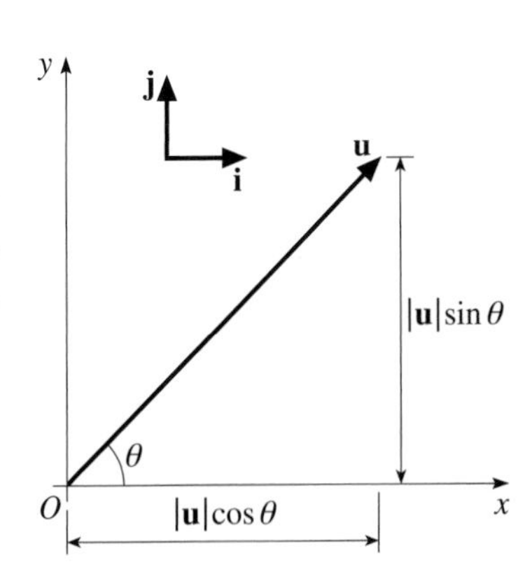

Figure 2.8

The velocity of the projectile is given by

$$\mathbf{v} = \dot{\mathbf{r}}(t) = (u\cos\theta)\mathbf{i} + (u\sin\theta - gt)\mathbf{j}.$$

The vector solution given by Equation (2.15) can be expressed as separate equations for the x- and y-coordinates as

$$x = ut\cos\theta, \tag{2.16}$$

$$y = ut\sin\theta - \tfrac{1}{2}gt^2. \tag{2.17}$$

So long as the ground is horizontal, we can define the **range** of the projectile to be the horizontal distance between the point of launch and the point of impact. To determine the projectile's range when the launch point and the impact point are in the same horizontal plane, note that the vertical coordinate of its position y will be zero at the launch and again when it hits the ground.

This definition of range is unlikely to be suitable where launch and impact are on an inclined plane, as in the ski-jump example in Exercise 2.4.

Putting $y = 0$ into Equation (2.17) gives

$$\begin{aligned} 0 &= ut\sin\theta - \tfrac{1}{2}gt^2 \\ &= t(u\sin\theta - \tfrac{1}{2}gt). \end{aligned}$$

This equation has two solutions, $t = 0$ and $t = (2u\sin\theta)/g$. At this latter time, the horizontal coordinate of the position x gives the range R of the projectile. From Equation (2.16), this is

$t = 0$ is the instant of launch.

$$R = u\frac{2u\sin\theta}{g}\cos\theta = \frac{2u^2\sin\theta\cos\theta}{g}.$$

Now $\sin 2\theta = 2\sin\theta\cos\theta$, so we have

See *Unit 1*, Section 3.

$$R = \frac{u^2\sin 2\theta}{g}. \tag{2.18}$$

The sine function never exceeds 1 in value, and we have $\sin 2\theta = 1$ when $2\theta = \frac{1}{2}\pi$, i.e. when $\theta = \frac{1}{4}\pi$. Since the launch angle must be between 0 and $\frac{1}{2}\pi$, other solutions can be ignored. So, for a given launch speed u, the maximum range R_{max} for a projectile on a horizontal surface (ignoring air resistance) is obtained using a launch angle of $\frac{1}{4}\pi$ to the horizontal, and this maximum range is

For a launch on horizontal ground, we must have $\theta > 0$. (For a launch from above ground level, such as from a cliff or bridge, we could have a launch angle below the horizontal, when θ would be negative.)

$$R_{\text{max}} = \frac{u^2}{g}. \tag{2.19}$$

From Equation (2.17), we see that y is a quadratic function of t, with a negative coefficient of t^2. So the graph of y against t is part of a parabola opening downwards. Such a parabola has a single stationary point where $\dot{y}(t) = 0$, and this will give the maximum value of y. Differentiating Equation (2.17) with respect to t gives

The condition $\dot{y}(t) = 0$ is equivalent to asserting that the vertical component of the velocity is zero when the projectile is at its maximum height.

$$\dot{y}(t) = u\sin\theta - gt,$$

and this is 0 when $u\sin\theta - gt = 0$, i.e. when $t = (u\sin\theta)/g$. Substituting $t = (u\sin\theta)/g$ into the right-hand side of Equation (2.17), the corresponding *maximum height* is given by

$$\begin{aligned} H &= u\left(\frac{u\sin\theta}{g}\right)\sin\theta - \frac{g}{2}\left(\frac{u\sin\theta}{g}\right)^2 \\ &= \frac{u^2\sin^2\theta}{g} - \frac{u^2\sin^2\theta}{2g} = \frac{u^2\sin^2\theta}{2g}. \end{aligned} \tag{2.20}$$

Substituting $t = (u\sin\theta)/g$ into the right-hand side of Equation (2.16), the x-component of the projectile's position at the point of maximum height is, using $\sin 2\theta = 2\sin\theta\cos\theta$,

$$\begin{aligned} x &= u\left(\frac{u\sin\theta}{g}\right)\cos\theta \\ &= \frac{u^2\sin\theta\cos\theta}{g} = \frac{u^2\sin 2\theta}{2g}. \end{aligned} \tag{2.21}$$

Thus the maximum height occurs when x is half the range R, as you might expect.

The results derived above apply to any projectile where the points of launch and impact are in the same horizontal plane (and air resistance is ignored). Some problems involving projectiles can conveniently be solved by direct use of these results.

Example 2.4

During a particular downhill run, a short but sharp rise causes a skier to leave the ground at $25\,\text{m}\,\text{s}^{-1}$ at an angle of $\frac{1}{6}\pi$ above the horizontal. The ground immediately beyond the rise is horizontal for 60 metres. After this, the slope is again downhill. Will the skier land on the level ground or on the downhill slope beyond it?

Solution

Model the skier as a particle launched from the end of the rise (see Figure 2.9). With $u = 25\,\text{m}\,\text{s}^{-1}$ and $\theta = \frac{1}{6}\pi$, the expression in Equation (2.18) for the range on a horizontal surface gives

$$R = \frac{25^2 \sin \frac{1}{3}\pi}{9.81} \simeq 55.17 \text{ metres.}$$

Since this is less than 60 metres, it would seem that the skier will land on the flat part of the run.

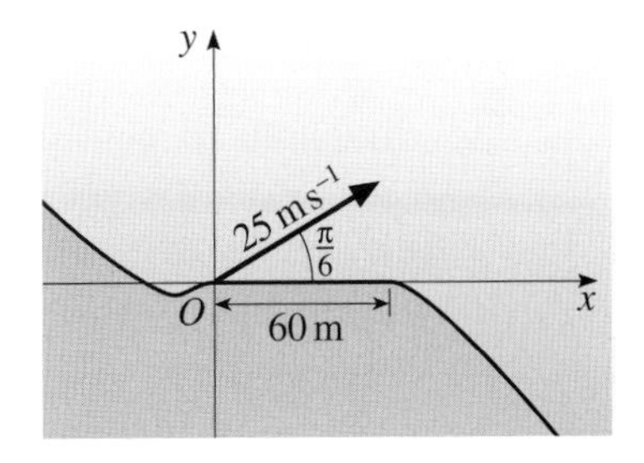

Figure 2.9

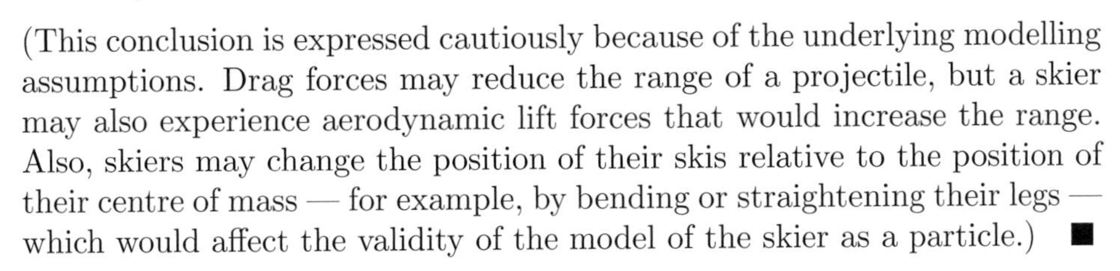
(This conclusion is expressed cautiously because of the underlying modelling assumptions. Drag forces may reduce the range of a projectile, but a skier may also experience aerodynamic lift forces that would increase the range. Also, skiers may change the position of their skis relative to the position of their centre of mass — for example, by bending or straightening their legs — which would affect the validity of the model of the skier as a particle.) ■

This example illustrates how efficiently some questions can be answered by use of general results, such as those giving the range and the maximum height of a projectile when the launch point and the impact point are in the same horizontal plane. When using the results in this subsection in this way, it is important to ensure that they are applicable. We could not, for example, use Equation (2.18) to determine how far the shot putter illustrated in Figure 2.7(b) would send the shot, since there the point of impact is *not* in the same horizontal plane as that of the launch. It is important to pay attention to the methodology used in deriving these results, since it can be used in other cases of projectile motion. In the absence of air resistance, we always arrive at the same vector differential equation (2.2) from Newton's second law. In general, we then need to identify the initial conditions appropriate to the particular situation, find the solution of Equation (2.2) satisfying those initial conditions, and use the solution to address the specific question(s) of interest in the particular problem.

**Exercise 2.6*

A ball kicked from a flat piece of ground at an angle of $\frac{1}{6}\pi$ above the horizontal lands 40 metres away from where it was kicked. What is the greatest height above the ground that the ball will have reached?

**Exercise 2.7*

Consider a projectile launched at an angle θ above the horizontal, from a point at a height h above the origin, with speed u. Take $t = 0$ to be the moment of launch, and use the coordinate system (and associated unit vectors) shown in Figure 2.10. Find the solution of Equation (2.2) satisfying these initial conditions.

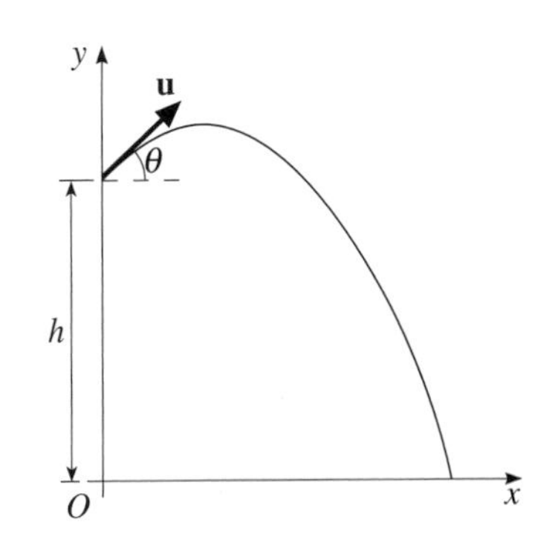

Figure 2.10

The vector solution obtained in Exercise 2.7 can be expressed as separate equations for the components x and y of the position of such a projectile at time t:

$$x = ut\cos\theta, \qquad (2.22)$$

$$y = h + ut\sin\theta - \tfrac{1}{2}gt^2. \qquad (2.23)$$

Equation (2.22) is identical to Equation (2.16) as the differential equation for x and its initial conditions are unchanged.

As one might expect, launch at a height h simply adds a term h to the y-coordinate.

We conclude this subsection with a summary of its main results.

Projectiles without air resistance

The equation of motion of a projectile subject only to the force of gravity is

$$\ddot{\mathbf{r}}(t) = -g\mathbf{j}, \qquad (2.2)$$

where $\mathbf{j}$ is a unit vector pointing vertically upwards. If the projectile is launched at time $t = 0$, from the point $x = 0$, $y = 0$, with launch speed u in the (x, y)-plane and launch angle θ above the horizontal, the solution of the equation of motion satisfying these initial conditions is

$$x = ut\cos\theta, \qquad (2.16)$$

$$y = ut\sin\theta - \tfrac{1}{2}gt^2. \qquad (2.17)$$

The maximum height H reached by such a projectile is

$$H = \frac{u^2\sin^2\theta}{2g}. \qquad (2.20)$$

The range R of such a projectile is

$$R = \frac{u^2\sin 2\theta}{g}. \qquad (2.18)$$

The maximum range R_{max} for a launch speed u is achieved with a launch angle $\theta = \frac{1}{4}\pi$ and is

$$R_{\text{max}} = \frac{u^2}{g}. \qquad (2.19)$$

If you encounter different initial conditions, you should go back to Equation (2.2) and find the appropriate solution by integration. However, if launch is from $x(0) = 0$, $y(0) = h$, then we need to modify the solutions of the equation of motion (2.2) given in Equations (2.16) and (2.17) by adding a term h to the right-hand side of Equation (2.17) as given in Equation (2.23). (In this case, the results for the range and the maximum height are *not* applicable.)

Exercise 2.8

A shot putter launches a shot at a speed of $13\,\text{m}\,\text{s}^{-1}$ at an angle of $\frac{1}{6}\pi$ above the horizontal from a height of 1.8 metres above ground level. How far will the shot travel in the horizontal direction before it hits the ground, assuming that the ground is horizontal?

Exercise 2.9

A stone is thrown from a height of 1.5 metres above horizontal ground at an angle of $\frac{1}{4}\pi$ above the horizontal and lands at a distance of 30 metres from the point where it was thrown. Estimate the speed with which it was thrown.

2.3 The trajectory of a projectile

There is a variety of problems you may be asked about the motion of projectiles. Some can be 'pigeonholed', perhaps requiring you to find the range, or to ensure that a target is hit. Others may require you to bring information about the flight of a projectile to bear on the problem in less predictable ways. We start this subsection with problems that involve hitting a target.

The trajectory of a projectile is the path it traces. To hit some target, say at P, we require that the point P lies on the trajectory. Suppose that a projectile has launch speed u and launch angle θ above the horizontal, and that it is launched from $(0, 0)$ at time $t = 0$. Then, from work in the previous subsection, we have

A launch angle *below* the horizontal would correspond to a negative value of θ.

$$x = ut\cos\theta, \tag{2.16}$$

$$y = ut\sin\theta - \tfrac{1}{2}gt^2. \tag{2.17}$$

If we have no interest in *when* the projectile hits a target, it is efficient to eliminate t to obtain an equation for the trajectory relating y and x directly. Equation (2.16) gives $t = x/(u\cos\theta)$, and substituting this into Equation (2.17) gives

$$\begin{aligned} y &= u\frac{x}{u\cos\theta}\sin\theta - \frac{g}{2}\left(\frac{x}{u\cos\theta}\right)^2 \\ &= x\tan\theta - x^2\frac{g}{2u^2}\sec^2\theta. \end{aligned} \tag{2.24}$$

We see that y is a quadratic function of x, and hence that the trajectory is part of a parabola.

As illustrated in Example 2.5 below, it is often convenient to replace $\sec^2\theta$ by $1 + \tan^2\theta$, giving

See *Unit 1*, Section 3.

$$y = x\tan\theta - x^2\frac{g}{2u^2}(1 + \tan^2\theta), \tag{2.25}$$

which is a quadratic equation in $\tan\theta$.

Example 2.5

A golfer wants to play a recovery shot through a copse of trees. There is a small gap in the foliage at a height of 12 metres and 40 metres in front of the golfer. The golfer knows that, with his usual swing, he hits the ball at about $35\,\mathrm{m\,s^{-1}}$. What angle of launch would enable the ball to hit the gap in the foliage?

Solution

The golfer wants the trajectory of the ball to pass through the point $x = 40$, $y = 12$ (working in SI units). So, from Equation (2.25) with $u = 35$, we have

$$\begin{aligned} 12 &= 40\tan\theta - 40^2\frac{9.81}{2\times 35^2}(1 + \tan^2\theta) \\ &= 40\tan\theta - 6.407(1 + \tan^2\theta), \end{aligned}$$

so

$$6.407\tan^2\theta - 40\tan\theta + 18.407 = 0.$$

This is a quadratic equation for $\tan\theta$ and has the two solutions

$$\tan\theta = 0.5002, \quad \tan\theta = 5.743.$$

Each of these gives a single value for θ in the range $0 \le \theta \le \frac{1}{2}\pi$, namely

$$\theta = 0.4638\ (26.58^\circ), \quad \theta = 1.398\ (80.12^\circ).$$

We see that there are two possible launch angles that strike the target (see Figure 2.11). In this example, the choice of a launch angle of about 27° is perhaps more likely to be suitable, since the other choice would have the ball descending through the foliage at a steep angle, when it would be more likely to hit part of a tree. ■

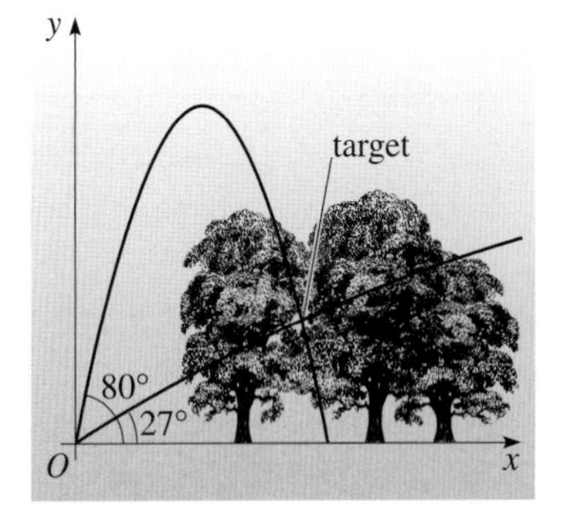

Figure 2.11 Two launch angles to hit the target

In any problem where we need to find a launch angle (given the launch speed) to hit a specified target, we arrive at a quadratic equation for $\tan\theta$, namely Equation (2.25). So long as this equation has two distinct real roots, there will be two launch angles that enable the target to be hit. Of course, the roots may coincide. In either case, we say that the target is **achievable**. On the other hand, we may arrive at a quadratic equation with no real roots. In this case, the target is not achievable — for the given launch speed, there is no launch angle that enables the target to be hit.

*Exercise 2.10

Suppose that a projectile has launch speed u at an angle θ above the horizontal, and that it is launched from $(0, h)$ at time $t = 0$. (That is, the projectile is launched at a height h above the origin.) By eliminating t from Equations (2.22) and (2.23), obtain an equation (relating y to x) for the trajectory of such a projectile.

We see from Exercise 2.10 that for a launch at a height h above the origin, we need to add only a term h to the right-hand side of Equation (2.25) for the trajectory. This result is frequently useful.

Trajectory of a projectile

For a projectile launched at time $t = 0$ from $(0, h)$ with launch speed u and launch angle θ above the horizontal, the trajectory has the equation

$$y = h + x\tan\theta - x^2\frac{g}{2u^2}\sec^2\theta. \qquad (2.26)$$

It is often convenient to use the trigonometric identity

$$\sec^2\theta = 1 + \tan^2\theta$$

to give

$$y = h + x\tan\theta - x^2\frac{g}{2u^2}(1 + \tan^2\theta), \qquad (2.27)$$

which is a quadratic equation in $\tan\theta$.

*Exercise 2.11

A basketball player is 2.6 metres (horizontally) from the goal. The goal is 3 metres above ground level. The player launches the ball at $7\,\mathrm{m\,s^{-1}}$, and from a height of 1.8 metres above ground level. What angle of launch should the player choose?

We now look at an example that requires more work to answer the posed question.

Example 2.6

This example concerns baseball fielders throwing the ball back to the catcher. Assume throughout that the point of launch and the point of impact are at the same horizontal level.

(a) A fielder can just throw a ball a distance of 60 metres. How fast can the fielder throw the ball?

(b) A fielder needs to throw a ball to the catcher from a distance of 58 metres. Assuming that the fielder throws directly to the catcher, at the speed calculated in part (a), what is the shortest time in which the fielder can return the ball to the catcher?

(c) Suppose that a second fielder is mid-way between the first fielder and the catcher (so that each gap is 29 metres), and that each fielder throws at the speed calculated in part (a). The first fielder throws to the second fielder, then the second fielder throws to the catcher. As well as the time in flight, the second fielder requires 0.3 seconds to catch and throw the ball. Would this 'relaying' result in a quicker return of the ball to the catcher?

Solution

(a) In the previous subsection we found that the maximum range of a projectile (for launch speed u) is achieved at a launch angle $\frac{1}{4}\pi$, and this maximum range is u^2/g (Equation (2.19)). So, for the fielder, we have $u^2/g = 60$, which gives

$$u = \sqrt{60g} = \sqrt{60 \times 9.81} = 24.26.$$

So the fielder can throw the ball at a speed of approximately $24.26\,\mathrm{m\,s^{-1}}$.

(b) Taking the point of launch as origin, and working in metres, the trajectory of the ball needs to pass through the point $(58, 0)$. So, using Equation (2.25), we need a launch angle θ where

$$0 = 58\tan\theta - 58^2 \frac{g}{2 \times 60g}(1 + \tan^2\theta).$$

It is simpler, as well as more accurate, to use $u = \sqrt{60g}$ here.

This can be rearranged as

$$\tan^2\theta - \frac{120}{58}\tan\theta + 1 = 0.$$

This quadratic equation has solutions $\tan\theta = 0.7696$ and $\tan\theta = 1.299$. The corresponding values of θ (between 0 and $\frac{1}{2}\pi$) are 0.6559 (37.58°) and 0.9149 (52.42°). Throwing the ball at either of these angles will return it to the catcher.

To find the time that it takes the ball to reach the catcher, we can use Equation (2.16). When $x = 58$ metres, the time t (in seconds) must satisfy

$$58 = ut\cos\theta = \sqrt{60g}\,t\cos\theta.$$

We obtain different times depending on the choice of the launch angle θ. With $\theta = 0.6559$, the time is 3.017 seconds. With $\theta = 0.9149$, the time is 3.920 seconds. As one might expect, the lower angle of launch gives the shorter flight time, so the fastest possible return time is 3.017 seconds.

(c) The total time to return the ball to the catcher is $2T + 0.3$ seconds, where T is the time (in seconds) to throw the ball 29 metres at the launch speed calculated in (a). To ensure that the ball passes through the point $(29, 0)$, we need a launch angle θ satisfying Equation (2.25) with these coordinates, that is,

$$0 = 29\tan\theta - 29^2 \frac{g}{120g}(1 + \tan^2\theta),$$

so that

$$\tan^2\theta - \frac{120}{29}\tan\theta + 1 = 0.$$

This has solutions $\tan\theta = 0.2577$ and $\tan\theta = 3.880$. The corresponding launch angles are 0.2522 (14.45°) and 1.319 (75.55°). Flight times are 1.234 seconds and 4.790 seconds. The lower launch angle gives the smaller flight time, and the total return time to the catcher for the 'relay' is

$$2 \times 1.234 + 0.3 = 2.769 \text{ seconds}.$$

This time *is* shorter than the time found in (b) for a direct throw. ■

In the previous subsection we saw that, for a launch speed u on a horizontal surface, the maximum range for a projectile is obtained with a launch angle $\frac{1}{4}\pi$ and is u^2/g (Equation (2.19)). We next consider the angle of launch required to give the maximum range when launch is from *above* ground level.

We continue to define the range to be the horizontal displacement between the point of launch and the point of impact, even for a launch above ground level. The following calculation of the maximum range brings together ideas about projectiles and methods from calculus. The approaches we shall use are chosen to minimize the complexity of the algebra; they are not always those that first come to mind.

This horizontal displacement measures the length of a shot put, for example.

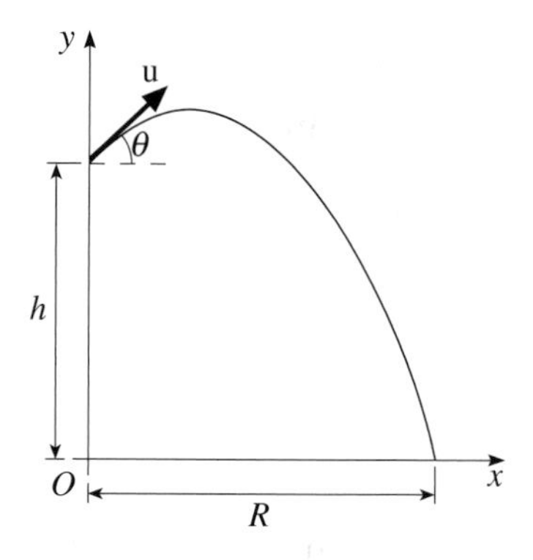

Figure 2.12

Consider a projectile launched with speed u from a point at a height h above the ground, which we assume is horizontal. We choose the origin and axes as shown in Figure 2.12, and $t = 0$ as the time of launch. If the launch angle is θ above the horizontal, the equation of the trajectory is

$$y = h + x\tan\theta - x^2\frac{g}{2u^2}(1+\tan^2\theta). \qquad (2.27)$$

Let R be the range. Then, since $(R, 0)$ lies on the trajectory, we have

$$0 = h + R\tan\theta - R^2\frac{g}{2u^2}(1+\tan^2\theta).$$

Defining $z = \tan\theta$ and $L = u^2/g$ gives

$$0 = h + Rz - \frac{R^2}{2L}(1+z^2). \qquad (2.28)$$

We assume that $-\frac{1}{2}\pi < \theta < \frac{1}{2}\pi$. Note that a negative value for θ corresponds to a launch angle below the horizontal.

For a given launch speed and height, h and L are constants. We want to maximize the range R by choice of the launch angle θ or, equivalently, by choice of z. The global maximum of a function can occur at a stationary point or at an end point of its domain. However, the endpoints of the domain, $\theta = -\frac{1}{2}\pi$ and $\theta = \frac{1}{2}\pi$, both lead to a range of $R = 0$ (the motion is straight up and down), so the maximum range must occur at a stationary point. In order to simplify the algebra, we shall consider R as a function of z, so we want to find values of z for which $dR/dz = 0$. Now implicit differentiation of Equation (2.28) with respect to z gives

Implicit differentiation was discussed in *Unit 1*, Section 5.

$$0 = \frac{d}{dz}\left(zR(z)\right) - \frac{1}{2L}\frac{d}{dz}\left((1+z^2)R(z)^2\right),$$

or

$$0 = \left(R + z\frac{dR}{dz}\right) - \frac{1}{2L}\left(2zR^2 + (1+z^2)2R\frac{dR}{dz}\right).$$

Setting $dR/dz = 0$ reduces this equation to

$$0 = R - \frac{zR^2}{L}.$$

So the maximum range occurs when $z = L/R$. Substituting $z = L/R$ into Equation (2.28) gives

$$\begin{aligned}0 &= h + R\frac{L}{R} - \frac{R^2}{2L}\left(1+\frac{L^2}{R^2}\right)\\ &= h + L - \frac{R^2}{2L} - \frac{L}{2}\\ &= h + \frac{L}{2} - \frac{R^2}{2L}.\end{aligned}$$

Hence

$$R = \sqrt{L^2 + 2Lh}. \qquad (2.29)$$

This maximum range is achieved when

$$\tan\theta = z = \frac{L}{R} = \frac{L}{\sqrt{L^2 + 2Lh}} = \frac{1}{\sqrt{1 + 2h/L}},$$

that is, when

$$\theta = \arctan\left(\frac{1}{\sqrt{1 + 2h/L}}\right). \qquad (2.30)$$

Strictly speaking we have not shown that the range given by Equation (2.29) *is* a maximum. All we have shown is that it is a stationary value, which could also be a minimum value, for example. However, physically we know that the projectile does have a maximum range and, as $z = L/R$ is the only stationary point, this stationary point must be a maximum. Alternatively, we could show mathematically that the stationary point given by $z = L/R$ is a maximum by considering the sign of the second derivative d^2R/dz^2.

Maximum range for an elevated launch

A projectile launched with speed u from a height h above ground level has maximum range R_{max} on horizontal ground given by

$$R_{max} = \sqrt{L^2 + 2Lh}, \qquad (2.29)$$

where $L = u^2/g$. This maximum range is achieved using the launch angle

$$\theta = \arctan\left(\frac{1}{\sqrt{1 + 2h/L}}\right). \qquad (2.30)$$

If $h = 0$, Equation (2.29) gives $R_{max} = L$, as it should, since L is the maximum range for a launch from ground level (when $h = 0$). Also, if $h > 0$, then $R_{max} > L$. As one might expect, a launch from above ground level achieves a maximum range greater (for the same launch velocity) than one at ground level. More generally, the greater the height of the launch point, the greater the maximum range.

With $h = 0$, Equation (2.30) gives $\theta = \arctan 1 = \frac{1}{4}\pi$, again corresponding to our previous result for a launch from ground level.

Exercise 2.12

At a tutorial, one of the students, who happens to be an expert shot putter, asserts that aiming to launch at an angle $\frac{1}{4}\pi$ has always been good enough for them. The student says that improving launch speed is the key to good shot putting. Assume that the student launches the shot from a height of 2 metres above ground level.

(a) The student can put a shot 17 metres with a launch angle $\frac{1}{4}\pi$ above the horizontal. Calculate the speed at which the shot is being launched to achieve this range.

(b) For launch at the speed calculated in part (a), use Equations (2.29) and (2.30) to find the optimum launch angle and the corresponding range.

(c) If the student achieves a launch speed 1% higher than that calculated in part (a) and launches at an angle $\frac{1}{4}\pi$ above the horizontal, what range will the student achieve?

Exercise 2.13

A footballer taking a free kick launches the ball from ground level so that it just clears a player who is 10 metres away and 2 metres high. The ball enters the goal 30 metres away at a height of 2.4 metres.

As usual in this unit, model the ball as a particle. This means that any swerve that a footballer may achieve by kicking the ball with spin will be overlooked.

(a) Take as the origin the point from which the ball was kicked. Let the launch speed be u and the launch angle above the horizontal be θ. Use Equation (2.24) twice to obtain two equations that u and θ must satisfy.

Multiply one of these equations by a suitable constant, so that the term $(g\sec^2\theta)/2u^2$ has the same coefficient in each equation. Then subtract one equation from the other to eliminate u, and thus obtain an equation that is satisfied by $\tan\theta$. Hence find the launch angle θ.

(b) At what speed was the ball kicked? What period of time elapsed from the moment the ball was kicked until it entered the goal?

2.4 Energy and projectile motion

For solving certain mechanics problems, conservation of mechanical energy provides an efficient approach. In *Unit 8* we showed that total mechanical energy is conserved for an object moving in one dimension subject to the influence of a force that depends only on the object's position; that is, we have

$$\text{kinetic energy} + \text{potential energy} = \text{a constant}$$

throughout the object's motion. Now, gravity is a force that depends only on an object's position, so we might hope that mechanical energy will be conserved for the motion of a projectile in the absence of air resistance, even though the motion is not in one dimension. The kinetic energy of a particle is $\frac{1}{2}mv^2$, where m is its mass and v is its speed. So, for a particle of mass m with velocity $\mathbf{v} = v_1\mathbf{i} + v_2\mathbf{j}$,

We emphasize 'in the absence of air resistance' here, because mechanical energy is *not* conserved when resistive forces are present, since such forces depend on the object's velocity.

$$\text{kinetic energy} = \tfrac{1}{2}m|\mathbf{v}|^2 = \tfrac{1}{2}m(v_1^2 + v_2^2). \qquad (2.31)$$

The potential energy due to gravity is $mg \times$ height, where the height is measured upwards from a chosen datum. For projectile models, it is natural to choose the datum at $y = 0$, and then

$$\text{potential energy} = mgy.$$

Using results established earlier, we now show that mechanical energy *is* conserved for a projectile not subject to air resistance. Consider a particle of mass m, launched with speed u at an angle θ above the horizontal. Without loss of generality, we can choose the origin as the point of launch, and $t = 0$ as the moment of launch. At time t, if the components of its velocity are v_1 in the x-direction and v_2 in the y-direction, differentiating Equations (2.16) and (2.17) gives

$$v_1 = u\cos\theta, \qquad (2.32)$$

$$v_2 = u\sin\theta - gt. \qquad (2.33)$$

The kinetic energy of the projectile is, from Equation (2.31),

$$\begin{aligned}
\tfrac{1}{2}m|\mathbf{v}|^2 &= \tfrac{1}{2}m(v_1^2 + v_2^2) \\
&= \tfrac{1}{2}m\left(u^2\cos^2\theta + (u\sin\theta - gt)^2\right) \\
&= \tfrac{1}{2}m(u^2\cos^2\theta + u^2\sin^2\theta - 2ugt\sin\theta + g^2t^2) \\
&= \tfrac{1}{2}m(u^2 - 2ugt\sin\theta + g^2t^2) \\
&= \tfrac{1}{2}m\left(u^2 - 2g(ut\sin\theta - \tfrac{1}{2}gt^2)\right).
\end{aligned}$$

$\cos^2\theta + \sin^2\theta = 1$

Using Equation (2.17), $y = ut\sin\theta - \frac{1}{2}gt^2$, we can write this as

$$\tfrac{1}{2}m|\mathbf{v}|^2 = \tfrac{1}{2}m(u^2 - 2gy).$$

Hence $\frac{1}{2}m|\mathbf{v}|^2 + mgy = \frac{1}{2}mu^2$.

The expression $\frac{1}{2}m|\mathbf{v}|^2 + mgy$ gives the total mechanical energy of the projectile at time t. We have shown it to be independent of t and equal to the kinetic energy at launch (when, because of our choice of datum, the potential energy is zero).

Conservation of mechanical energy

The mechanical energy of a projectile subject only to the force of gravity is conserved during its motion.

This result can be useful in answering certain questions, particularly where we wish to relate a projectile's speed to its height.

Exercise 2.14

A stone thrown at $11\,\mathrm{m\,s^{-1}}$ hits a target at a height of 1 metre above and a horizontal distance of 10 metres from the point from where it was thrown. Use the conservation of mechanical energy to find the speed of the stone when it hits the target.

Exercise 2.15

Consider a particle launched from the origin with speed u at an angle θ above the horizontal. Using energy considerations, find the greatest distance above the ground that the object will reach (assuming the ground to be horizontal), and check your result against that given by Equation (2.20).

End-of-section Exercises

Exercise 2.16

(a) Find the solution of the differential equation $\ddot{\mathbf{r}}(t) = -g\mathbf{j}$ satisfying the initial conditions $\dot{\mathbf{r}}(0) = v\mathbf{j}$ and $\mathbf{r}(0) = a\mathbf{i} + b\mathbf{j}$, where the direction of $\mathbf{i}$ is horizontal and the direction of $\mathbf{j}$ is vertically upwards.

(b) If the motion of a projectile is described by the equations in part (a), how must it have been launched? Describe the subsequent motion. Is your description reflected in the solution you have found?

Exercise 2.17

(a) A cricket ball thrown at $20\,\mathrm{m\,s^{-1}}$ is caught 20 metres away from the thrower. At what angle to the horizontal was it thrown? (Assume that the point of launch and the catch are at the same height above the ground.)

(b) A cricket ball is thrown in the same way as in part (a). What is the highest tree that the ball could clear on the way? At what horizontal distance from the thrower is this maximum height achieved?

(c) A man standing on one side of a line of trees about 20 metres high sees that he has a clear path enabling him to run fast through the trees to the other side. Standing 10 metres from the trees, he offers a friend a bet that, starting from that point, he can throw a cricket ball over the trees, run through, and catch it when it comes down on the other side. His friend knows that the man can throw a cricket ball about 50 metres on level ground, that he is a good runner and can catch well. If you were the friend, would you take the bet?

Exercise 2.18

In a fairground variation on a coconut shy, square targets with sides of 0.1 metre are placed vertically 20 metres from the thrower, with their lower edges 3 metres above, and parallel to, the ground. Balls are thrown at these targets. In order to dislodge a target, a ball must to be travelling at around $12\,\mathrm{m\,s^{-1}}$ or more when it hits.

(a) A contestant can throw in a controlled way at $15\,\mathrm{m\,s^{-1}}$, but is concerned whether, after such a throw, the ball will be travelling fast enough if it hits. Could it dislodge a target?

(b) Assuming that launch speed is $15\,\mathrm{m\,s^{-1}}$ and the point of launch is 1 metre above ground level, what range of launch angles will hit the target?

3 Resisted projectiles

In the previous section you were introduced to methods of analysing the motion of projectiles on the assumption that air resistance can be neglected. Here we shall consider how air resistance may affect projectile motion. In *Unit 6* you met two models for the way the air resistance force, $\mathbf{R}$ say, on an object depends on the object's velocity $\mathbf{v}$ and size. For a smooth spherical object of diameter D, the linear model of air resistance $\mathbf{R} = -c_1 D\mathbf{v}$ is valid for values of $D|\mathbf{v}|$ up to about 10^{-5} (in SI units). The quadratic model of air resistance $\mathbf{R} = -c_2 D^2|\mathbf{v}|\mathbf{v}$ is valid for $D|\mathbf{v}|$ between about 10^{-2} and about 1 (in SI units). (For air, we have $c_1 \simeq 1.7 \times 10^{-4}$ and $c_2 \simeq 0.20$.)

A cricket ball has diameter about 0.07 metres. If this is thrown at $15\,\mathrm{m\,s^{-1}}$, we have $D|\mathbf{v}| = 1.05$. This is typical of the many sporting and athletic examples considered in Section 2, and we see that the linear model is not appropriate for these. The value of $D|\mathbf{v}| = 1.05$ is only just outside the range of validity for the quadratic model, so we shall consider the quadratic model here.

To describe resisted projectile motion in two dimensions, we shall use (as in Section 2) a horizontal x-axis and vertically upwards y-axis with corresponding Cartesian unit vectors $\mathbf{i}$ and $\mathbf{j}$. The forces on the projectile consist of its weight $\mathbf{W} = -mg\mathbf{j}$ and the resistive force $\mathbf{R}$, which is given by

$$\begin{aligned}\mathbf{R} &= -c_2 D^2|\mathbf{v}|\mathbf{v}\\ &= -c_2 D^2\left(\sqrt{\dot{x}^2 + \dot{y}^2}\right)(\dot{x}\mathbf{i} + \dot{y}\mathbf{j}).\end{aligned}$$

Newton's second law gives

$$\begin{aligned} m(\ddot{x}\mathbf{i}+\ddot{y}\mathbf{j}) &= m\ddot{\mathbf{r}} \\ &= \mathbf{R}+\mathbf{W} \\ &= -c_2D^2\dot{x}\sqrt{\dot{x}^2+\dot{y}^2}\,\mathbf{i} - c_2D^2\dot{y}\sqrt{\dot{x}^2+\dot{y}^2}\,\mathbf{j} - mg\mathbf{j}. \end{aligned}$$

Dividing by m and putting $c = c_2D^2/m$ gives

$$\ddot{x}\mathbf{i}+\ddot{y}\mathbf{j} = -c\dot{x}\sqrt{\dot{x}^2+\dot{y}^2}\,\mathbf{i} - c\dot{y}\sqrt{\dot{x}^2+\dot{y}^2}\,\mathbf{j} - g\mathbf{j}.$$

Equating the components in the **i**- and **j**-directions on both sides of this equation gives the pair of differential equations in the box below.

Modelling a projectile subject to quadratic air resistance

For a smooth spherical object of mass m and diameter D, subject only to the forces of gravity and air resistance, and assuming the quadratic model of air resistance, we have

$$\begin{aligned} \ddot{x} &= -c\dot{x}\sqrt{\dot{x}^2+\dot{y}^2}, \\ \ddot{y} &= -c\dot{y}\sqrt{\dot{x}^2+\dot{y}^2} - g, \end{aligned} \qquad (3.1)$$

where x and y are the horizontal and vertically upwards coordinates of the projectile's position, and $c = c_2D^2/m$, with $c_2 \simeq 0.20$.

There are $\dot{x}$ and $\dot{y}$ terms in both of these differential equations, and we consequently refer to them as *coupled*. What is more, they involve the square root of the sum of the squares of derivatives, and so are *non-linear*. We cannot solve these differential equations exactly. However, they can be handled numerically on a computer.

In the remainder of this section you will use your computer and a multimedia package to investigate examples of projectile motion. The multimedia package will take you through the analysis of some examples captured on video (a shot put and thrown balls of various types). From the video, data have been extracted on launch velocities and heights. Measurements of D and m were also made for each object. Using numerical solutions of Equations (3.1) generated by the computer algebra package, you will be able to calculate the range predicted by the model, taking air resistance into account. For each example, this prediction can then be compared with the range actually achieved and also with that predicted by the model in Section 2 where air resistance was ignored.

Now work through the multimedia package for this unit.

PC

There is a computer file that can be used to solve Equations (3.1). To use it, you need to know values for the mass m and diameter D of the projectile being investigated, and also its launch height, launch speed and launch angle. You will use this file to investigate the effect of launch speed on the range of a projectile subject to air resistance.

Use your computer to complete the following activity.

Activity 3.1

A tennis ball with mass $m = 0.06$ kilograms and diameter $D = 0.065$ metres is launched at a height of 2 metres with launch angle $\frac{1}{4}\pi$.

(a) For the launch speeds listed below (in m s^{-1}), find the range predicted by the quadratic air resistance model and the range predicted by the model in Section 2 in which air resistance is ignored.

(i) 10 (ii) 20 (iii) 30 (iv) 50 (v) 100 (vi) 200

(b) In broad terms, how does the ratio

$$\frac{\text{range with air resistance included}}{\text{range with air resistance ignored}}$$

change as the launch speed is increased?

Outcomes

After studying this unit you should:

- be able to apply Newton's second law in vector form to problems in more than one dimension;
- be able to calculate the force exerted by the seat on a passenger in a car in constant acceleration up or down an inclined plane;
- be able to solve problems concerning motion over a hump-backed bridge of given profile with a constant horizontal component of speed;
- be able to calculate the velocity and acceleration of a particle whose position in space is a given function of time, and use this to determine forces on vehicles and passengers following such specified paths;
- in a model of motion that involves a normal reaction between an object and a surface, where the object is not anchored to the surface in any way, be aware that if the model implies a normal reaction that is negative, then such motion is likely to be impossible;
- be able to integrate a vector function;
- be able to interpret terminology introduced here concerning projectile motion;
- be able to solve problems relating to the motion of a projectile in the absence of air resistance;
- be aware that total mechanical energy is conserved for projectile motion without air resistance, and use this in solving appropriate problems;
- be able to use your computer to solve problems concerning the motion of a projectile subject to air resistance governed by a quadratic model.

Solutions to the exercises

Section 1

1.1 The forces on the passenger are the passenger's weight **W** and the force **R** exerted by the seat. Suppose that **R** makes an angle α with the slope, as shown in the figure below. We know the component (magnitude $\frac{1}{2}g$) of the acceleration down the slope and the component (magnitude 0) normal to the slope. We shall choose axes in these two directions, as shown in the figure.

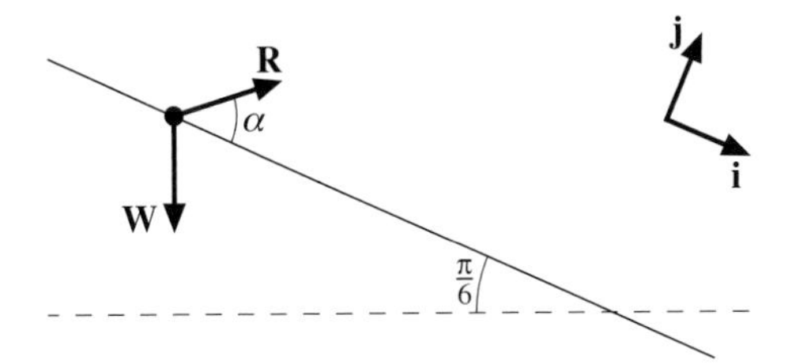

Then

$$\mathbf{W} = mg\sin\tfrac{1}{6}\pi\,\mathbf{i} - mg\cos\tfrac{1}{6}\pi\,\mathbf{j}$$
$$= \tfrac{1}{2}mg\mathbf{i} - \tfrac{1}{2}\sqrt{3}mg\mathbf{j},$$

$$\mathbf{R} = |\mathbf{R}|\cos\alpha\,\mathbf{i} + |\mathbf{R}|\sin\alpha\,\mathbf{j}$$

and

$$\ddot{\mathbf{r}} = \tfrac{1}{2}g\mathbf{i}.$$

Newton's second law gives

$$\mathbf{R} + \mathbf{W} = m\ddot{\mathbf{r}},$$

or

$$(|\mathbf{R}|\cos\alpha\,\mathbf{i} + |\mathbf{R}|\sin\alpha\,\mathbf{j}) + (\tfrac{1}{2}mg\mathbf{i} - \tfrac{1}{2}\sqrt{3}\,mg\mathbf{j}) = \tfrac{1}{2}mg\mathbf{i}.$$

Equating the **i**-components of this equation gives

$$|\mathbf{R}|\cos\alpha + \tfrac{1}{2}mg = \tfrac{1}{2}mg.$$

Hence

$$|\mathbf{R}|\cos\alpha = 0,$$

which implies that either $|\mathbf{R}| = 0$ or $\alpha = \frac{1}{2}\pi$.

Equating the **j**-components gives

$$|\mathbf{R}|\sin\alpha - \tfrac{1}{2}\sqrt{3}mg = 0,$$

so

$$|\mathbf{R}|\sin\alpha = \tfrac{1}{2}\sqrt{3}mg.$$

From this equation we deduce that $|\mathbf{R}|$ cannot be zero, so we must have

$$\alpha = \tfrac{1}{2}\pi$$

and

$$|\mathbf{R}| = \tfrac{1}{2}\sqrt{3}mg.$$

So the force exerted by the seat on the passenger acts perpendicular to the slope and has magnitude $\frac{1}{2}\sqrt{3}mg$.

1.2 We saw in the text that the force exerted by the seat is $R_2\mathbf{j}$, where R_2 is given by Equation (1.5) as

$$R_2 = m\left(g + \frac{2\pi^2hu^2}{L^2}\cos\left(\frac{2\pi ut}{L}\right)\right) \quad \left(0 \le t \le \frac{L}{u}\right).$$

We have $m = 90$, $h = 4$ and $L = 30$.

(a) With $u = 10$, the force exerted by the seat has magnitude

$$90\left(9.81 + \frac{2\pi^2 \times 4 \times 10^2}{30^2}\cos\left(\tfrac{2}{3}\pi t\right)\right) \quad (0 \le t \le 3).$$

The magnitude is greatest when $\cos\left(\frac{2}{3}\pi t\right) = 1$, i.e. when $t = 0$ or $t = 3$. This greatest magnitude is 1672 N.

The magnitude is smallest when $\cos\left(\frac{2}{3}\pi t\right) = -1$, i.e. when $t = 1.5$. This least magnitude is 93.33 N.

(The passenger's weight has magnitude 882.9 N, so the magnitude of the force exerted by the seat is about twice that of the passenger's weight at its greatest, and only about 10% of it at its smallest.)

(b) With $u = 15$, the force exerted by the seat, by Equation (1.5), has magnitude

$$90\left(9.81 + \frac{2\pi^2 \times 4 \times 15^2}{30^2}\cos(\pi t)\right) \quad (0 \le t \le 2).$$

The magnitude is greatest when $\cos(\pi t) = 1$, i.e. when $t = 0$ or $t = 2$. This greatest magnitude is 2659 N.

The expression for R_2 is smallest when $\cos(\pi t) = -1$, i.e. when $t = 1$. This least value is -893.6 N.

It might be possible for the seat to exert a negative (downward) force on the passenger — via a seat belt. However, it is not possible for the road to exert a downward force on the car, and the vertical component of the force between car and road and that between seat and passenger becomes negative at the same instant. So, at this speed, the car will leave the ground, and the least magnitude of the force between seat and passenger is, in fact, zero (it will not actually become negative).

(c) At a horizontal speed u, the magnitude of the force exerted by the road on the car (as given by Equation (1.5)) is least at $t = L/(2u)$. This least magnitude will be zero if

$$9.81 - \frac{2\pi^2 \times 4u^2}{30^2} = 0,$$

i.e. if

$$u = \sqrt{\frac{9.81 \times 30^2}{8\pi^2}} \simeq 10.57.$$

So the car will just leave the ground if it is travelling with a horizontal speed of about $10.57\,\mathrm{m\,s^{-1}}$. It will not leave the ground if its horizontal speed is less than this.

1.3 We have $x = ut$. Then, for $0 \le t \le 20/u$,

$$\mathbf{r} = x\mathbf{i} + y\mathbf{j}$$
$$= ut\mathbf{i} + \tfrac{1}{160}(30u^2t^2 - u^3t^3)\mathbf{j}.$$

Differentiating with respect to t, we obtain

$$\dot{\mathbf{r}} = u\mathbf{i} + \tfrac{1}{160}(60u^2t - 3u^3t^2)\mathbf{j},$$
$$\ddot{\mathbf{r}} = \tfrac{1}{160}(60u^2 - 6u^3t)\mathbf{j}.$$

Since $\ddot{\mathbf{r}}$ has a zero **i**-component, the force exerted on a passenger (of mass m, say) by the seat acts vertically upwards. If $\mathbf{R} = R_1\mathbf{i} + R_2\mathbf{j}$ is the force exerted by the seat on the passenger, we have $R_1 = 0$ and the total force on the passenger is $(R_2 - mg)\mathbf{j}$.

So the **j**-component of Newton's second law gives

$$R_2 - mg = \tfrac{1}{160}m(60u^2 - 6u^3t).$$

Hence

$$R_2 = m\left(g + \tfrac{1}{160}(60u^2 - 6u^3t)\right) \quad (0 \le t \le 20/u).$$

This expression decreases with t and will have its minimum value at $t = 20/u$. At this time, we have

$$R_2 = m\left(g + \tfrac{1}{160}\left(60u^2 - 6u^3\frac{20}{u}\right)\right) = m\left(g - \tfrac{3}{8}u^2\right).$$

A feeling of near weightlessness will occur if this value of R_2 is about zero, which occurs if $g \simeq \frac{3}{8}u^2$, i.e. if $u \simeq \sqrt{8 \times 9.81/3} \simeq 5.115$.

So a feeling of near weightlessness will occur at the end of the climbing section of the track if the horizontal speed is about $5.115\,\mathrm{m\,s^{-1}}$.

1.4 Choosing the unit vector $\mathbf{i}$ in the x-direction and the unit vector $\mathbf{j}$ in the y-direction, we have

$$\mathbf{r} = 3t\mathbf{i} + 4t^2\mathbf{j},$$
$$\dot{\mathbf{r}} = 3\mathbf{i} + 8t\mathbf{j},$$
$$\ddot{\mathbf{r}} = 8\mathbf{j}.$$

(a) If $\mathbf{R}$ is the force exerted on the car by the track and $\mathbf{W}$ is the weight of the car and any passengers, then Newton's second law applied to the car gives

$$\mathbf{R} + \mathbf{W} = m\ddot{\mathbf{r}},$$

where m is the mass of the car and passengers. Let $\mathbf{k}$ be a unit vector vertically upwards. Then $\mathbf{W} = -mg\mathbf{k}$ and

$$\begin{aligned}\mathbf{R} &= m\ddot{\mathbf{r}} - \mathbf{W} \\ &= m(8\mathbf{j}) - (-mg\mathbf{k}) \\ &= m(8\mathbf{j} + 9.81\mathbf{k}).\end{aligned}$$

So $\mathbf{R}$ makes an angle θ with the horizontal (see the figure below), where $\tan\theta = 9.81/8$, giving

$$\theta = 0.8867 \text{ radians} = 50.80°.$$

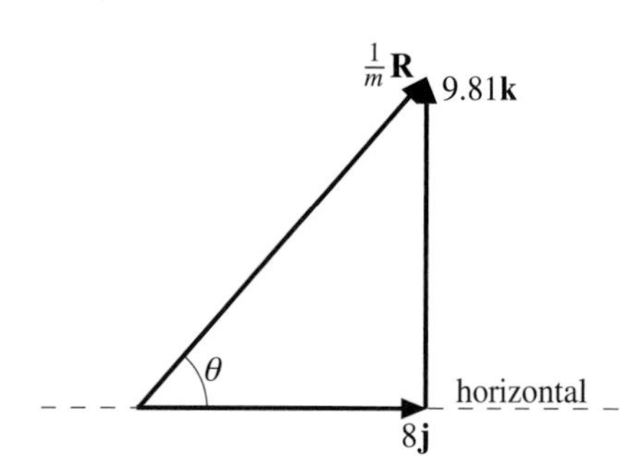

(b) The force exerted on a passenger by the seat is the same as that exerted on the car by the track, except that m is now the mass of the passenger. The reaction force $m(8\mathbf{j} + 9.81\mathbf{k})$, with $m = 100$, has magnitude

$$100\sqrt{8^2 + 9.81^2} \simeq 1266.$$

So the force exerted by the seat on the passenger is approximately 1266 N.

1.5 **(a)** We have

$$\mathbf{r} = a\cos bt\,\mathbf{i} + a\sin bt\,\mathbf{j} + (h - \tfrac{1}{4}gt^2)\mathbf{k},$$

so

$$\dot{\mathbf{r}} = -ab\sin bt\,\mathbf{i} + ab\cos bt\,\mathbf{j} - \tfrac{1}{2}gt\,\mathbf{k}$$

and

$$\ddot{\mathbf{r}} = -ab^2\cos bt\,\mathbf{i} - ab^2\sin bt\,\mathbf{j} - \tfrac{1}{2}g\,\mathbf{k}.$$

(b) The weight of the car is $\mathbf{W} = -mg\,\mathbf{k}$. If we denote the force exerted by the track on the car by $\mathbf{R}$, Newton's second law applied to the car is

$$\mathbf{R} + \mathbf{W} = m\ddot{\mathbf{r}},$$

so

$$\begin{aligned}\mathbf{R} &= m\ddot{\mathbf{r}} - \mathbf{W} \\ &= (-mab^2\cos bt\,\mathbf{i} - mab^2\sin bt\,\mathbf{j} - \tfrac{1}{2}mg\,\mathbf{k}) + mg\,\mathbf{k} \\ &= m(-ab^2\cos bt\,\mathbf{i} - ab^2\sin bt\,\mathbf{j} + \tfrac{1}{2}g\,\mathbf{k}).\end{aligned}$$

(c) The magnitude of the force exerted by the track on the car is

$$\begin{aligned}|\mathbf{R}| &= m\sqrt{a^2b^4\cos^2 bt + a^2b^4\sin^2 bt + \tfrac{1}{4}g^2} \\ &= m\sqrt{a^2b^4 + \tfrac{1}{4}g^2},\end{aligned}$$

using the identity $\cos^2 bt + \sin^2 bt = 1$. This is constant, as it is independent of time t.

Section 2

2.1 We have

$$\begin{aligned}\int \mathbf{c}\,dt &= \int (c_1\mathbf{i} + c_2\mathbf{j})\,dt \\ &= \left(\int c_1\,dt\right)\mathbf{i} + \left(\int c_2\,dt\right)\mathbf{j} \\ &= (c_1t + d_1)\mathbf{i} + (c_2t + d_2)\mathbf{j} \\ &= \mathbf{c}t + \mathbf{d},\end{aligned}$$

where $\mathbf{d} = d_1\mathbf{i} + d_2\mathbf{j}$ is an arbitrary constant vector.

2.2 Example 2.3 predicts that $X = u\sqrt{2h/g}$, i.e.

$$\frac{X^2}{h} = \frac{2u^2}{g}.$$

The launch speed u, and hence the quantity $2u^2/g$, should be the same for each run of the projectile demonstrator. Calculating X^2/h for the three data points, we obtain

0.1051, 0.1023, 0.1041.

These are as close to being equal as we are likely to get, given the accuracy to which the measurements were taken. From these values, we see that $2u^2/g$ must be about 0.1038 (the average of the above three values), so

$$u \simeq \sqrt{\frac{0.1038 \times 9.81}{2}} \simeq 0.7136.$$

So the ball must leave the ramp with a speed of about $0.7\,\mathrm{m\,s^{-1}}$.

2.3 We shall choose the y-axis vertically upwards and the x-axis horizontal. You may have chosen the origin at the top of the cliff (in which case you should use Equation (2.10)). We can equally well choose the origin at the bottom of the cliff at beach level, and we shall do this. Suppose that the car left the cliff with a speed u, travelling in a horizontal direction (at right angles to the cliff). Then the initial conditions are exactly the same as in Example 2.3, but with $h = 18$. We can use the solution of Equation (2.2) derived in Example 2.3, which was

$$\mathbf{r}(t) = ut\mathbf{i} + (h - \tfrac{1}{2}gt^2)\mathbf{j},$$

or, separated into components,

$$x = ut, \qquad \text{(S.1)}$$

$$y = h - \tfrac{1}{2}gt^2. \qquad \text{(S.2)}$$

We know that $x = 8$ when $y = 0$ (assuming that the car hit the ground exactly 8 metres from the cliff and modelling the car as a particle). So, from Equation (S.1), the car hit the ground at $t = 8/u$. Substituting this into Equation (S.2) gives

$$0 = 18 - \tfrac{1}{2}g(64/u^2).$$

Thus, as u is positive,

$$u = \sqrt{\frac{64 \times 9.81}{2 \times 18}} \simeq 4.176.$$

So the car left the cliff at a speed of just over $4\,\mathrm{m\,s^{-1}}$.

2.4 **(a)** Suppose that the jumper's speed on take off at O is u. The sum of the kinetic and potential energies must be the same at A and at O (assuming that no energy is lost in skiing down the slope). The kinetic energy at A is zero and at O is $\frac{1}{2}mu^2$, where m is the jumper's mass. Taking the x-axis as the datum, the potential energy is $15mg$ at A and zero at O. So, equating the total energies at O and A, we have

$$\tfrac{1}{2}mu^2 = 15mg.$$

Thus $u^2 = 30g$ and so, as u is positive,

$$u = \sqrt{30 \times 9.81} \simeq 17.16.$$

So the jumper's speed on leaving O is about $17\,\mathrm{m\,s^{-1}}$.

(b) Since the launch velocity is in the horizontal direction, we can use Equation (2.11), $y = -gx^2/(2u^2)$. Since $u^2 = 30g$ (from part (a)), this becomes

$$y = -\tfrac{1}{60}x^2.$$

(c) The line OB has equation $y = -x$.

(d) The coordinates (x, y) of the point B must satisfy both $y = -x$ and $y = -\frac{1}{60}x^2$. So the x-coordinate of B must satisfy $-x = -\frac{1}{60}x^2$, i.e.

$$x^2 = 60x.$$

The solution $x = 0$ corresponds to the point O, so at B we have $x = 60$. Thus B has coordinates $(60, -60)$. The distance OB is $\sqrt{60^2 + 60^2}$, i.e. about 84.85 metres.

(e) There are various factors affecting the length of jump obtained that are not included in this simple model of the jumper as a particle unaffected by resistive forces. The jumper may get a push start at A (potentially increasing u and increasing the length of the jump), but will surely lose some energy through resistive forces while skiing from A to O (thereby reducing u and decreasing the length of the jump). Air resistance in flight may reduce the distance of the jump, but a good jumper will use the skis to gain aerodynamic lift and so increase the length of jump achieved. The method of take off may lead to a launch velocity whose direction is above the horizontal, which again would increase the length of the jump. So some of these factors will increase the length of jump achieved, while others will reduce it.

2.5 **(a)** Let the speed of the buggy at take off be u. For this part of the question it is convenient to use a coordinate system different from that used to give the equation of the ramp profile. Choose an origin at the point of take off, with a Y-axis vertically upward and an X-axis horizontal in the direction of take off. On landing, the buggy has (X, Y)-coordinates $(5, -1)$. The trajectory of a projectile launched horizontally from the origin at speed u is given by Equation (2.11) as

$$Y = -\frac{gX^2}{2u^2}.$$

For the trajectory to pass through $(5, -1)$, we need

$$-1 = -\frac{9.81 \times 5^2}{2u^2},$$

that is,

$$u = \sqrt{\frac{9.81 \times 5^2}{2}} \simeq 11.07.$$

So the speed of the buggy at take off is about $11\,\mathrm{m\,s^{-1}}$.

(b) The ramp has the profile given by Equation (1.2), although we have only 'part of a hump-backed bridge', because of the restricted domain of x given. We calculated the vertical component of the force in Equation (1.5) as

$$R_2 = m\left(g + \frac{2\pi^2hu^2}{L^2}\cos\left(\frac{2\pi ut}{L}\right)\right),$$

where t is the time since the buggy started up the ramp, and $h = 1$.

From Equation (1.3), the highest point of the ramp is reached at $t = L/(2u)$ (when $\cos(2\pi ut/L) = -1$). So $R_2 = 0$ at the point of take off if

$$m\left(g - \frac{2\pi^2hu^2}{L^2}\right) = 0,$$

that is,

$$L = \pi u\sqrt{\frac{2h}{g}}$$

$$= \pi \times 11.07\sqrt{\frac{2 \times 1}{9.81}} \simeq 15.71.$$

So the horizontal length $0.5L$ of the ramp is approximately 7.854 metres.

2.6 In the text, we obtained Equation (2.18) for the range, namely $R = u^2 \sin 2\theta / g$. With $\theta = \frac{1}{6}\pi$, the kick has range 40 metres, so the launch speed u must satisfy

$$u^2 = \frac{40g}{\sin \frac{1}{3}\pi} = \frac{80g}{\sqrt{3}}.$$

We also obtained the expression (2.20) for the greatest height $H = (u^2 \sin^2 \theta)/2g$ reached by a projectile. With $\theta = \frac{1}{6}\pi$ and $u^2 = 80g/\sqrt{3}$, this gives

$$H = \frac{80g \times \sin^2 \frac{1}{6}\pi}{2g\sqrt{3}} = \frac{10}{\sqrt{3}} \simeq 5.774.$$

So the greatest height reached by the ball is about 5.774 metres.

2.7 We need to find the solution of $\ddot{\mathbf{r}}(t) = -g\mathbf{j}$ satisfying $\dot{\mathbf{r}}(0) = \mathbf{u}$, where $\mathbf{u} = (u\cos\theta)\mathbf{i} + (u\sin\theta)\mathbf{j}$ and $\mathbf{r}(0) = h\mathbf{j}$ (since the point of launch is $(0, h)$). The integral of $\ddot{\mathbf{r}}(t) = -g\mathbf{j}$ is

$$\dot{\mathbf{r}}(t) = -gt\mathbf{j} + \mathbf{c}.$$

Substituting $t = 0$ and using the initial condition $\dot{\mathbf{r}}(0) = \mathbf{u}$, we must have $\mathbf{c} = \mathbf{u}$.

Integrating again gives

$$\mathbf{r}(t) = -\tfrac{1}{2}gt^2\mathbf{j} + \mathbf{u}t + \mathbf{d}.$$

Substituting $t = 0$ and using the initial condition $\mathbf{r}(0) = h\mathbf{j}$, we must have $\mathbf{d} = h\mathbf{j}$.

Hence the required solution is

$$\begin{aligned}\mathbf{r}(t) &= -\tfrac{1}{2}gt^2\mathbf{j} + (ut\cos\theta)\mathbf{i} + (ut\sin\theta)\mathbf{j} + h\mathbf{j} \\ &= (ut\cos\theta)\mathbf{i} + (h + ut\sin\theta - \tfrac{1}{2}gt^2)\mathbf{j}.\end{aligned}$$

2.8 Taking the origin to be at ground level, and using Equations (2.22) and (2.23), the position of the shot at a time t after the launch is given by

$$\begin{aligned}x &= 13t\cos \tfrac{1}{6}\pi, \\ y &= 1.8 + 13t\sin \tfrac{1}{6}\pi - \tfrac{1}{2} \times 9.81t^2.\end{aligned} \qquad \text{(S.3)}$$

To find the time when the shot hits the ground, we substitute $y = 0$ in Equation (S.3) and solve the resulting quadratic equation for t. The solutions are $t = 1.560$ and $t = -0.2352$. The negative solution represents a time before the shot is launched and so can be rejected. At $t = 1.560$, we have $x = 17.57$.

So the shot lands at a horizontal distance of 17.57 metres from the point of launch.

2.9 Taking the origin to be at ground level, we can use Equations (2.22) and (2.23) with $h = 1.5$ and $\theta = \frac{1}{4}\pi$. Suppose that the launch speed is u. Then Equation (2.22) gives $x = ut\cos\frac{1}{4}\pi = ut/\sqrt{2}$. If the stone hits the ground when $t = T$, we have $30 = uT/\sqrt{2}$, so $T = 30\sqrt{2}/u$. We know that $y = 0$ when $t = T$, so substituting into Equation (2.23) gives

$$\begin{aligned}0 &= 1.5 + u\frac{30\sqrt{2}}{u}\frac{1}{\sqrt{2}} - \frac{g}{2}\left(\frac{30\sqrt{2}}{u}\right)^2 \\ &= 31.5 - \frac{900g}{u^2}.\end{aligned}$$

This gives $u = 30\sqrt{9.81/31.5} \simeq 16.74$.

So the launch speed was approximately $16.74\,\mathrm{m\,s^{-1}}$.

2.10 From Equations (2.22) and (2.23) we have

$$x = ut\cos\theta,$$
$$y = h + ut\sin\theta - \tfrac{1}{2}gt^2.$$

From the first equation, $t = x/(u\cos\theta)$. Substituting this into the second equation gives

$$\begin{aligned}y &= h + u\frac{x}{u\cos\theta}\sin\theta - \frac{g}{2}\left(\frac{x}{u\cos\theta}\right)^2 \\ &= h + x\tan\theta - x^2\frac{g}{2u^2}\sec^2\theta.\end{aligned}$$

Alternatively, using $\sec^2\theta = 1 + \tan^2\theta$,

$$y = h + x\tan\theta - x^2\frac{g}{2u^2}(1 + \tan^2\theta).$$

2.11 We choose the origin to be at ground level, vertically below the point of launch. So the equation of the trajectory of the basketball is Equation (2.27) with $h = 1.8$ and $u = 7$ (using SI units). In order for the ball to pass through the net, we want the point $x = 2.6$, $y = 3$ to be on this trajectory. Hence

$$3 = 1.8 + 2.6\tan\theta - (2.6)^2\frac{9.81}{2 \times 7^2}(1 + \tan^2\theta).$$

This simplifies to the quadratic equation

$$0.6767\tan^2\theta - 2.6\tan\theta + 1.877 = 0 \qquad \text{(S.4)}$$

for $\tan\theta$.

(Alternatively, and more efficiently, you may have chosen the origin to be the point from which the ball was launched. However, this leads to the same equation (S.4) for $\tan\theta$.)

This equation for $\tan\theta$ has the two solutions, namely

$$\tan\theta = 2.879 \quad \text{and} \quad \tan\theta = 0.9633.$$

Each of these gives a single value for θ in the range $0 \le \theta \le \frac{1}{2}\pi$,

$$\theta = 1.236\ (70.85^\circ) \quad \text{and} \quad \theta = 0.7667\ (43.93^\circ).$$

We see that there are two possible launch angles that enable the target to be hit. In this example, the choice of a launch angle of approximately 71° is more likely to be suitable, since this has the ball descending towards the net at the steeper angle, so the basketball is less likely to catch on the rim of the net.

2.12 (a) We choose the origin to be at ground level, vertically below the point of launch. So the equation of the trajectory of the shot is Equation (2.26) with $h = 2$ and $\theta = \frac{1}{4}\pi$ (using SI units). The trajectory must pass through the point of impact, namely $x = 17$, $y = 0$. So the launch speed u must satisfy the equation

$$0 = 2 + 17 - 17^2\frac{9.81}{2u^2}2.$$

(Alternatively, you may have chosen the origin to be the point from which the shot is launched. Then the equation of the trajectory is Equation (2.24) and the point of impact is $x = 17$, $y = -2$. However, you should arrive at the same equation for u as above.)

We have $u^2 = (17^2 \times 9.81)/19$, so $u \simeq 12.22$.

So the launch speed is about $12.22\,\mathrm{m\,s^{-1}}$.

(b) With u as calculated in (a), the parameter L in Equations (2.29) and (2.30) has the value $u^2/g \simeq 15.21$. We also have $h = 2$, so the value of θ giving the maximum range is (from Equation (2.30))

$$\theta = \arctan\left(\frac{1}{\sqrt{1+2h/L}}\right)$$

$$= \arctan\left(\frac{1}{\sqrt{1+4/15.21}}\right) = 0.7272\ (41.66^\circ).$$

The range achieved with this optimum launch angle is (from Equation (2.29))

$$R = \sqrt{L^2 + 2Lh} = \sqrt{15.21^2 + 4 \times 15.21} \simeq 17.09.$$

So the optimum launch angle is about 41.66°, with a range of approximately 17.09 metres.

(c) An improvement of 1% on the launch speed $12.22\,\mathrm{m\,s^{-1}}$ calculated in (a) would give a launch speed $12.22 \times 1.01 = 12.34\,\mathrm{m\,s^{-1}}$. With this launch speed and a launch angle $\frac{1}{4}\pi$, choosing the origin to be at ground level, vertically below the point of launch, the equation of the trajectory of the shot (Equation (2.26)) is

$$y = 2 + x - x^2 \frac{9.81}{2 \times 12.34^2} 2.$$

At the point of impact $y = 0$, which leads to the quadratic equation

$$0 = 2 + x - 0.064\,45x^2.$$

This has solutions $x = 17.31$ and $x = -1.793$.

We can reject the negative solution, which represents the point behind the putter where the trajectory intersects ground level. So the range of the put will be approximately 17.31 metres.

(We can see from the answers to (b) and (c) that the student is right in saying that a small increase in launch speed is more effective in increasing the range than is getting the optimum launch angle. However, although slight, the improvement in range (of 9 cm) resulting from putting at the optimum angle could be the difference between winning and coming nowhere! So one might as well try to achieve the optimum launch angle.)

2.13 **(a)** The trajectory must pass through the points $(10, 2)$ and $(30, 2.4)$. So, using Equation (2.24) twice, we have

$$2 = 10\tan\theta - 100\frac{g}{2u^2}\sec^2\theta, \qquad \text{(S.5)}$$

$$2.4 = 30\tan\theta - 900\frac{g}{2u^2}\sec^2\theta. \qquad \text{(S.6)}$$

Multiplying Equation (S.5) by 9 gives

$$18 = 90\tan\theta - 900\frac{g}{2u^2}\sec^2\theta. \qquad \text{(S.7)}$$

Subtracting Equation (S.6) from Equation (S.7) gives

$$15.6 = 60\tan\theta.$$

So $\tan\theta = 0.26$ and $\theta = 0.2544\ (14.57^\circ)$.

(b) Substituting $\theta = 0.2544$ into Equation (S.5) gives

$$2 = 10\tan(0.2544) - \frac{50g}{u^2}\sec^2(0.2544),$$

so

$$u^2 = \frac{50 \times 9.81\sec^2(0.2544)}{10\tan(0.2544) - 2} = 872.8$$

and $u \simeq 29.54$.

So the ball was kicked at approximately $29.54\,\mathrm{m\,s^{-1}}$.

Using Equation (2.16), we have $x = ut\cos\theta$. We know that the ball entered the goal when $x = 30$, so $t = 30/(29.54\cos(0.2544)) \simeq 1.049$.

So just over 1 second after having been kicked, the ball entered the goal.

2.14 If the stone has mass m, its initial kinetic energy is $\frac{1}{2}mu^2$, where $u = 11$. Between launch and hitting the target, its potential energy has increased by mgh, with $h = 1$. If it hits the target at speed v, we must have

$$\tfrac{1}{2}mv^2 + mgh = \tfrac{1}{2}mu^2.$$

Putting $u = 11$ and $h = 1$, we obtain

$$v^2 = 11^2 - 2 \times 9.81 = 101.4.$$

So the speed of the stone when it hits the target is about $10.07\,\mathrm{m\,s^{-1}}$.

2.15 Let the mass of the projectile be m, and take ground level as the datum for potential energy. The total energy at launch is $\frac{1}{2}mu^2$. At the highest point in its flight, the vertical component of the velocity will be zero, while the horizontal component is $u\cos\theta$ (by Equation (2.32)). If the height above the ground at this point is H, we have, by conservation of mechanical energy,

$$\tfrac{1}{2}mu^2 = \tfrac{1}{2}mu^2\cos^2\theta + mgH.$$

Thus

$$mgH = \tfrac{1}{2}mu^2(1 - \cos^2\theta) = \tfrac{1}{2}mu^2\sin^2\theta.$$

So the maximum height attained is

$$H = \frac{u^2\sin^2\theta}{2g},$$

as given by Equation (2.20).

2.16 **(a)** We solve the differential equation by integrating twice. Integrating once gives

$$\dot{\mathbf{r}}(t) = -gt\mathbf{j} + \mathbf{c}.$$

Putting $t = 0$ and using the initial condition $\dot{\mathbf{r}}(0) = v\mathbf{j}$, the constant vector $\mathbf{c}$ must satisfy $\mathbf{c} = v\mathbf{j}$. So we have

$$\dot{\mathbf{r}}(t) = (v - gt)\mathbf{j}.$$

Integrating again, we obtain

$$\mathbf{r}(t) = (vt - \tfrac{1}{2}gt^2)\mathbf{j} + \mathbf{d}.$$

Putting $t = 0$ and using the initial condition $\mathbf{r}(0) = a\mathbf{i} + b\mathbf{j}$, the constant vector $\mathbf{d}$ must satisfy $\mathbf{d} = a\mathbf{i} + b\mathbf{j}$. So the required solution is

$$\mathbf{r}(t) = (vt - \tfrac{1}{2}gt^2)\mathbf{j} + a\mathbf{i} + b\mathbf{j}$$

$$= a\mathbf{i} + (b + vt - \tfrac{1}{2}gt^2)\mathbf{j}. \qquad \text{(S.8)}$$

(b) The initial velocity of the projectile is a multiple of $\mathbf{j}$ and so (assuming $v > 0$) is directly upwards. It is launched from the point (a, b). Since the object is thrown directly upwards, and gravity is the only force acting, the object will stay on the same vertical line. So the x-component of its position should not change. And indeed we do have, in the solution for $\mathbf{r}(t)$ in Equation (S.8), a constant $\mathbf{i}$-component (giving the x-component of position) that is equal to its initial value a.

2.17 **(a)** The throw has range $R = 20$, so, using Equation (2.18) with $u = 20$, we have

$$\sin 2\theta = \frac{Rg}{u^2} = \frac{20 \times 9.81}{20^2} = 0.4905,$$

where θ is the launch angle.

Caution is needed here. The angle θ must lie between 0 and $\frac{1}{2}\pi$, so 2θ is between 0 and π. There are *two* angles with $\sin 2\theta = 0.4905$ in this range:

$$2\theta = 0.5127 \quad \text{and} \quad 2\theta = \pi - 0.5127 = 2.629,$$

that is,

$$\theta = 0.2563\ (14.69^\circ) \quad \text{and} \quad \theta = 1.314\ (75.31^\circ).$$

So the ball was launched at about either 15° or 75° to the horizontal.

(b) We saw in Equation (2.20) that the greatest height reached by such a projectile is $u^2 \sin^2\theta/(2g)$. Here $u = 20$. A launch angle of 75° will achieve a greater height than one of 15°, so we take $\theta = 1.314$. Then the greatest height reached by the ball is

$$H = \frac{20^2 \sin^2(1.314)}{2 \times 9.81} \simeq 19.08.$$

This height of about 19 m is above the point of launch, which might be up to 2 m above the ground, depending on the height of the thrower. So a tree of 20 m, or even 21 m, would be cleared. We saw in Equation (2.21) that a projectile attains its maximum height when x is half the range. Here the range is 20 m, so the maximum height is achieved at a horizontal distance of 10 m from the thrower.

(c) The man can throw 50 m on level ground. Ignoring any small difference between the launch and the impact heights, his maximum range (see Equation (2.19)) is u^2/g (at a launch angle $\frac{1}{4}\pi$). So he can throw at a speed u, where $u^2 = 50g$, so that $u \simeq 22.15$.

If the man throws at $20\,\mathrm{m\,s^{-1}}$, as he is able to, and uses a launch angle 1.314, he should clear the trees, as we saw in part (b). How long will this give him to run through the trees to catch the ball? Assuming that the peak of the trajectory is directly above the trees, he has to run 20 m. This is in the x-direction. The ball's velocity has an x-component $u\cos\theta = 20\cos(1.314)$. So $x = 20$ when $t = 20/(20\cos(1.314)) \simeq 3.944$. So the ball is in flight for about 3.944 s.

If the man can run at $8\,\mathrm{m\,s^{-1}}$ (which is equivalent to running the 100 metres in 12.5 seconds), then he will cover 20 m in 2.5 s. That would leave 1.444 s to get moving after he has thrown the ball and to get into position to catch it. He looks likely to be able to do it, so it is a bad bet to take!

2.18 **(a)** Conservation of mechanical energy provides an efficient approach here. Suppose that the ball hits the target at a speed v. The launch height is not given. If we assume that the point of launch is at ground level (it will in fact be higher), then the estimate of the speed at which the ball will hit the target will be on the low side. Allowing for hitting a target at its top, the ball will be 3.1 m higher when it hits than when it is thrown. Taking the launch position as the datum for the potential energy, conservation of mechanical energy gives

$$\tfrac{1}{2}u^2 = \tfrac{1}{2}v^2 + gh,$$

where $h = 3.1$ and $u = 15$. Hence

$$v = \sqrt{15^2 - 2 \times 3.1 \times 9.81} \simeq 12.81.$$

This speed of $12.81\,\mathrm{m\,s^{-1}}$ is comfortably above the $12\,\mathrm{m\,s^{-1}}$ required to dislodge a target.

(b) Choosing the point of launch as the origin, the target is at $(20, a)$, where $2 \le a \le 2.1$ (allowing for a target of height 0.1 m). We need this point to lie on the trajectory, whose equation is

$$y = x\tan\theta - x^2\frac{g}{2u^2}(1 + \tan^2\theta).$$

So we need, for a somewhere between 2 and 2.1,

$$a = 20\tan\theta - 20^2\frac{9.81}{2 \times 15^2}(1 + \tan^2\theta). \tag{S.9}$$

For $a = 2$, Equation (S.9) has solutions

$$\tan\theta = 1.440 \quad \text{and} \quad \tan\theta = 0.8539,$$

that is,

$$\theta = 0.9637\ (55.22^\circ) \quad \text{and} \quad \theta = 0.7068\ (40.49^\circ).$$

For $a = 2.1$, Equation (S.9) has solutions

$$\tan\theta = 1.419 \quad \text{and} \quad \tan\theta = 0.8742,$$

that is,

$$\theta = 0.9570\ (54.83^\circ) \quad \text{and} \quad \theta = 0.7184\ (41.16^\circ).$$

So the launch angle needs to be either between 40.49° and 41.16° or between 54.83° and 55.22°. We see that there is very little margin for error!

UNIT 15 Modelling heat transfer

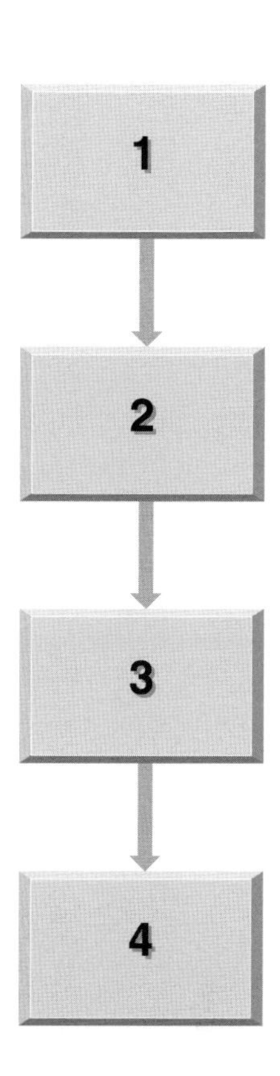

Study guide for Unit 15

The unit makes use of ideas relating to energy (from *Unit 8*) and first-order differential equations (from *Unit 2*). Some of the ideas here are picked up again in *Units 16* and *23*.

This unit contains four sections: Sections 2 and 3 require roughly equal study time; however, Sections 1 and 4 are somewhat shorter. Ideally this unit should be studied in the order in which it is presented.

Note that generally in this unit the intermediate and final answers of calculations are expressed to four significant figures, although full calculator accuracy was used throughout the calculations.

Introduction

Before the oil crisis of 1973, most people in the United Kingdom took cheap energy for granted and did not worry very much about the heat that was lost through their walls, windows and roofs. Suddenly, fuel costs increased dramatically and householders were urged to conserve energy, especially by insulating their walls and roofs, double-glazing their windows and lagging their hot-water tanks. Even today householders have similar concerns, recognizing that, as well as saving money, reducing energy consumption reduces environmental pollution and conserves finite stocks of fossil fuels.

This unit develops models that could be used to answer questions such as the following.

- How much does it cost to heat up a tank full of hot water?
- What thickness of insulation should be applied to a hot-water tank?
- What thickness of insulation should I use in my loft, and what savings would I make over a year?
- What should the gap be in double-glazing?
- Would triple glazing be better than double-glazing?
- Is it better to insulate the roof, insulate the walls or double-glaze the windows of my house?

The common factor in answering all these questions is the need to consider the transfer of heat energy between different regions of space.

Heat is a form of energy, and to remind you of this we shall often refer to *heat energy* rather than just heat in this unit.

The essential factor in considering the transfer of heat energy is the existence of a temperature difference, combined with the rule that the net transfer of heat energy takes place *from* regions of higher temperature *to* regions of lower temperature. For example, the fact that heat energy is transferred from a heated room to the cooler atmosphere outside the house, through the walls, is only too clear to the householder who has to pay the fuel bills. Also, the heat energy reaches the air in the room via, say, a central heating radiator, which is itself at a temperature above that of the room.

Heat is only one of many forms of energy, and energy can be converted from one form to another. For instance, in many electricity generating stations the chemical energy stored in gas, oil or coal is converted into heat energy, which then drives the turbines giving them kinetic energy. This kinetic energy is converted by the turbines into electrical energy and transmitted to the home where it may, in turn, be converted into kinetic energy (in a drill, vacuum cleaner, etc.) or light energy (in light bulbs, television, etc.) or heat energy (in an electric kettle, oven, electric fire, etc.).

This unit, however, does not discuss the topic of energy conversion, but concentrates on the transfer of heat energy from one region of space to another. The fact that the discussion will be restricted to transfers of heat energy does not mean that our examples will lack variety. There are in fact three distinct modes of heat energy transfer, and the unit develops models for each of these three modes.

The models introduced in this unit are widely used, for example to predict the rate at which heat energy is being transferred between different regions (or the amount of heat energy transferred in a given time) or to predict the way the temperature varies inside a region. In particular, this unit develops models for the loss of heat energy through the walls of a house and from a cylindrical pipe containing a hot fluid. Although these two basic models may appear, at first sight, to be very restrictive, they can be used as a basis for answering all the questions posed earlier.

Section 1 introduces the basic ideas of heat energy and temperature, and the three modes of heat energy transfer, namely conduction, convection and radiation. Conduction is discussed in more detail in Section 2, for steady-state situations. Section 3 discusses convection, again for the steady state, and develops models of situations where both conduction and convection are important. Finally, Section 4 considers the third mode of heat energy transfer, radiation, and how steady-state situations involving all three modes of heat energy transfer can be modelled.

1 Heat and temperature

In studying this unit, it is important that you are clear about the difference between the concepts of temperature and heat. This difference is spelled out in Subsection 1.1, which also discusses the relationship between these concepts. Subsection 1.2 introduces the three modes of heat energy transfer, namely conduction, convection and radiation, which we shall consider in more detail in the remainder of this unit.

1.1 The relationship between heat and temperature

You probably already know that **temperature** is a measure of the warmth of an environment, an object or a substance. If I told you that the room in which I am writing this unit has a temperature of 18°C, you could guess that I am wearing normal indoor clothing (although I do have a sweater on). However, the temperature outside is -1°C, and so when I take my dog for a walk I shall put on a coat, a scarf and a woolly hat. Internationally, temperatures are commonly measured in degrees Celsius (abbreviated to °C), which is the temperature scale in which water freezes at 0°C and boils at 100°C. Other scales of temperature are sometimes used — for example, when I was younger, temperatures in the United Kingdom were usually measured in degrees Fahrenheit (abbreviated to °F), which is a scale in which water freezes at 32°F and boils at 212°F. However, the important concept is that temperature is a measure of how hot something is, in the same way as speed is a measure of how fast something is moving. In this course we denote temperatures using the symbol Θ.

Degrees Celsius are sometimes referred to as 'degrees centigrade'.

The SI unit of temperature is actually not °C but the *kelvin*, as is described later.

Heat, on the other hand, is a form of energy, also known as **heat energy** or **thermal energy**. If the temperature of a substance increases, then heat energy has been given to the substance; conversely, if the temperature of a substance decreases, then heat energy has been taken away from the substance. Moreover, when heat energy is given to or taken from a substance then its temperature increases or decreases, respectively. In this course we denote heat energy in particular, and energy in general, by the symbol E.

We shall generally use the term *heat energy* in this unit.

In the above discussion of the connection between temperature and heat energy we have assumed that the substance does not change state. For example, it requires 226×10^4 joules of heat energy to convert 1 kg of water at its boiling point into steam *at the same temperature*.

To determine the relationship between temperature and heat energy, various experiments have been performed over the years. Typically, these experiments add energy at a constant rate to a substance, which is thermally isolated from its surroundings, and measure the temperature at different times. For example, water could be heated in a vacuum flask containing a heating element and a thermometer. These experiments have provided the following relationship between temperature and heat energy.

Thermal isolation is necessary to minimize any heat energy losses to the surrounding environment.

Relating heat and temperature

The change in the heat energy of a mass m of a substance when its temperature is changed from Θ_1 to Θ_2 is given by

$$E_2 - E_1 = mc(\Theta_2 - \Theta_1), \quad (1.1)$$

where E_1 is the heat energy when the temperature is Θ_1 and E_2 is the heat energy when the temperature is Θ_2. The parameter c depends on the nature of the substance being heated, and is called the *specific heat capacity* or sometimes the *specific heat* of the substance.

The model assumes that the substance has a uniform temperature at any given time.

The SI unit of temperature is the **kelvin**, represented by the symbol K. A temperature of zero kelvins is taken to be the lowest temperature attainable, which is called **absolute zero**. This temperature is equivalent to $-273.2°C$ (to 4 significant figures). The relationship between temperatures measured in kelvins and degrees Celsius is

$$\text{temperature in K} = \text{temperature in }°\text{C} + 273.2,$$

so that, for example, 20°C is equivalent to 293.2 K. Also note that a rise in temperature of 1 K is equal to a rise in temperature of 1°C, so it is possible to quote temperatures in degrees Celsius (°C) when using formulae such as Equation (1.1), which involve a temperature *difference*.

The kelvin is named after the British physicist Lord Kelvin (1824–1907).

The scale in which temperature is measured in kelvins is called the **absolute scale**.

Note that we write 'K' not '°K'.

The SI unit for heat energy is the same as that for other forms of energy, namely the joule (denoted by J, where $1\,\text{J} = 1\,\text{kg}\,\text{m}^2\,\text{s}^{-2}$). The SI units for specific heat capacity c are $\text{J}\,\text{kg}^{-1}\,\text{K}^{-1}$ (i.e. joules per kilogram per kelvin). Thus the **specific heat capacity** of a substance is the amount of heat energy, in joules, required to raise the temperature of 1 kilogram of the substance by 1 kelvin.

See *Unit 8*.

As has already been mentioned, the specific heat capacity is different from substance to substance. For example, it takes approximately 30 times less heat energy to raise the temperature of 1 kilogram of mercury by 1°C than to raise the temperature of the same mass of water by the same amount. Also, the specific heat capacity of a substance depends slightly on temperature and, in the case of a gas, on pressure. Approximate specific heat capacities for various substances, at a temperature of 293 K ($\simeq$ 20°C) for solids and liquids, and at standard temperature and pressure (STP) for gases, are given in Table 1.1.

Standard temperature and pressure (STP) for a gas is a temperature of 0°C and a pressure of $101\,325\,\text{N}\,\text{m}^{-2}$.

Table 1.1 Specific heat capacities

Substance	Specific heat capacity c ($\text{J}\,\text{kg}^{-1}\,\text{K}^{-1}$)
Water	4 190
Ethyl alcohol	2 500
Mercury	140
Crown glass	670
Mild steel	420
Copper	385
Air	993
Hydrogen	14 300
Oxygen	913

Source: R. M. Tennent (ed.) (1971) *Science data book*, Oliver and Boyd.

Although it is not used directly in Equation (1.1), another quantity that will prove useful in this unit is the rate at which heat energy is produced (e.g. by the heating element in a kettle) or transmitted or dissipated. The SI unit for measuring this quantity is the **watt** (denoted by W), where one watt equals one joule per second ($1\,\mathrm{W} = 1\,\mathrm{J\,s^{-1}}$). If, for example, the element in a kettle has a power rating of 3000 watts, it will (as long as it is switched on) use electrical energy at the rate of 3000 joules per second to produce heat energy at the same rate. The watt is a rather small unit for many of the situations in which it is used, and so it is more common to find the power rating of heating elements expressed in kilowatts (i.e. thousands of watts, denoted by kW). For example, one-bar electric fires commonly have 1 kW elements, immersion heaters in water tanks commonly have 3 kW elements and electric kettles commonly have between 2 and 3 kW elements.

The watt is named after the British engineer James Watt (1736–1819).

The *power rating* of a heating source is simply the rate at which that source produces heat energy.

$1\,\mathrm{kW} = 1000\,\mathrm{W}$

Exercise 1.1

(a) Use Equation (1.1) and Table 1.1 to calculate the change in the heat energy of 2 kg of water when its temperature is raised from 20°C to 80°C.

(b) The water in (a) was heated in an electric kettle with a 2 kW element. Assuming that all the electrical energy is used only in heating the water, estimate how long it will take to raise the water temperature from 20°C to 80°C.

(c) In (b) it is assumed that the electrical energy is used only to heat the water. What else would it be used to heat, in practice? Is the answer to (b) an underestimate or an overestimate of the actual time taken?

1.2 The three modes of heat transfer

There are three modes of **heat energy transfer**, or **heat transfer** for short, namely *conduction*, *convection* and *radiation*.

In **conduction**, heat energy is transferred from one part of a substance to another part because the faster vibration of molecules in the hotter part (i.e. the part at a higher temperature) excites the molecules, atoms or electrons in an adjacent cooler part so that they, in turn, move faster. In this way heat energy is passed through the substance from the parts at a higher temperature to those at a lower temperature. There is no macroscopic (i.e. large-scale) movement of any part of the substance involved in this mode of heat transfer.

The conduction of heat energy takes place in all solids, liquids and gases. However, the molecules in solids and liquids are packed fairly tightly, whereas the molecules in gases are widely spaced. Conduction in gases is determined by the rate at which the kinetic energy of the gas molecules can be transferred by random collisions, which occur relatively infrequently. So gases are poor conductors of heat energy compared with solids and liquids, with the result that, in modelling heat transfer, the conduction of heat energy through gases is often ignored (at least in a first model). In fact, although liquids are generally better conductors of heat energy than gases, apart from mercury, they too are generally poor conductors compared with solids. Consequently, in modelling heat transfer, the conduction of heat energy in liquids is also often ignored.

One example of conduction is the loss of heat energy through the walls of a warm room. The inside surface of the wall is at a higher temperature than the outside surface and, as a result, heat energy passes through the wall by conduction. Another example is the transfer of heat energy from the inside of a pipe carrying hot water to the outside of the pipe.

The second mode of heat transfer, **convection**, is associated only with *fluids* (i.e. liquids and gases). In convection, heat energy is transferred by virtue of the movement of the fluid. A saucepan of water being heated on a gas ring is a suitable example. Heat energy from the burning gas is conducted through the bottom of the saucepan and transmitted to the parts of the water nearest the bottom of the pan. This raises the temperature of that part of the water and consequently makes it less dense. The hotter water then rises and mixes with the main body of the water, transmitting heat energy to it. It is replaced near the bottom of the pan by cooler water from above, and the process continues. The resulting movements of the water are referred to as *convection currents*. If convection currents are caused purely by the kind of variation in density with temperature described in the case of the water in the saucepan, the process is known as **natural** or **free convection**. If the fluid movement, and therefore the rate of heat transfer, were to be increased by the use of a stirrer or a pump, for example, then it would be **forced convection**. Examples of heat transfer by forced convection are cooling a cup of hot tea by blowing over the surface, and baking in a fan oven. Convection is particularly important as a mode of heat transfer near the interface between the fluid and another substance.

The third mode of heat transfer is **thermal radiation**, often referred to simply as **radiation**. A familiar example of radiation is the way that heat energy reaches us from the sun. Radiation can take place through any substance — solid, liquid or gas — and even through a vacuum. However, opaque substances are largely opaque to radiation, in that very little heat energy is transferred through them by radiation, with the result that, in modelling heat transfer, the radiation of heat energy through opaque substances can usually be ignored.

The mechanism by which the heat energy travels is called *electromagnetic radiation*. This course is not the place for a detailed discussion of electromagnetic radiation, but it is worth mentioning that radio and television signals, light and X-rays are all examples of it.

Every substance — solid, liquid or gas — continuously emits part of its heat energy by radiation and gains heat energy by radiation from the other substances around it. For a given substance, the net rate at which it gains or loses heat energy by radiation depends on its temperature, as well as the nature of its surface (in the case of solids and liquids). The higher the temperature of the substance, the greater the amount of heat energy it radiates in a given time. A highly polished surface is a poor radiator and also a poor absorber of radiation; this is why in a vacuum flask the surfaces that face each other across the vacuum are highly polished reflectors. A matt black surface is a good radiator and a good absorber of radiation. Gases are poor radiators of heat compared with solids or liquids, with the result that, in modelling heat transfer, the radiation of heat energy by gases is often ignored.

Example 1.1

A cavity wall of a house consists of a layer of breeze-blocks, an air gap and a layer of bricks, as shown in Figure 1.1. Assume that the conduction of heat energy through air is negligible, that the radiation of heat energy from air is negligible, and that the breeze-blocks and bricks are opaque to radiation. Identify the modes of heat transfer involved in the transfer of heat energy through the wall from the inside of the house, which is warm, to the outside on a cold, windy day.

Solution

The modes of heat transfer are:

(a) natural convection from the warm air inside the house to the inside surface of the breeze-block layer;

(b) radiation from objects inside the house to the inside surface of the breeze-block layer;

(c) radiation from the inside surface of the breeze-block layer to objects inside the house;

(d) conduction through the breeze-block layer;

(e) natural convection from the outer surface of the breeze-block layer to the air in the gap;

(f) radiation from the outer surface of the breeze-block layer to the inner surface of the brick layer;

(g) natural convection from the air in the gap to the inner surface of the brick layer;

(h) radiation from the inner surface of the brick layer to the outer surface of the breeze-block layer;

(i) conduction through the brick layer;

(j) forced convection from the outside surface of the brick layer to the cold air outside the house;

(k) radiation from the outside surface of the brick layer to the surroundings outside the house;

(l) radiation from the surroundings outside the house to the outside surface of the brick layer. ■

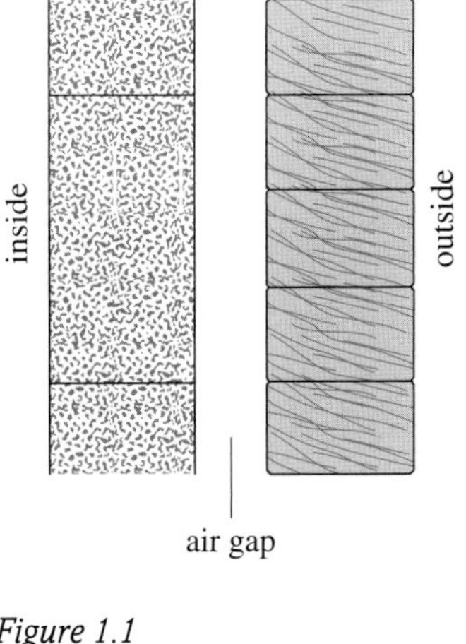

Figure 1.1

***Exercise 1.2**

A china cup full of hot milky tea is placed on a wooden table, as shown in Figure 1.2. Assume that the conduction of heat energy through tea is negligible (so that the temperature of the bulk of the tea can be assumed to be uniform) and that china, wood and milky tea are opaque to radiation. Identify the modes of heat transfer present in the cooling of the cup of tea.

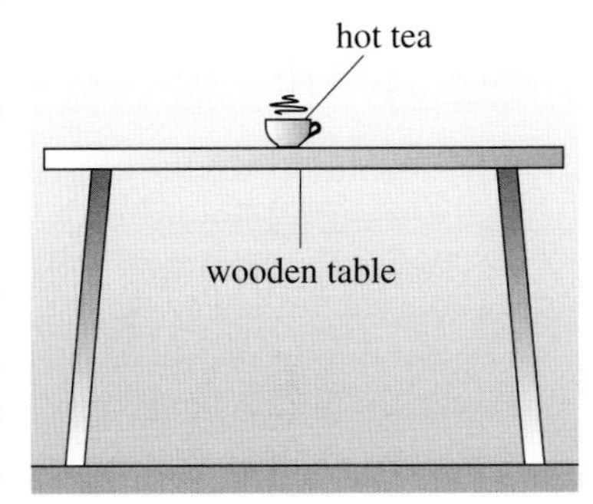

Figure 1.2

Although, as Example 1.1 and Exercise 1.2 illustrate, more than one mode of heat transfer is present in most physical situations, in this unit, for the sake of simplicity, we shall consider each mode separately (at least at first).

End-of-section Exercises

Exercise 1.3

An immersion heater is rated at 3 kW. It is used to heat the water in a well-insulated tank that contains 100 kg of water. How long will it take to heat the water from 15°C to 60°C, assuming that all the electrical energy is used only in heating the water? Do you think that your answer is reasonably close to reality?

Exercise 1.4

An empty room in a house has a volume of $40\,\mathrm{m}^3$. On a cold morning the room has a temperature of $0°\mathrm{C}$, and you wish to raise the temperature of the room to $20°\mathrm{C}$ in 30 minutes by using an electric fire. Ignoring heat losses through the walls, doors, windows, floor and ceiling, what is the minimum rating of an electric fire that could achieve this? Do you think that your answer is reasonably close to reality?

You may assume that the density of air is $1.293\,\mathrm{kg\,m^{-3}}$.

2 Conduction

In this and subsequent sections of this unit we shall develop models for the transfer of heat energy through the walls of a house. We shall begin, in this section, by setting up a simple model based on just one of the three modes of heat transfer, namely conduction. Subsection 2.2 provides a brief discussion of a physical law that we shall need in our modelling. Subsection 2.4 extends the model to a different situation, that of conduction through a pipe. In later sections, we shall extend our model to take into account the effects of convection and radiation.

2.1 Heat loss through a wall: initial assumptions

For our first model of the conduction of heat energy through a wall, we restrict ourselves to walls that consist of a single layer of material, such as the stone walls found in old cottages.

Multilayered walls are considered in Sections 3 and 4.

We shall model our solid wall as a **flat rectangular slab**, by which we mean a solid with six rectangular faces, the breadth (or thickness) of which is significantly less than its height or length, as illustrated in Figure 2.1. We shall refer to the two largest faces of the slab as the *surfaces* of the slab; in the case of a solid wall, one of the surfaces represents the inside surface of the wall and the other the outside surface. (We shall be able to apply our heat transfer model not only to solid walls but also, for example, to solid doors, to single-glazed windows and even to slab-shaped volumes of fluids.) The two surfaces of the slab have the same area, as does any cross-section parallel to these surfaces.

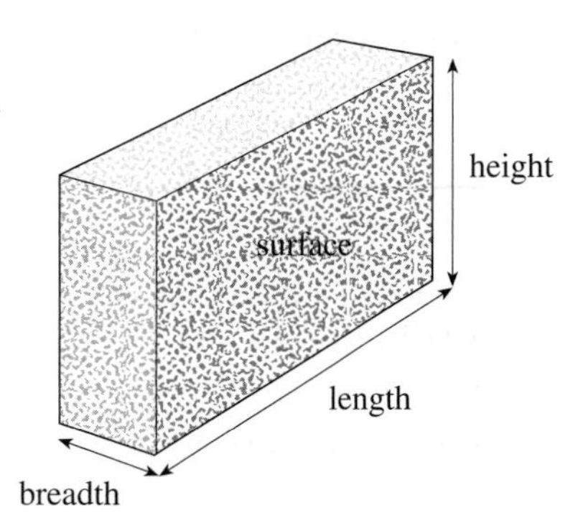

Figure 2.1

The purpose of the model is to enable us to calculate the rate of heat energy loss due to conduction through a solid wall (or through anything else that can be modelled by a slab) when one surface of the wall (the 'inside' or 'inner' surface) is at a higher temperature than the other surface (the 'outside' or 'outer' surface).

****Exercise 2.1***

List four or five factors (e.g. the temperature on the inside surface of the slab) that you think are the most important in determining the rate of heat energy loss due to conduction through a slab. How would you expect the rate of heat energy loss to change as these factors are varied?

The solution to Exercise 2.1 will help us later when we come to define the variables and parameters for our model, and to formulate relationships between them. But first, we need to list the simplifying assumptions that will enable us to develop our first, simple model of heat transfer through a wall by conduction. Here is an initial list of simplifying assumptions.

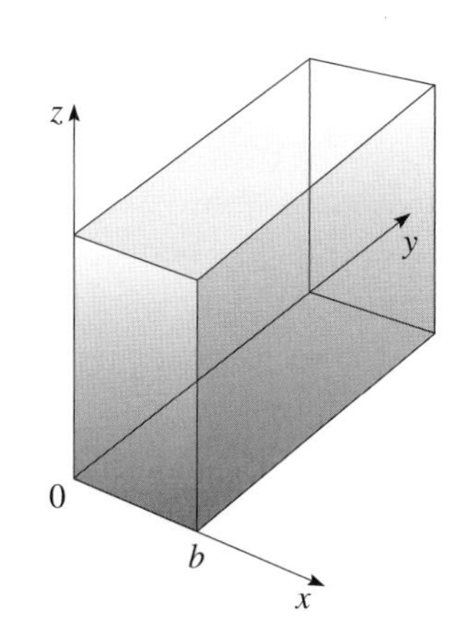

Figure 2.2

(1) The wall is of uniform construction, so that we ignore the facts that the wall is likely to be made up from a variety of different materials (e.g. bricks, stones, mortar, plaster) and is likely to contain doors and/or windows. (Heat energy losses through doors and windows could be incorporated later in a revised model.)

(2) The wall can be represented as a slab. In consequence, we can choose coordinates so that the inside surface of the wall is in the plane $x = 0$ and the outside is in the plane $x = b$ ($b > 0$), where b is the thickness of the wall (see Figure 2.2).

(3) The temperature in the wall is the same in each plane $x =$ constant. This implies that the temperature in the wall at any given time depends on x and not on y or z, i.e. it means that we assume the temperature does not change as we get near the top, bottom or ends of the wall.

(4) The wall is in a **steady state**, which means that the temperature at any given point is independent of the time. This means, for example, that we ignore the fact that the temperatures inside and outside a house can vary considerably between day and night. (Variations over time could be included later in a revised model.)

Variations over time are considered in *Unit 16*.

Assumptions (3) and (4) imply that the temperature at a point in the wall, being independent of time t and the spatial coordinates y and z, depends only on the spatial coordinate x. We can, therefore, represent the temperature by a variable $\Theta = \Theta(x)$, $0 \leq x \leq b$, where $\Theta(x)$ is the temperature at any point in the wall at a perpendicular distance x from the inside surface.

In particular, this implies that the temperatures on the inside and outside surfaces of the wall are uniform and constant.

*Exercise 2.2

Under assumptions (1) to (4), what is the direction of the transfer of heat energy through a wall? You may assume that the (inside) surface $x = 0$ of the wall is at a higher temperature than the (outside) surface $x = b$.

The function $\Theta(x)$ gives, in theory, a complete description of the temperature distribution in the wall. The question now is how to find this distribution, and how to find the rate of heat transfer by conduction through the wall. In order to do this, we have to make a further assumption, known as *Fourier's law*, about the relationship between the temperature distribution and the resulting rate of heat transfer.

Before discussing Fourier's law, it is worth noting that the **rate of heat transfer** is vector quantity, as it possesses both magnitude and direction (the direction of the heat transfer). However, in this unit we shall only be concerned with the *magnitude* of the rate of heat transfer, denoted by q; the direction will always be from a region of higher temperature to one of lower temperature. Also, we shall refer to q as the rate of heat transfer, even though strictly speaking q only gives the magnitude, since the direction will be obvious from the context.

A vector approach to heat transfer is contained in *Unit 23*.

2.2 Fourier's law

The model that we shall use for steady-state conduction through a wall is based on theoretical work done by the French mathematician Joseph Fourier in the early nineteenth century, which has since been amply confirmed by experiment. Fourier's law gives quantitative expression to the idea that conduction transfers heat energy from hotter to cooler places, by postulating that the rate of heat transfer is determined by how rapidly the temperature varies with position.

Jean Baptiste Joseph Fourier (1768–1830)

In the case of our slab, temperature is a function of the x-coordinate and the rate of change of temperature with position is given by $d\Theta/dx$, which is referred to as the **temperature gradient**. Now Fourier's postulation was that the rate of heat transfer q is proportional to the temperature gradient. Also, assumptions (1) to (3) in Subsection 2.1 lead to the reasonable postulation that q is proportional to the surface area, A, of the slab. Combining these two postulations, we obtain

$$q \propto A\frac{d\Theta}{dx},$$

where $\propto$ means 'is proportional to'. Now, the rate of heat transfer q is positive (from the warm inside to the cool outside) and (measured in the same direction) the temperature gradient $d\Theta/dx$ is negative. So, because q and $d\Theta/dx$ have opposite signs, it is conventional to write

It is true in general that, if measured in the same direction, the rate of heat transfer and the temperature gradient must have opposite signs.

$$q = -\kappa A\frac{d\Theta}{dx}, \qquad (2.1)$$

where κ is a *positive* constant of proportionality, called the **thermal conductivity** of the uniform material of which we assume the slab is made. Equation (2.1) gives *Fourier's law* in the case of our slab; it provides the required model of the rate of heat transfer by conduction through our wall. In SI units thermal conductivity κ is measured in watts per metre per kelvin ($\mathrm{W\,m^{-1}\,K^{-1}}$).

The thermal conductivity of a substance varies slightly with temperature. However, in this unit, we shall assume that it is a constant for any given substance. Table 2.1 shows some typical values of κ for various solid materials at 293 K ($\simeq 20°\mathrm{C}$).

This assumption is a reasonable one when temperature differences are not too large.

Table 2.1 Thermal conductivities

Material	Thermal conductivity κ ($\mathrm{W\,m^{-1}\,K^{-1}}$)
Pure copper	385
Stainless steel	150
Mild steel	63
China	1.5
Crown glass	1.0
Brick	0.6
Breeze-block	0.2
Wood	0.15
Concrete	0.1
Cork	0.05

Source: R. M. Tennent (ed.) (1971) *Science data book*, Oliver and Boyd.

Equation (2.1) gives a special case of Fourier's law, applicable to the case of the slab. The general form of the law is as follows.

Fourier's law

Consider a surface S, which is everywhere perpendicular to the direction of heat transfer and is sufficiently small that the temperature gradient $d\Theta/dn$ normal (i.e. perpendicular) to the surface can be considered constant over the surface. The rate q of heat transfer by conduction across the surface is

$$q = -\kappa A \frac{d\Theta}{dn}, \tag{2.2}$$

where κ is the thermal conductivity of the uniform material containing S and A is the area of S.

In *Unit 23*, we shall see how Equation (2.2) can be expressed more elegantly using vector notation.

We shall use this more general form of Fourier's law in Subsection 2.4 when we consider conduction through a pipe.

2.3 Heat loss through a wall: a first model

In order to use Equation (2.1) to determine the rate of transfer of heat energy by conduction through our wall, we need to know how the rate of heat transfer q depends on t and x. Since we are assuming a steady state, Θ is independent of t; hence, by Equation (2.1), q must also be independent of t. To determine how q depends on x, consider a slice of the slab stretching from $x = x_1$ to $x = x_2$ (see Figure 2.3). Now, since Θ is independent of t, the temperature at any point in the slice is always constant. This means that the heat energy of the slice is constant. We can deduce that the rate of heat transfer into the slice through the plane $x = x_1$, in the direction of increasing x, must be equal to the rate of heat transfer out of the slice through the plane $x = x_2$, again in the direction of increasing x (or else the heat energy of the slice would vary). Therefore, since the choice of slice is arbitrary, the rate of heat transfer must be constant for all x, i.e. q is independent of x. To summarize, q is independent of both t and x, i.e. the rate of heat transfer by conduction through the wall is constant.

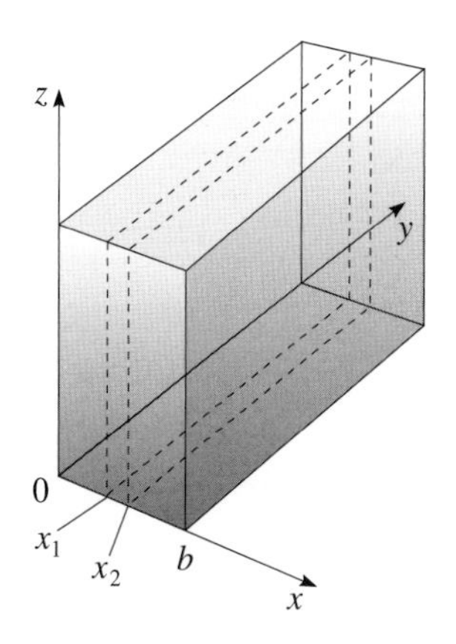

Figure 2.3

So our task is to use Fourier's law, in the form

$$q = -\kappa A \frac{d\Theta}{dx}, \tag{2.1}$$

knowing that q is a constant, to find the rate of transfer of heat energy through a slab of thickness b when we know the temperatures of the two surfaces $x = 0$ and $x = b$. We denote these two temperatures by Θ_1 and Θ_2, respectively, i.e. $\Theta(0) = \Theta_1$ and $\Theta(b) = \Theta_2$, and assume that $\Theta_1 > \Theta_2$.

As q, κ and A are all constants, Fourier's law tells us that

$$\frac{d\Theta}{dx} = -\frac{q}{\kappa A}, \tag{2.3}$$

is also constant. This differential equation can be solved by direct integration to give

$$\Theta(x) = -\frac{q}{\kappa A}x + C, \tag{2.4}$$

where C is a constant. Putting $x = 0$ in Equation (2.4) and using the boundary condition $\Theta(0) = \Theta_1$ gives $C = \Theta_1$, whence

$$\Theta(x) = -\frac{q}{\kappa A}x + \Theta_1. \tag{2.5}$$

Putting $x = b$ in Equation (2.5) and using the boundary condition $\Theta(b) = \Theta_2$ gives

$$\Theta_2 = -\frac{q}{\kappa A}b + \Theta_1. \tag{2.6}$$

Hence, rearranging Equation (2.6), a model of the rate of heat transfer by conduction through the slab is

$$q = \frac{\kappa A(\Theta_1 - \Theta_2)}{b}. \tag{2.7}$$

Steady-state conduction through a uniform slab

In the steady state, the rate of heat transfer q by conduction through a slab of constant cross-sectional area A and thickness b, made of uniform material with thermal conductivity κ, is given by

$$q = \frac{\kappa A(\Theta_1 - \Theta_2)}{b}, \tag{2.7}$$

where Θ_1 and Θ_2 ($\Theta_1 > \Theta_2$) are the temperatures of the two surfaces of the slab.

As Equation (2.7) involves a temperature *difference*, it can be used with either the Celsius or the absolute temperature scale.

Using Equation (2.7) to substitute for q in Equation (2.5) gives

$$\Theta(x) = \Theta_1 - \frac{\Theta_1 - \Theta_2}{b}x \tag{2.8}$$

as the temperature distribution in the slab. This linear relationship is illustrated in Figure 2.4. Using Equation (2.7) to substitute for q in Equation (2.3) gives

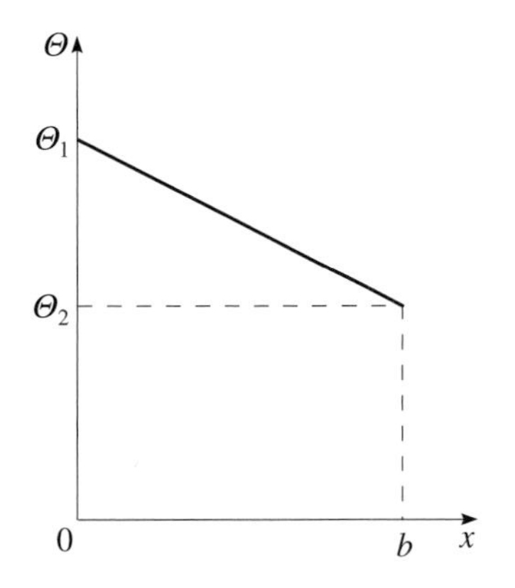

Figure 2.4

$$\frac{d\Theta}{dx} = -\frac{\Theta_1 - \Theta_2}{b} \tag{2.9}$$

as the temperature gradient in the slab. (Equation (2.9) is written in this way to emphasize that, for $\Theta_1 > \Theta_2$, the temperature gradient is negative.)

*Exercise 2.3

Does Equation (2.7) depend on the factors that you thought of as important in Exercise 2.1? Does q increase or decrease as A, $\Theta_1 - \Theta_2$ and b increase? Is this what you predicted in your solution to Exercise 2.1?

*Exercise 2.4

The solid brick walls of a house are 210 mm thick. The air inside the house is at a temperature of 18°C and the air outside is at a temperature of 10°C. Assume that the surfaces of the walls are at the temperature of the air with which they are in contact.

(a) What, according to the steady-state conduction model, is the rate of heat transfer through the walls, per square metre of wall surface?

(b) What is the temperature gradient of the wall?

(c) What is the temperature at a point in the wall 50 mm from the inside surface?

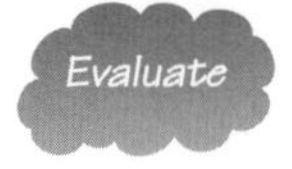

In Exercise 2.4 we have seen that our model predicts that the rate of heat transfer by conduction per unit area through a 210 mm solid brick wall, when the inside and outside temperatures are 18°C and 10°C, is $22.86\,\mathrm{W\,m^{-2}}$. Experimentally, the rate of heat transfer per unit area is found to be $16.8\,\mathrm{W\,m^{-2}}$, which is significantly lower. One of the main reasons for this discrepancy is the assumption we made in Exercise 2.4 that the temperature on the inside surface of the wall is the same as the temperature of the air inside the house, and similarly for the temperature on the outside surface of the wall. However, if you touch the inside surface of a wall, you should notice that it feels colder than the air inside the house; similarly, the outside surface feels warmer than the air outside the house. So this assumption is not a good one. The less than perfect thermal contact between the surfaces of the wall and the air is caused by convection. In Section 3 we shall develop a revised model for heat transfer through a wall by incorporating the effects of convection at the inside and outside surfaces of the wall.

2.4 Conduction through a pipe

We shall end this section by discussing conduction through the walls of a cylindrical pipe — for example central heating pipes, which carry hot water to the radiators and are surrounded by cooler air. We shall assume again a steady state, as defined earlier, and also that heat transfer takes place *radially* (i.e. at each point in the pipe wall, the direction of heat transfer is away from the centre of the pipe).

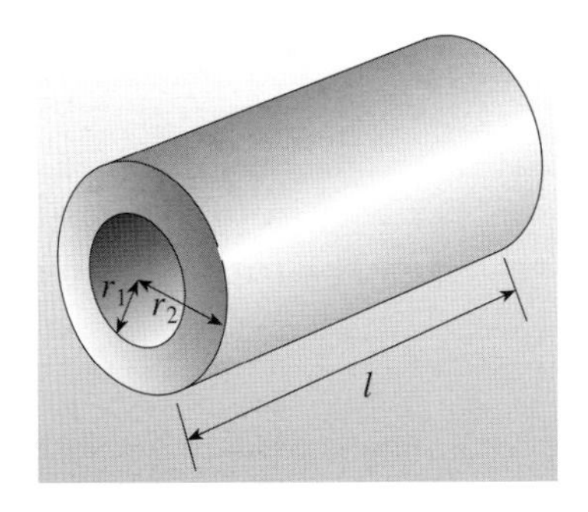

Figure 2.5

The main difference between this case and conduction through a slab is that here the cross-sectional area A through which heat energy is transferred is not constant. This becomes clear when we consider the cross-section of a pipe such as that shown in Figure 2.5. The pipe is of length l, and has inner radius r_1 and outer radius r_2 (so the thickness of the pipe wall is $r_2 - r_1$). The inner surface of the pipe has area $A_1 = 2\pi r_1 l$ and the outer surface has area $A_2 = 2\pi r_2 l$, and $A_2 > A_1$. For any radius r, where $r_1 \le r \le r_2$, the cross-sectional cylindrical surface defined by r (shown in Figure 2.6) has area $A = 2\pi r l$, so the cross-sectional area depends on the radius.

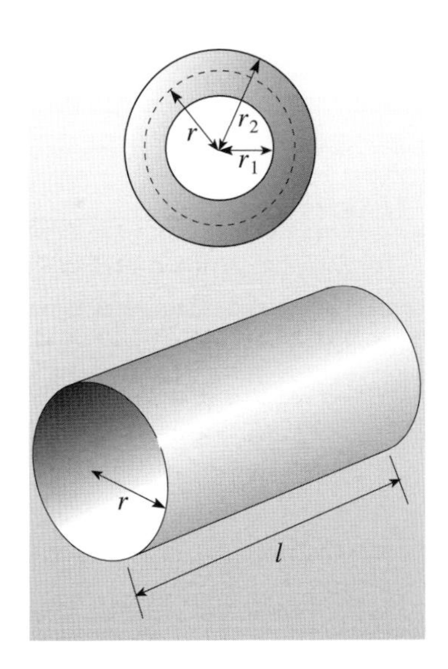

Figure 2.6

Now for any cross-sectional cylindrical surface of radius r inside the pipe wall (so that $r_1 \le r \le r_2$), symmetry tells us that the temperature at all points of this surface will be the same. It follows that the steady-state temperature Θ in the pipe wall is a function only of r, and the temperature gradient is $d\Theta/dr$. Furthermore, under the assumption that heat transfer takes place radially, the direction of the transfer of heat energy across this cylindrical surface is everywhere perpendicular to the surface. So, by the general form of Fourier's law (Equation (2.2)), the heat transfer rate is

$$q = -\kappa A \frac{d\Theta}{dr},$$

where in this case the area A is a function of r.

Using $A = 2\pi r l$, we obtain

$$q = -\kappa \times (2\pi r l) \times \frac{d\Theta}{dr},$$

and hence

$$\frac{d\Theta}{dr} = -\frac{q}{2\pi\kappa r l} = -\frac{q}{2\pi\kappa l}\frac{1}{r}. \qquad (2.10)$$

Using an argument similar to that used in Subsection 2.3, we can deduce that, in the steady state, q is a constant, i.e. q does not vary with r. Thus, Equation (2.10) can be solved by direct integration to give the general solution

$$\Theta = -\frac{q}{2\pi\kappa l}\ln r + C,$$

where C is a constant.

We can find the constant C and the rate of heat transfer q if we know the temperatures at the inner and outer surfaces of the pipe. We shall denote the temperature on the inner surface $r = r_1$ of the pipe by Θ_1 and the temperature on the outer surface $r = r_2$ by Θ_2, and we shall assume that $\Theta_1 > \Theta_2$, i.e. that the inner surface is hotter than the outer surface, so that heat energy is transferred from the inside to the outside of the pipe. Using these two boundary conditions, we obtain

$$\Theta_1 = -\frac{q}{2\pi\kappa l}\ln r_1 + C \quad \text{and} \quad \Theta_2 = -\frac{q}{2\pi\kappa l}\ln r_2 + C.$$

Remember that q is constant and hence has the same value at every radius.

Subtracting the second equation from the first, we have

$$\Theta_1 - \Theta_2 = \frac{q}{2\pi\kappa l}(\ln r_2 - \ln r_1) = \frac{q}{2\pi\kappa l}\ln\left(\frac{r_2}{r_1}\right),$$

so

$$q = \frac{2\pi\kappa l(\Theta_1 - \Theta_2)}{\ln(r_2/r_1)}. \tag{2.11}$$

Steady-state conduction through a uniform cylinder

In the steady state, the rate of heat transfer q by conduction through a cylinder of inner radius r_1, outer radius r_2 and length l, made of uniform material with thermal conductivity κ, is given by

$$q = \frac{2\pi\kappa l(\Theta_1 - \Theta_2)}{\ln(r_2/r_1)}, \tag{2.11}$$

where Θ_1 and Θ_2 are the temperatures of the inner and outer surfaces of the cylinder, respectively.

Again, as Equation (2.11) involves a temperature difference, it can be used with either the Celsius or the absolute temperature scale.

*Exercise 2.5

A copper pipe, of internal diameter 13 mm and external diameter 15 mm, carries hot water at a temperature of 80°C through a room at a temperature of 20°C. Assuming that the surfaces of the pipe have the same temperature as the temperature of the fluid with which they are in contact, predict the rate at which heat energy is conducted through the wall of a one-metre length of the pipe.

Note that we have specified the diameters of the pipe, rather than the radii.

Exercise 2.6

(a) Show that the temperature Θ at a radius r inside the wall of the pipe discussed in this subsection can be modelled by

$$\Theta = \Theta_1 - \frac{\Theta_1 - \Theta_2}{\ln(r_2/r_1)}\ln\left(\frac{r}{r_1}\right). \tag{2.12}$$

(b) For the pipe specified in Exercise 2.5, what is the temperature in the pipe wall at a radius of 7 mm, according to the model?

End-of-section Exercises

Exercise 2.7

A glass window has an area of $2\,m^2$ and a thickness of 4 mm. The inside surface of the window has a temperature of 20°C and the outside surface a temperature of 10°C. Predict the rate of transfer of heat energy by conduction through the window.

Exercise 2.8

A cylindrical tea-urn has an outside diameter of 350 mm and a height of 515 mm. It has a circular lid and stands on a wooden table. It is made from stainless steel 3 mm thick. It is required to estimate the rate of loss of heat energy from the tea-urn when it is full of water maintained at a temperature of 100°C (by means of a thermostatically controlled heating element) when the temperature of the surrounding air is 20°C. We assume that the inside surface of the tea-urn is at the temperature of the water it contains, and that the outside surface of the tea-urn is at the temperature of the surrounding air.

(a) Estimate the rate of loss of heat energy by conduction through the cylindrical sides of the tea-urn.

(b) Modelling the lid of the tea-urn as a uniform flat circular slab, estimate the rate of loss of heat energy by conduction through the lid of the tea-urn.

(c) Assuming that there is a no significant loss of heat energy through the bottom of the tea-urn (as wood is a poor conductor of heat energy), use the results of (a) and (b) to estimate the total rate of loss of heat energy by conduction from the tea-urn. Comment on your answer.

Exercise 2.9

A storage vessel may be modelled as a hollow sphere of uniform material. The internal and external radii are r_1 and r_2, respectively. The temperatures of the inner and outer spherical surfaces are Θ_1 and Θ_2, respectively (where $\Theta_1 > \Theta_2$), and the thermal conductivity of the material of the vessel is κ.

(a) Show that the steady-state heat transfer rate for conduction through the wall of the vessel can be modelled by

The surface area of a sphere of radius r is $4\pi r^2$.

$$q = 4\pi\kappa\left(\frac{1}{r_1} - \frac{1}{r_2}\right)^{-1}(\Theta_1 - \Theta_2).$$

(b) Show that if the storage vessel is made of mild steel, and $\Theta_1 = 20°C$, $\Theta_2 = 15°C$ and $r_1 = 0.1\,m$, then without insulation the heat transfer rate for conduction through the wall of the vessel cannot be kept below 395 W however large the outside radius r_2 is made.

3 Convection and U-values

In this section we continue the task of developing a model for the transfer of heat energy through a slab such as a solid wall, window or door, of given thickness, when we know the temperatures of the air on either side of the slab. In Section 2 we built up a model for the heat transfer through the slab by conduction. Here, in Subsections 3.1 and 3.2, we improve on that model by incorporating the effects of convection in the air in contact with the slab at both its surfaces. Subsection 3.3 shows how our model can be applied to pipes. We continue to assume a steady-state situation.

The effects of radiation are considered in Section 4.

3.1 A simple model of convection

It was remarked in Subsection 2.3 that a model for heat transfer through a wall that incorporates only conduction in the wall, and assumes that there is a perfect transfer of heat energy between the surfaces of the wall and the surrounding air, does not compare very well with reality. In the case of a house wall, heat energy is transferred not only through the wall, but also from the warm air in the room to the wall, and from the wall to the cool air outside. There are, therefore, two regions where there is transfer of heat energy between a fluid (air) and a surface. In the case of a pipe containing hot water, the heat energy is transferred from the hot water inside to the cool air outside, and again there are two surfaces where a solid is in contact with a fluid (water–pipe and pipe–air) across which heat transfer takes place. In either case, since there is a fluid present, convection will play a major part in the heat transfer process. The purpose of our improved model is to incorporate not only the heat transfer due to conduction through the solid wall or pipe but also to allow for the effects of both free and forced convection in the fluids in contact with the wall or pipe.

Exercise 3.1

The distinguishing feature of heat transfer by convection is fluid motion. Bearing this in mind, list the factors that you think are the most important in determining the rate of transfer of heat energy due to convection, between a fluid and a surface.

Considered in detail, convection turns out to be a rather complicated matter, not at all easy to analyse. As you might expect, fluid mechanics plays a very important part in any thorough consideration of convection. Fortunately, in spite of this, it is possible to get some quite useful results based on a very simple description of the main features of convection, together with some of the practical experience that has been accumulated over the years.

Figure 3.1 shows a solid–fluid boundary. We shall assume the heat transfer is taking place from the solid (say, a house wall) to the fluid (say, atmospheric air). This means the temperature of the surface of the wall, where it touches the air, must be higher than the air temperature at some distance from the house. The parts of the air near the wall are heated by conduction and radiation before they move away to join the main body of the air, being replaced by cooler air, which in turn is heated. The result is that the air very near the wall has a temperature higher than that of the main body of the air, which we will assume to be at a uniform temperature, referred to as its **ambient temperature**. The temperature drop between the wall and the main body of the air, which enables the transfer of heat energy to take place, occurs in a thin layer of the air quite near the surface of the wall.

This effect is very evident if you touch the outside surface of a pipe containing hot water!

This is sketched in Figure 3.1, where Θ_1 represents the surface temperature of the wall and Θ_2 represents the ambient temperature of the main body of the air.

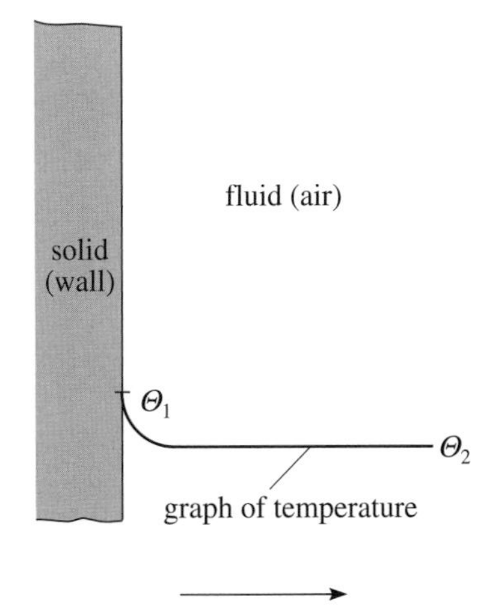

Figure 3.1

The same general argument applies when the direction of the heat transfer is from the fluid to the solid — the temperature drop from fluid to solid again occurs in a thin layer of fluid immediately next to the surface of the solid. In this layer the fluid is giving up some of its heat energy to the solid, mainly by conduction.

Furthermore, the same general arguments apply for convection at the surface between two fluids (e.g. the surface between the tea in a cup and the surrounding air).

Although the detailed physical process of convection is quite complicated, we can make some simple qualitative observations.

- If the temperature difference $\Theta_1 - \Theta_2$ increases, then so does the magnitude of the rate of heat transfer (hotter surfaces lose heat energy at a faster rate than do cooler surfaces).
- If the temperature difference is zero, then the rate of heat transfer is also zero.
- If the temperature difference $\Theta_1 - \Theta_2$ changes sign (so that the air is now hotter than the wall, for example), then the direction of heat transfer also changes (so that heat energy is now transferred from the air to the wall).

These observations are consistent with the assumption that the rate of heat transfer by convection is proportional to the temperature difference. Furthermore, as we would expect the rate of heat transfer by convection to increase with the area of the surface, it is reasonable to assume that the rate of heat transfer is proportional to the surface area. These postulations lead to the following simple model of heat energy transfer by convection, commonly used by chemical engineers, architects and heating engineers.

Steady-state heat transfer by convection

If a fluid meets a surface, then the rate of heat transfer q between the surface and the fluid due to convection in the steady state is given by

$$q = hA(\Theta_1 - \Theta_2), \qquad (3.1)$$

where A is the area of the surface and h is a positive constant called the **convective heat transfer coefficient**. The temperature Θ_1 is the higher of the temperature of the surface of the substance and the ambient temperature of the fluid, and the temperature Θ_2 is the lower of these two, so that $\Theta_1 > \Theta_2$.

As Equation (3.1) involves a temperature difference, it can be used with either the Celsius or the absolute temperature scale.

Equation (3.1) looks similar to Equation (2.7), which we used to model conduction through a slab, with h substituted for κ/b. In fact, h is a different sort of coefficient, as it takes into account the geometry of the surface, the nature of the adjacent fluid, and the relative velocity between the fluid and the surface. Unlike Equation (2.7), Equation (3.1) is a suitable model for any surface, even if it is not flat.

In SI units the convective heat transfer coefficient h is measured in watts per square metre per kelvin ($\mathrm{W\,m^{-2}\,K^{-1}}$).

*Exercise 3.2

An electrically heated plate of area $0.04\,\mathrm{m}^2$ dissipates heat by convection at a rate of 750 W to air at an ambient temperature of 20°C. If the surface of the plate has a constant temperature of 200°C, determine the convective heat transfer coefficient between the plate and the air.

With temperature differences of this magnitude, radiation will also be an important mode of heat transfer.

Table 3.1 gives an indication of the ranges of typical values of the convective heat transfer coefficient h for different conditions. Because h depends not only on the particular fluid but also on the fluid velocity, the dimensions and shape of the surface and the details of the fluid motion near the surface, it is not possible to give a table of exact values.

Table 3.1 Ranges of values of the convective heat transfer coefficient

Process	Fluid	Convective heat transfer coefficient h ($\mathrm{W\,m^{-2}\,K^{-1}}$)
Free convection	Gas	2–25
	Liquid	50–1000
Forced convection	Gas	25–250
	Liquid	50–20 000

Source: F. P. Incropera and D. P. de Witt (1990) *Introduction to heat transfer*, Wiley.

As seen in Table 3.1, heat energy losses due to convection are significantly larger when the convection is forced than when the convection is free. This is why the 'wind chill' factor is so important in cold weather. Even when the air temperature is the same, a wind will result in significantly greater heat energy losses from the body.

In this unit we shall mostly be concerned with convective heat transfer in air and water, and shall assume the values for the convective heat transfer coefficient given in Table 3.2. However, when using these values, it is important to remember that the actual value in a real situation may be considerably different.

Table 3.2 Assumed values of the convective heat transfer coefficient

Process	Fluid	Convective heat transfer coefficient h ($\mathrm{W\,m^{-2}\,K^{-1}}$)
Free convection	Air	10
	Water	500
Forced convection	Air	150
	Water	1000

3.2 Heat loss through a wall: a second model

We are now in a position to be able to construct a reasonably realistic model for the heat energy loss through a solid house wall, in the steady state, that incorporates the effects of conduction as well as convection. Our task is to find a relationship that gives the rate of heat energy loss q in terms of the ambient temperature Θ_{in} of the air inside the house and the ambient temperature Θ_{out} of the air outside the house, where we shall assume that $\Theta_{\text{in}} > \Theta_{\text{out}}$.

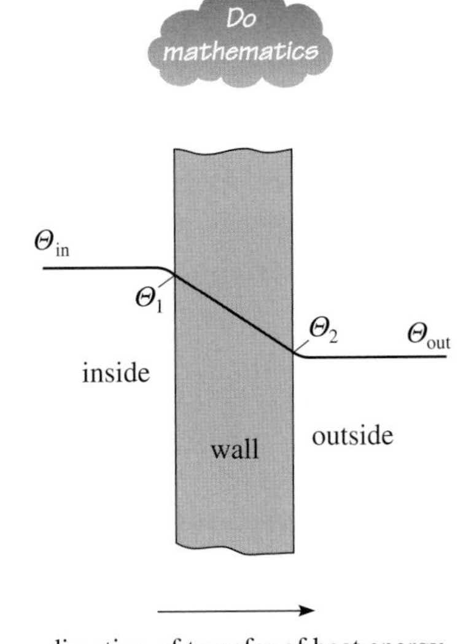

direction of transfer of heat energy

Figure 3.2

Figure 3.2 shows part of the cross-section of a solid wall, together with a sketch of the temperature variation from the air inside to the air outside. Assuming that the wall is opaque to radiation (as most walls essentially are), the temperature drop $\Theta_1 - \Theta_2$ across the wall is exclusively due to conduction through the wall, and so, using Equation (2.7), the rate of heat transfer through the wall is

$$q = \frac{\kappa A(\Theta_1 - \Theta_2)}{b}. \tag{3.2}$$

We shall assume that the temperature drop $\Theta_2 - \Theta_{\text{out}}$ between the outside surface of the wall and the main body of air outside is principally due to convection. Hence, using Equation (3.1), the rate of heat transfer is

In fact, as you will see in Section 4, radiation has a significant part to play here.

$$q = h_{\text{out}} A(\Theta_2 - \Theta_{\text{out}}), \tag{3.3}$$

where h_{out} is the convective heat transfer coefficient at the outside wall surface. Similarly, at the inside wall surface the rate of heat transfer is

$$q = h_{\text{in}} A(\Theta_{\text{in}} - \Theta_1), \tag{3.4}$$

where h_{in} is the convective heat transfer coefficient at the inside surface.

Now, using an argument similar to that in Subsection 2.3, we can deduce that, in the steady state, the rate of heat transfer q takes the same constant value at each stage of the heat transfer process, given by Equations (3.2)–(3.4). Hence we can use these three equations to find a relationship between this constant value of q and Θ_{in} and Θ_{out}, by eliminating Θ_1 and Θ_2. This can be done by writing Equation (3.4) as

$$\Theta_{\text{in}} - \Theta_1 = \frac{q}{Ah_{\text{in}}},$$

Equation (3.2) as

$$\Theta_1 - \Theta_2 = \frac{qb}{A\kappa}$$

and Equation (3.3) as

$$\Theta_2 - \Theta_{\text{out}} = \frac{q}{Ah_{\text{out}}}.$$

Adding these three equations, we eliminate Θ_1 and Θ_2 and obtain

$$\Theta_{\text{in}} - \Theta_{\text{out}} = \frac{q}{A}\left(\frac{1}{h_{\text{in}}} + \frac{b}{\kappa} + \frac{1}{h_{\text{out}}}\right).$$

Hence

$$q = \left(\frac{1}{h_{\text{in}}} + \frac{b}{\kappa} + \frac{1}{h_{\text{out}}}\right)^{-1} A(\Theta_{\text{in}} - \Theta_{\text{out}}) = UA(\Theta_{\text{in}} - \Theta_{\text{out}}), \tag{3.5}$$

where

$$U = \left(\frac{1}{h_{\text{in}}} + \frac{b}{\kappa} + \frac{1}{h_{\text{out}}}\right)^{-1}. \tag{3.6}$$

The coefficient U is usually referred to as the ***U*-value** for the wall. The U-value is the overall heat transfer coefficient for the wall and the surface effects combined, and Equation (3.5) gives the rate of heat transfer in terms of the overall temperature drop $\Theta_{\text{in}} - \Theta_{\text{out}}$.

In the technical literature, you may see

$$R = \frac{1}{U} = \frac{1}{h_{\text{in}}} + \frac{b}{\kappa} + \frac{1}{h_{\text{out}}}$$

referred to as the **thermal resistance** or ***R*-value** of the wall. It is called the thermal *resistance* because an increase in the value of R results in a decrease in the rate of heat energy transfer q. (There are strong analogies with resistances in the theory of electrical circuits.)

Steady-state heat transfer by conduction and convection through a uniform slab

In the steady state, the rate of heat transfer q by conduction and convection through a slab of constant cross-sectional area A and thickness b, made of uniform material with thermal conductivity κ, bounded on either side by a fluid, is given by

$$q = UA(\Theta_{\text{in}} - \Theta_{\text{out}}), \tag{3.5}$$

where Θ_{in} and Θ_{out} ($\Theta_{\text{in}} > \Theta_{\text{out}}$) are the ambient temperatures at either side of the slab and

$$U = \left(\frac{1}{h_{\text{in}}} + \frac{b}{\kappa} + \frac{1}{h_{\text{out}}}\right)^{-1}, \tag{3.6}$$

where h_{in} and h_{out} are the convective heat transfer coefficients for the two surfaces of the slab.

The SI units of U are the same as those of the convective heat transfer coefficient h, namely $\text{W m}^{-2}\,\text{K}^{-1}$.

*Exercise 3.3

According to Equation (3.5), does q increase or decrease as A, $\Theta_{\text{in}} - \Theta_{\text{out}}$ and h_{out} increase? Is this what you would expect intuitively?

*Exercise 3.4

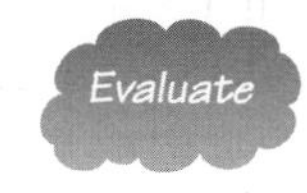

The solid brick walls of a house are 210 mm thick. The air inside the house is at an ambient temperature of 18°C, and the air outside is at an ambient temperature of 10°C. The convective heat transfer coefficients are $10\,\text{W m}^{-2}\,\text{K}^{-1}$ for the inside and $150\,\text{W m}^{-2}\,\text{K}^{-1}$ for the outside (as given in Table 3.2).

(a) Calculate the U-value for the walls.

(b) What, according to the steady-state conduction and convection model, is the heat transfer rate through the walls, per square metre of wall surface? Compare your answer with the one you obtained in the solution to Exercise 2.4(a).

(c) What are the temperatures at the inside and outside surfaces of the walls?

This exercise extends Exercise 2.4 to include the effects of convection.

Calculations similar to those above can be performed for cavity walls. Figure 3.3 shows the structure of a typical exterior cavity wall of a modern house in the UK. The wall is effectively made up of three layers — breeze-block, air and brick. The heat transfer through the layers of breeze-block and brick can be dealt with quite simply — it is almost entirely by conduction. The problem is the air in the gap between the brick and the breeze-block. Because air can circulate, convection plays an important part in heat transfer across the gap. It turns out that, for gaps up to about 15 mm, the heat transfer by conduction and convection across the air gap can be modelled as though the air gap was a substance of thermal conductivity $\kappa = 0.0241\,\text{W m}^{-1}\,\text{K}^{-1}$, i.e. by using Equation (2.7)

$$q = \frac{\kappa A(\Theta_1 - \Theta_2)}{b},$$

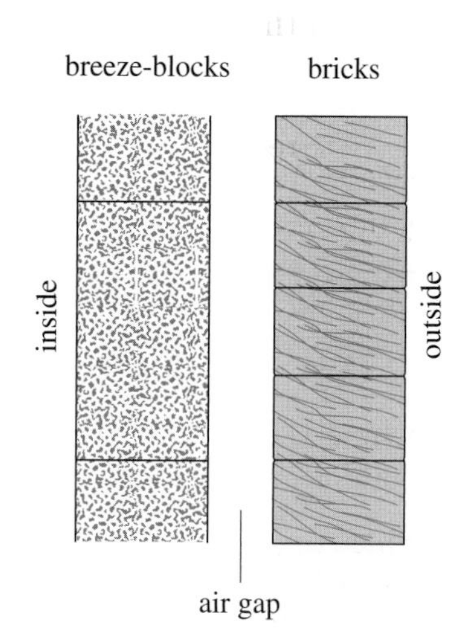

Figure 3.3

In reality, most of the heat transfer across the gap is by radiation. This is considered in Section 4.

where b is the thickness of the gap. If the air gap is more than 15 mm, the heat transfer by conduction and convection is almost independent of the thickness of the gap, and so is better modelled by

$$q = h_c A(\Theta_1 - \Theta_2), \tag{3.7}$$

where h_c is a *combined heat transfer coefficient*, which takes into account both conduction and convection, whose value is about $1.75\,\mathrm{W\,m^{-2}\,K^{-1}}$.

Steady-state heat transfer by conduction and convection across an air gap

The rate of heat transfer q across an air gap of constant cross-sectional area A in the steady state can be modelled for gaps of up to about 15 mm in width by

$$q = \frac{\kappa A(\Theta_1 - \Theta_2)}{b}, \tag{2.7}$$

where $\kappa = 0.0241\,\mathrm{W\,m^{-1}\,K^{-1}}$ and b is the thickness of the gap. For gaps wider than about 15 mm, a better steady-state model is

$$q = h_c A(\Theta_1 - \Theta_2), \tag{3.7}$$

where $h_c = 1.75\,\mathrm{W\,m^{-2}\,K^{-1}}$ is the **combined heat transfer coefficient**. In both cases Θ_1 and Θ_2 are the temperatures of the surfaces at either side of the air gap, with $\Theta_1 > \Theta_2$.

Example 3.1

Find an algebraic formula for the U-value for heat transfer by conduction and convection through a double-glazed window where each pane has thickness b and surface area A, and the air gap between the panes has width w ($w < 15$ mm), as shown in Figure 3.4. Write down the corresponding formula for steady-state heat transfer.

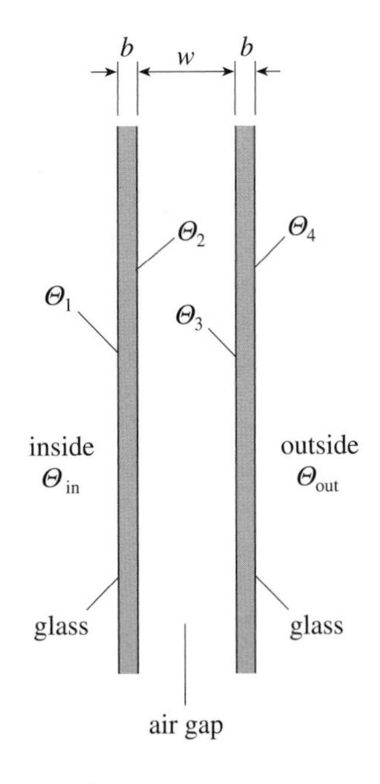

Figure 3.4

Solution

The rate of heat transfer by convection at the inside and outside of the double-glazed unit, using Equation (3.1), is

$$q = h_{in} A(\Theta_{in} - \Theta_1) \quad \text{and} \quad q = h_{out} A(\Theta_4 - \Theta_{out}),$$

where the temperatures are as shown in Figure 3.4, and h_{in} and h_{out} are the convective heat transfer coefficients for the inside and outside surfaces.

Using Equation (2.7), the rate of heat transfer by conduction through the panes is

$$q = \frac{\kappa_g A(\Theta_1 - \Theta_2)}{b} \quad \text{and} \quad q = \frac{\kappa_g A(\Theta_3 - \Theta_4)}{b},$$

where the temperatures are as shown in Figure 3.4, and κ_g is the thermal conductivity of the glass.

Since the width of the air gap is $w < 15$ mm, the rate of heat transfer through the air gap, using Equation (2.7), is

$$q = \frac{\kappa_a A(\Theta_2 - \Theta_3)}{w},$$

where the temperatures are as shown in Figure 3.4 and κ_a is the 'thermal conductivity' of the air gap.

We can rewrite these equations as follows:

$$\Theta_{\text{in}} - \Theta_1 = \frac{q}{h_{\text{in}}A}$$

$$\Theta_1 - \Theta_2 = \frac{qb}{\kappa_{\text{g}}A},$$

$$\Theta_2 - \Theta_3 = \frac{qw}{\kappa_{\text{a}}A},$$

$$\Theta_3 - \Theta_4 = \frac{qb}{\kappa_{\text{g}}A},$$

$$\Theta_4 - \Theta_{\text{out}} = \frac{q}{h_{\text{out}}A}.$$

Since, in the steady state, q takes the same constant value at each stage of the heat transfer process, adding these equations together gives

$$\Theta_{\text{in}} - \Theta_{\text{out}} = \frac{q}{A}\left(\frac{1}{h_{\text{in}}} + \frac{b}{\kappa_{\text{g}}} + \frac{w}{\kappa_{\text{a}}} + \frac{b}{\kappa_{\text{g}}} + \frac{1}{h_{\text{out}}}\right).$$

Hence the U-value for heat transfer by conduction and convection through the double-glazed window is

$$U = \left(\frac{1}{h_{\text{in}}} + \frac{b}{\kappa_{\text{g}}} + \frac{w}{\kappa_{\text{a}}} + \frac{b}{\kappa_{\text{g}}} + \frac{1}{h_{\text{out}}}\right)^{-1}.$$

The corresponding rate of heat transfer is

$$q = UA(\Theta_{\text{in}} - \Theta_{\text{out}}). \quad \blacksquare$$

*Exercise 3.5

The walls of a house are cavity walls consisting of two layers of brick 105 mm thick separated by an air gap of 30 mm. The ambient temperatures inside and outside the house are 18°C and 10°C respectively. What, according to the steady-state conduction and convection model, is the heat transfer rate per square metre of wall surface? Compare your answer with the one you obtained for a solid wall in the solution to Exercise 2.4(a).

For a real house wall we would also need to consider, for example, the layer of plaster on the inside of the wall and the surface decoration layer (paint or wallpaper). Other parts of a house are equally complex: for example, from the ceiling of an upstairs bedroom to the outside there is usually a layer of plasterboard, a mixed layer of wood and fibreglass, a large air layer, another mixed layer of wood and felt, and finally a layer of slates or tiles. Combining the heat transfers through all these layers is a daunting task. Fortunately, these sorts of calculations are required so regularly that tables of the U-values of common building elements are published (see Table 3.3).

*Exercise 3.6

Calculate the rate of heat transfer through a pitched felted roof with 100 mm of insulation and of ceiling area 50 m^2 if the inside temperature is 20°C and the outside temperature is 6°C.

As you can see from Table 3.3, the effect of insulating an element of a house is to decrease its U-value. A lower U-value results in a lower rate of heat energy loss and so lower heating bills. However, each progressive increase in the thickness of insulation has a smaller effect on the overall U-value and hence on the saving on heating bills.

Table 3.3 U-values of common building elements

Building element	U-value ($\mathrm{W\,m^{-2}\,K^{-1}}$)
Walls	
Solid brick	2.1
Brick–breeze-block cavity (unfilled)	1.0
Brick–breeze-block cavity (filled)	0.6
Floors	
Solid concrete	0.8
Suspended timber	0.7
Either of above with 50 mm polystyrene	0.5
Roof	
Pitched with felt, no insulation	2.0
Pitched with felt, 50 mm insulation	0.6
Pitched with felt, 100 mm insulation	0.3
Flat roof, 25 mm insulation	0.9
Flat roof, 50 mm insulation	0.7
Windows	
Wooden frame, single-glazed	5.0
Wooden frame, double-glazed	2.9
Metal frame, single-glazed	5.8
Metal frame, double-glazed	3.7
Doors	
Solid wood	2.4

Source: T102, *Block 1: Heat*, Table 3.

Tables of U-values such as this, which are used by designers of buildings, incorporate the effects of radiation as well as conduction and convection.

For pitched roofs, the area A in Equation (3.5) is the area of the ceiling, rather than the area of the roof.

3.3 Convection and conduction through a pipe

U-values apply only to things that can be modelled as slabs. They cannot be used, for example, for cylindrical pipes because of the varying area across which heat energy transfer takes place. However, a model equivalent to Equation (3.5) can be derived for such pipes.

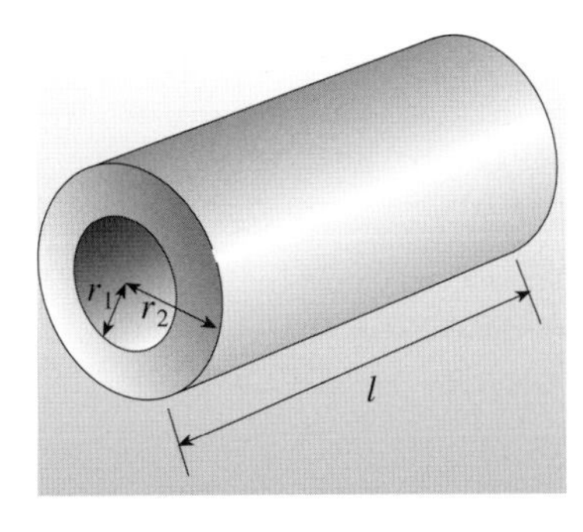

Figure 3.5

Consider the cylindrical pipe shown in Figure 3.5. Equation (3.1) for heat transfer by convection at the inner and outer surfaces gives

$$q = 2\pi h_{\mathrm{in}} r_1 l(\Theta_{\mathrm{in}} - \Theta_1) \quad \text{and} \quad q = 2\pi h_{\mathrm{out}} r_2 l(\Theta_2 - \Theta_{\mathrm{out}}),$$

where h_{in} and h_{out} are the convective heat transfer coefficients at the inside and outside surfaces of the pipe, Θ_1 and Θ_2 are the temperatures of the inside and outside surfaces of the pipe, and Θ_{in} and Θ_{out} are the ambient temperatures inside and outside the pipe (with $\Theta_{\mathrm{in}} > \Theta_{\mathrm{out}}$).

The heat transfer by conduction through the pipe wall is given by Equation (2.11) as

$$q = \frac{2\pi\kappa l(\Theta_1 - \Theta_2)}{\ln(r_2/r_1)},$$

where κ is the thermal conductivity of the pipe. Hence

$$\Theta_{in} - \Theta_1 = \frac{q}{2\pi h_{in} r_1 l},$$

$$\Theta_1 - \Theta_2 = \frac{q\ln(r_2/r_1)}{2\pi\kappa l},$$

$$\Theta_2 - \Theta_{out} = \frac{q}{2\pi h_{out} r_2 l}.$$

Since, in the steady state, q takes the same constant value at each stage of the heat transfer process, adding these three equations we eliminate Θ_1 and Θ_2 to obtain

$$\Theta_{in} - \Theta_{out} = \frac{q}{2\pi l}\left(\frac{1}{h_{in} r_1} + \frac{1}{\kappa}\ln\left(\frac{r_2}{r_1}\right) + \frac{1}{h_{out} r_2}\right).$$

Thus

$$q = 2\pi l\left(\frac{1}{h_{in} r_1} + \frac{1}{\kappa}\ln\left(\frac{r_2}{r_1}\right) + \frac{1}{h_{out} r_2}\right)^{-1}(\Theta_{in} - \Theta_{out}). \qquad (3.8)$$

Steady-state heat transfer by conduction and convection through a uniform cylinder

In the steady state the rate of heat transfer q by conduction and convection through a cylinder of inner radius r_1, outer radius r_2 and length l, made of uniform material with thermal conductivity κ, bounded on either side by a fluid, is given by

$$q = 2\pi l\left(\frac{1}{h_{in} r_1} + \frac{1}{\kappa}\ln\left(\frac{r_2}{r_1}\right) + \frac{1}{h_{out} r_2}\right)^{-1}(\Theta_{in} - \Theta_{out}), \qquad (3.8)$$

where h_{in} and h_{out} are the convective heat transfer coefficients at the inside and outside surfaces of the cylinder, and Θ_{in} and Θ_{out} are the ambient temperatures inside and outside the cylinder (with $\Theta_{in} > \Theta_{out}$).

*Exercise 3.7

A copper pipe, of internal diameter 13 mm and external diameter 15 mm, carries hot water at an ambient temperature of 80°C through a room at an ambient temperature of 20°C. The convective heat transfer coefficients are $10\,\mathrm{W\,m^{-2}\,K^{-1}}$ at the outside surface of the pipe and $1000\,\mathrm{W\,m^{-2}\,K^{-1}}$ at the inside surface.

We considered this problem previously in Exercise 2.5, but neglected the effects of convection there.

Predict the steady-state rate of heat transfer by conduction and convection through a one-metre length of the pipe. Compare your answer with the one you obtained in the solution to Exercise 2.5.

End-of-section Exercises

Exercise 3.8

A glass window has an area of $2\,\text{m}^2$ and a thickness of 4 mm. The ambient temperature inside the window is 20°C and outside is 10°C. The convective heat transfer coefficients are $10\,\text{W}\,\text{m}^{-2}\,\text{K}^{-1}$ for the inside surface of the window and $150\,\text{W}\,\text{m}^{-2}\,\text{K}^{-1}$ for the outside surface.

(a) Calculate the U-value for the window.

(b) What, according to the steady-state conduction and convection model, is the rate of heat energy loss through the window? Compare your answer with the one you obtained in the solution to Exercise 2.7.

(c) What are the temperatures at the two glass surfaces?

Exercise 3.9

The window in Exercise 3.8 is replaced by a double-glazed unit, where each pane of glass is 4 mm thick and the air gap is 20 mm wide. The combined heat transfer coefficient for the air gap is $1.75\,\text{W}\,\text{m}^{-2}\,\text{K}^{-1}$.

(a) Calculate the U-value for the window.

(b) What, according to the steady-state conduction and convection model, is the rate of heat energy loss through the window? Compare your answer with the one you obtained in the solution to Exercise 3.8(b).

Exercise 3.10

In this exercise you are asked to investigate the effects of lagging a cylindrical pipe. Consider a length l of cylindrical pipe, of internal radius r_1 and external radius r_2, constructed from a material with thermal conductivity κ. Suppose that the ambient temperatures inside and outside the pipe are Θ_{in} and Θ_{out} (where $\Theta_{\text{in}} > \Theta_{\text{out}}$) and that the convective heat transfer coefficients at the inside and outside surfaces of the pipe are h_{in} and h_{out}. The pipe is to be fitted with a uniform thickness of lagging, whose thermal conductivity is κ_{lag}, so that the external radius of the lagged pipe is r_3.

(a) Show that the rate of heat transfer by conduction and convection through the lagged pipe can be modelled in the steady state by

$$q = 2\pi l \left(\frac{1}{h_{\text{in}} r_1} + \frac{1}{\kappa} \ln\left(\frac{r_2}{r_1}\right) + \frac{1}{\kappa_{\text{lag}}} \ln\left(\frac{r_3}{r_2}\right) + \frac{1}{h_{\text{out}} r_3} \right)^{-1} (\Theta_{\text{in}} - \Theta_{\text{out}}).$$

(b) What, according to the steady-state conduction and convection model, is the rate of heat transfer through an *unlagged* pipe for which $l = 1\,\text{m}$, $r_1 = 0.004\,\text{m}$, $r_2 = 0.005\,\text{m}$, $\kappa = 50\,\text{W}\,\text{m}^{-1}\,\text{K}^{-1}$, $h_{\text{in}} = 1000\,\text{W}\,\text{m}^{-2}\,\text{K}^{-1}$ and $h_{\text{out}} = 10\,\text{W}\,\text{m}^{-2}\,\text{K}^{-1}$ when it contains a hot liquid whose ambient temperature is $\Theta_{\text{in}} = 50$°C, the ambient temperature of the air outside being $\Theta_{\text{out}} = 20$°C?

(c) The pipe is lagged using a material for which $\kappa_{\text{lag}} = 0.1\,\text{W}\,\text{m}^{-1}\,\text{K}^{-1}$. By using the model in part (a) to predict the rates of heat energy loss from the *lagged* pipe in two cases, first when the thickness of lagging is such that $r_3 = 0.02\,\text{m}$ and then $r_3 = 0.03\,\text{m}$, show that, according to the models, the rate of heat energy loss from a cylindrical pipe can be increased, as well as decreased, by lagging.

(d) Estimate the thickness of lagging for which the rate of heat energy loss from the pipe is a maximum.

4 Radiation

So far in this unit we have concentrated on modelling heat transfer by conduction and convection. In this last section we shall briefly discuss the third mode of heat transfer, radiation.

4.1 Modelling radiation

The nature of radiation

Consider a substance enclosed in a vacuum and at a higher temperature than its surroundings. An example of this is a hot liquid in a vacuum flask. Experience tells us that the substance eventually cools until its temperature is the same as its surroundings. As the substance is enclosed in a vacuum, the transfer of heat energy cannot be due to conduction or convection. The mode of heat transfer in this case is (**thermal**) **radiation**. As was mentioned in Subsection 1.2, radiation occurs from all substances, whether solid, liquid or gas. If you are indoors, heat energy is being radiated by everything that surrounds you: the walls, the floor, the ceiling, the furniture and even the air. At the same time you are yourself emitting radiative energy to your surroundings.

Radiation is caused by changes in the configuration of the electrons in the atoms or molecules of a substance. It is transported from one substance to another by electromagnetic waves. In the spectrum of electromagnetic waves, the wavelengths of thermal radiation extend from approximately 0.1 to 100 μm, including the infrared part, the visible part and some of the ultraviolet part of the spectrum, as Figure 4.1 illustrates.

$1 \mu\text{m} = 1 \times 10^{-6}\,\text{m}$ (where μm stands for 'micrometre').

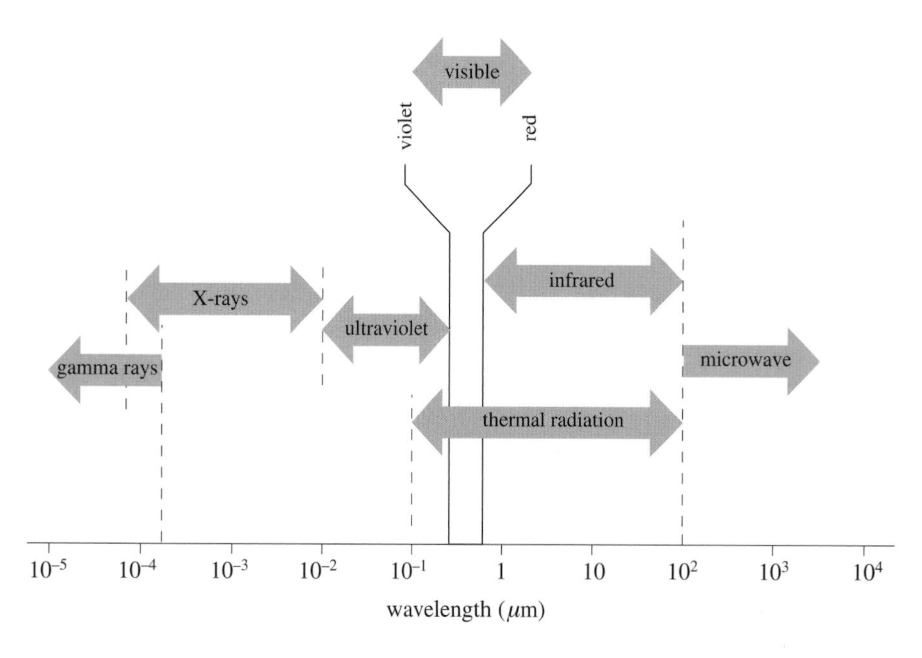

Figure 4.1 Spectrum of electromagnetic radiation

Emission of radiation

The amount of radiation emitted by a surface depends on the temperature of the surface and the nature of the surface. A good model of the rate of emission of radiation from a surface is the following.

Rate of emission of radiation

The rate of emission q of radiation from a surface of area A is

$$q = \varepsilon\sigma A\Theta^4, \qquad (4.1)$$

where ε is the **emissivity** of the surface ($0 < \varepsilon \leq 1$), σ is the **Stefan–Boltzmann constant**, whose value is $5.670 \times 10^{-8}\,\mathrm{W\,m^{-2}\,K^{-4}}$, and Θ is the *absolute* temperature of the surface, measured in kelvins.

Notice that the rate of emission of radiation depends on the absolute temperature of the surface and not on a temperature difference.

The emissivity of a surface is a dimensionless quantity that varies widely with the nature of the surface: it is close to 0 for highly polished surfaces (which is why the surfaces in a vacuum flask which face each other across the vacuum space are silvered) and close to 1 for matt surfaces. When $\varepsilon = 1$, we have the maximum possible rate of emission of radiation, and a surface with emissivity 1 is called a **black-body**. However, in reality, no surface is a perfect black-body (though some surfaces are good approximations to one). So, in practice, all surfaces have $\varepsilon < 1$; such a surface is called a **grey-body**.

When $\varepsilon = 1$, Equation (4.1) is often referred to as the **Stefan–Boltzmann law**.

Exercise 4.1

A 2 kW electric fire is to be constructed using a cylindrical element of diameter 10 mm and length 0.3 m. Assume that the principal mode of heat transfer is radiation, that the surroundings are at a sufficiently low temperature so that the radiation from the surroundings to the element can be ignored, and that the element radiates as a black-body. Predict the temperature of the element.

Absorption, reflection and transmission of radiation

When radiation falls on the surface of a substance, some is absorbed by the substance, some is reflected back into the surroundings and some is transmitted through the substance. Many solids are opaque to radiation, in that they do not transmit radiation, and so we can neglect the transmission of radiation when we consider the radiation falling on the surface of an opaque solid. This means that if, for example, 80% of the radiation falling on a solid surface is absorbed, then 20% is reflected and none is transmitted. The proportion of the radiation falling on a surface that is absorbed is called the **absorptivity** of the surface. It can be shown that the absorptivity of a surface is equal to its emissivity — this result is called **Kirchoff's law**. This means that there is one coefficient, the emissivity, that characterizes the emission, the absorption and the reflection of radiation.

Since a black-body has emissivity 1, it absorbs all radiation falling on it and reflects none.

Rate of absorption of radiation

The rate of absorption q of radiation by an opaque surface is well modelled by

$$q = \varepsilon \times \text{total radiation falling on the surface},$$

where ε is the emissivity of the surface.

Exchange of radiation

Any substance not only emits radiation to its surroundings but also absorbs it from the surroundings: in other words, there is an *exchange* of radiation. The exchange of radiation between two surfaces depends on the geometry of the surfaces as well as their nature. This is because the radiation from a surface is emitted in all directions and, in general, only a proportion of this will fall on the other surface, as illustrated in Figure 4.2.

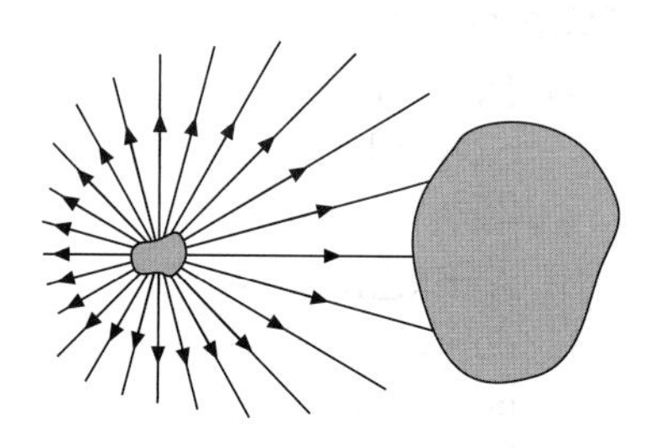

Figure 4.2

Even for a geometrically simple situation such as two parallel infinite flat surfaces, where all the radiation emitted by one surface falls on the second surface, the situation is complicated by the fact that not all the radiation falling on the second surface is absorbed: some of it is reflected. In its turn this reflected radiation falls on the first surface where, in its turn, it is both absorbed and reflected. This process of absorption and reflection at the two surfaces continues, decreasing in intensity at each successive reflection (as illustrated diagrammatically in Figure 4.3).

This situation could model the gap in a cavity wall.

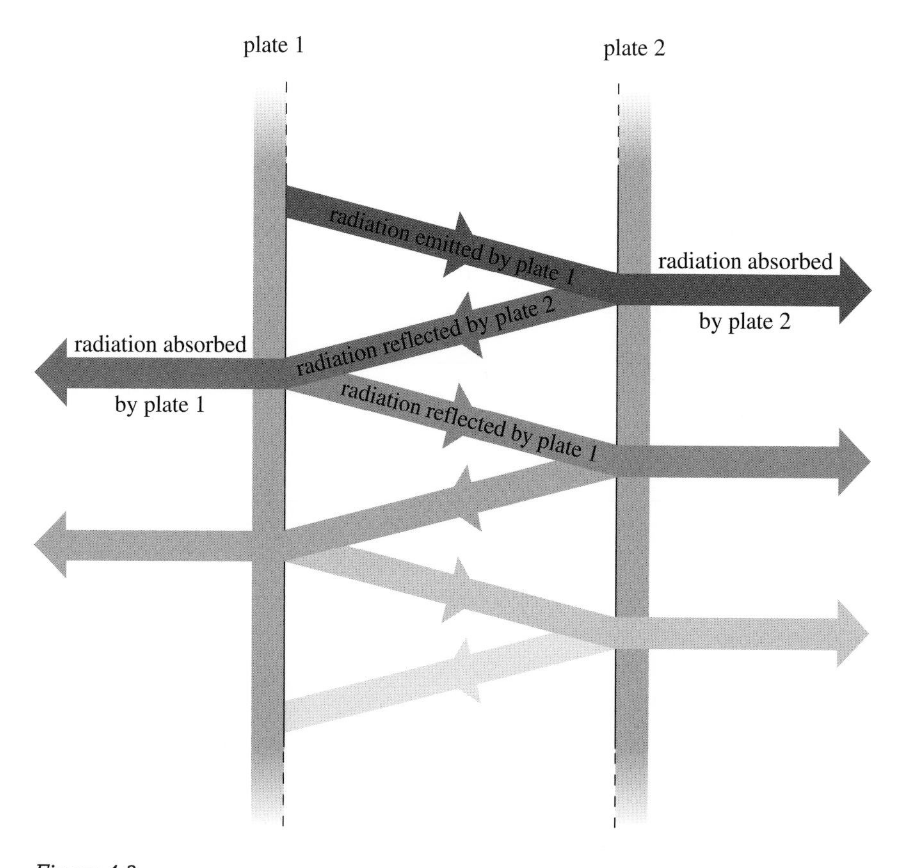

Figure 4.3

Similarly, the radiation initially emitted from the second surface is reflected backwards and forwards across the gap, with a proportion of the radiation being absorbed every time it falls on a surface. If the two surfaces have emissivities (and absorptivities) ε_1, ε_2 and temperatures Θ_1, Θ_2 respectively, the net rate of transfer of radiation per unit area from surface 1 to surface 2 is

$$\frac{q}{A} = \frac{\sigma(\Theta_1^4 - \Theta_2^4)}{\dfrac{1}{\varepsilon_1} + \dfrac{1}{\varepsilon_2} - 1}. \tag{4.2}$$

You are not expected to be able to derive this expression for yourself (although it only involves summing an infinite geometric series).

Exercise 4.2

(a) Predict the rate of transfer of radiation, per square metre, through the cavity between two parallel brick walls whose surface temperatures are 25°C and 5°C, given that the emissivity of a brick surface is 0.9.

(b) A radiation shield, consisting of a thin polished aluminium sheet of emissivity 0.05, is inserted in the cavity between the two walls. The sheet is sufficiently thin so that you can assume that the temperatures on its two surfaces are the same. Also, in the steady state, the temperature of the sheet is constant and the rate of heat transfer is the same at either side of the sheet. Assuming that radiation is the only mode of heat transfer, estimate the temperature of the aluminium radiation shield and the rate of transfer of radiation, per square metre, between the two brick walls.

4.2 Combined modes of heat transfer and U-values

In Subsection 3.2 we considered how to calculate the rate of transfer of heat energy, in the steady state, when both conduction and convection are involved. These estimates were simple to calculate, because the rate of heat transfer for both these modes is proportional to the temperature difference. However, the rate of transfer of heat energy by radiation involves the fourth power of the (absolute) temperature, which makes the calculation of combined heat transfers involving radiation more difficult. Indeed, heat transfer problems that incorporate radiation usually involve solving quartic equations. However, when small temperature differences are involved, it is possible to approximate these quartic equations by linear equations. For example, consider Equation (4.2). We have

$$\begin{aligned} q &= (\varepsilon_1^{-1} + \varepsilon_2^{-1} - 1)^{-1}\sigma A(\Theta_1^4 - \Theta_2^4) \\ &= (\varepsilon_1^{-1} + \varepsilon_2^{-1} - 1)^{-1}\sigma A(\Theta_1^2 + \Theta_2^2)(\Theta_1^2 - \Theta_2^2) \\ &= (\varepsilon_1^{-1} + \varepsilon_2^{-1} - 1)^{-1}\sigma A(\Theta_1^2 + \Theta_2^2)(\Theta_1 + \Theta_2)(\Theta_1 - \Theta_2) \\ &= h_{\text{rad}}\, A(\Theta_1 - \Theta_2), \end{aligned}$$

where

$$h_{\text{rad}} = (\varepsilon_1^{-1} + \varepsilon_2^{-1} - 1)^{-1}\sigma(\Theta_1 + \Theta_2)(\Theta_1^2 + \Theta_2^2).$$

The price we have to pay for this simplification is that the coefficient h_{rad} is now dependent on the temperatures involved. However, if only small temperature differences are involved, we can use an average temperature, such as $\Theta_{\text{mean}} = \frac{1}{2}(\Theta_1 + \Theta_2)$, instead of Θ_1 and Θ_2 in order to calculate an approximate value for h_{rad}. The resulting approximation for Equation (4.2) is

$$q \simeq h_{\text{rad}}\, A(\Theta_1 - \Theta_2), \qquad (4.3)$$

where $h_{\text{rad}} = 4(\varepsilon_1^{-1} + \varepsilon_2^{-1} - 1)^{-1}\sigma\,\Theta_{\text{mean}}^3$ and $\Theta_{\text{mean}} = \frac{1}{2}(\Theta_1 + \Theta_2)$.

Exercise 4.3

Compare the results obtained by using Equation (4.2) and its linear approximation given by Equation (4.3), for $\Theta_2 = 10$°C, when $\Theta_1 = 15$, 20, 30, 40, 60, 80 and 100°C.

You need to use *absolute* temperatures when using Equations (4.2) and (4.3).

It is the linear approximation given by Equation (4.3) that is used in tables of U-values, such as Table 3.3, which incorporate the effects of conduction, convection and radiation.

End-of-section Exercises

Exercise 4.4

The surface of a spaceship has an emissivity of 0.1 and a temperature of 5°C. Assuming that the temperature of space is 0 K and that space is essentially a vacuum, so that no conduction or convection is possible, predict the rate of loss of heat energy per unit area from the surface of the spaceship.

*Exercise 4.5

The gap in a cavity wall is 30 mm wide. The two surfaces bordering the gap both have emissivity 0.9. One surface has a constant temperature of 5°C and the other a constant temperature of 15°C.

(a) Predict the steady-state rate of heat transfer, by all appropriate modes, per unit area, when the gap is filled with air.

(b) Predict the rate of heat transfer, by all appropriate modes, per unit area, when the gap is filled with a foam which has thermal conductivity $0.026\,\mathrm{W\,m^{-1}\,K^{-1}}$. Assume that no radiation is transmitted through the foam.

Outcomes

After studying this unit you should be able to:

- understand the relationship between heat energy and temperature;
- identify when the three modes of heat transfer, namely conduction, convection and radiation, are relevant;
- apply simple models for conduction, convection and radiation, either singly or in combination, to steady-state situations.

Solutions to the exercises

Section 1

1.1 **(a)** From Table 1.1, for water $c = 4190\,\mathrm{J\,kg^{-1}\,K^{-1}}$, so from Equation (1.1) we have

$$E_2 - E_1 = mc(\Theta_2 - \Theta_1) = 2 \times 4190 \times (80 - 20)$$
$$= 502\,800\,\mathrm{J},$$

i.e. the model predicts that there is an *increase* in heat energy of 5.028×10^5 J.

(Note that as Equation (1.1) involves a temperature difference, we can use the Celsius scale for temperature, rather than the absolute scale.)

(b) The element produces heat energy at a rate of $2000\,\mathrm{J\,s^{-1}}$. Thus the time to produce 5.028×10^5 J is

$$\frac{5.028 \times 10^5}{2 \times 10^3} = 251.4 \text{ seconds}$$
$$\simeq 4 \text{ minutes } 11 \text{ seconds.}$$

(c) Some of the electrical energy is used to heat the kettle itself, and some is used to heat the air surrounding the kettle. The rate at which electrical energy is used to heat the water is therefore less than that which was assumed in part (b), so the time obtained is an *underestimate*.

1.2 The modes of transfer of heat energy involved are:

(a) natural convection from the hot tea to the inside surface of the cup;

(b) conduction through the cup;

(c) conduction through the table from the bottom surface of the cup;

(d) natural convection from the hot tea to the top surface of the tea;

(e) natural convection from the outer curved surface of the cup, from the surfaces of the table and from the top surface of the tea to the surrounding air;

(f) radiation from the outer curved surface of the cup, from the surfaces of the table and from the top surface of the tea to the surroundings;

(g) radiation from the surroundings to the outer curved surface of the cup, the surfaces of the table and the top surface of the tea.

We have ignored the heat transfer between the bottoms of the table legs and the floor!

1.3 From Table 1.1, the specific heat capacity of water is $c = 4190\,\mathrm{J\,kg^{-1}\,K^{-1}}$, so the heat energy required to increase the temperature of the water from 15°C to 60°C is

$$E_2 - E_1 = mc(\Theta_2 - \Theta_1) = 100 \times 4190 \times (60 - 15)$$
$$= 1.8855 \times 10^7\,\mathrm{J}.$$

The power rating of the heater is 3000 W, so the time to produce 1.8855×10^7 J is

$$\frac{1.8855 \times 10^7}{3000} = 6285 \text{ seconds}$$
$$\simeq 1 \text{ hour } 45 \text{ minutes.}$$

So the time taken to heat the water is predicted to be about $1\frac{3}{4}$ hours.

We have ignored the heat energy required to heat the material of the tank itself and the heat losses to the surroundings. Both of these factors will increase the estimate of the time. However, if the tank is well insulated, the answer is probably close to the actual time needed to heat the water.

1.4 The mass of the air in the room is $40 \times 1.293 = 51.72$ kg. From Table 1.1, the specific heat capacity of air is $993\,\mathrm{J\,kg^{-1}\,K^{-1}}$, so Equation (1.1) predicts that the heat energy required to heat the air from 0°C to 20°C is

$$E_2 - E_1 = mc(\Theta_2 - \Theta_1) = 51.72 \times 993 \times 20$$
$$= 1.027 \times 10^6\,\mathrm{J}.$$

In order to achieve this in 30 minutes, the minimum rating of the heater must be

$$\frac{1.027 \times 10^6}{30 \times 60} = 570.6\,\mathrm{W}.$$

So we would require a heater that is rated at just over $\frac{1}{2}$ kW.

As we have neglected the heat energy required to heat the walls, doors, windows, floor and ceiling of the room, as well as the heat losses to the surroundings, this answer is likely to be a gross underestimate. (In reality, for a non-empty room, we would have to consider the heating of the furniture, and so on, too.)

Section 2

2.1 My list is:

(a) the thickness of the slab;

(b) the surface area of the slab;

(c) the material from which the slab is made;

(d) the temperature on the inside surface of the slab;

(e) the temperature on the outside surface of the slab.

As the thickness of the slab increases, I would expect the rate of heat energy loss to decrease. However, I would expect the rate of heat energy loss to increase as the surface area increases. Indeed, symmetry suggests to me that the rate of heat energy loss is likely to be proportional to the surface area: if we double the surface area, I would expect the rate of heat energy loss also to double. Some materials, such as copper, are good conductors of heat energy, and slabs constructed from these materials will have high rates of heat energy loss; other materials, such as polystyrene foam, are bad conductors of heat energy, and slabs constructed from these materials will have low rates of heat energy loss. Finally, I would expect the rate of heat energy loss to depend on the temperature difference across the slab, rather than on the actual temperatures on the surfaces, and I would expect any increase in the temperature difference to result in an increase in the rate of heat energy loss.

2.2 Heat energy is transferred from regions of higher temperature to those of lower temperature. As the temperature is a function of the coordinate x and not y or z, i.e. $\Theta = \Theta(x)$, the direction of the transfer must be parallel to the x-axis. As $\Theta(0) > \Theta(b)$, the direction of transfer of heat energy must be parallel to the x-axis in the direction of positive x.

2.3 Equation (2.7) expresses the rate of heat energy loss q in terms of the thickness b of the slab, the surface area A of the slab, the thermal conductivity κ of the slab (which depends on the material from which the slab is made), and the temperatures Θ_1 and Θ_2 of the inside and outside surfaces of the slab. These are exactly the five factors listed in Solution 2.1.

The rate of transfer of heat energy increases as A and $\Theta_1 - \Theta_2$ increase, but decreases as b increases, as predicted in Solution 2.1. (Also note that q is directly proportional to A, as expected, and to $\Theta_1 - \Theta_2$, and is inversely proportional to b.)

2.4 **(a)** From Table 2.1, $\kappa = 0.6\,\mathrm{W\,m^{-1}\,K^{-1}}$. Substituting this and the values $\Theta_1 = 18°\mathrm{C}$, $\Theta_2 = 10°\mathrm{C}$, $b = 0.21\,\mathrm{m}$ into Equation (2.7), we have

$$\begin{aligned}\frac{q}{A} &= \frac{\kappa(\Theta_1 - \Theta_2)}{b}\\ &= \frac{0.6 \times (18 - 10)}{0.21}\\ &= 22.86\,\mathrm{W\,m^{-2}}.\end{aligned}$$

So the rate of heat transfer by conduction per square metre of wall surface is $22.86\,\mathrm{W\,m^{-2}}$.

(b) The temperature gradient is given by Equation (2.9). Since this involves a temperature difference, we can use the temperatures in degrees Celsius. So with $\Theta_1 = 18°\mathrm{C}$, $\Theta_2 = 10°\mathrm{C}$ and $b = 0.21\,\mathrm{m}$, we have

$$\begin{aligned}\frac{d\Theta}{dx} &= -\frac{\Theta_1 - \Theta_2}{b}\\ &= -\frac{18 - 10}{0.21}\\ &= -38.10\,\mathrm{K\,m^{-1}}.\end{aligned}$$

So the temperature gradient is $-38.10\,\mathrm{K\,m^{-1}}$.

(c) We can employ Equation (2.8) in order to determine the temperature at a point. If we use SI units, we have $\Theta_1 = 291.2\,\mathrm{K}$, $\Theta_2 = 283.2\,\mathrm{K}$, $b = 0.21\,\mathrm{m}$ and $x = 0.05\,\mathrm{m}$, so the temperature at $x = 0.05\,\mathrm{m}$ is

$$\begin{aligned}\Theta &= \Theta_1 - \frac{\Theta_1 - \Theta_2}{b}x\\ &= 291.2 - \frac{291.2 - 283.2}{0.21} \times 0.05\\ &= 289.30\,\mathrm{K}.\end{aligned}$$

So, in degrees Celsius, the temperature 50 mm from the inside surface is 16.10°C.

(Note that the same result is obtained by using degrees Celsius rather than kelvins as the unit of temperature.)

2.5 Using Equation (2.11) with $r_1 = 0.0065\,\mathrm{m}$, $r_2 = 0.0075\,\mathrm{m}$, $\Theta_1 = 80°\mathrm{C}$, $\Theta_2 = 20°\mathrm{C}$, $l = 1\,\mathrm{m}$ and $\kappa = 385\,\mathrm{W\,m^{-1}\,K^{-1}}$ (from Table 2.1), we obtain

$$\begin{aligned}q &= \frac{2\pi\kappa l(\Theta_1 - \Theta_2)}{\ln(r_2/r_1)}\\ &= \frac{2\pi \times 385 \times 1 \times (80 - 20)}{\ln(0.0075/0.0065)}\\ &= 1.014 \times 10^6\,\mathrm{W}.\end{aligned}$$

Thus the rate of heat transfer by conduction through the wall of a one-metre length of the pipe is predicted to be 1014 kW.

(Note that the assumption that the outer surface of the pipe is at the same temperature as the air in the room is clearly not reasonable — just try touching the hot-water pipes in your home! An improved model, which disposes of this assumption by taking into account the effects of convection, is considered in the next section.)

2.6 **(a)** By Equation (2.11), the rate of heat transfer by conduction through the pipe wall is modelled as

$$q = \frac{2\pi\kappa l(\Theta_1 - \Theta_2)}{\ln(r_2/r_1)}.$$

However, Equation (2.11) also applies to that part of the pipe wall lying between radius r_1 and radius r, so

$$q = \frac{2\pi\kappa l(\Theta_1 - \Theta)}{\ln(r/r_1)}.$$

Equating these two expressions for q, we obtain

$$\frac{\Theta_1 - \Theta}{\ln(r/r_1)} = \frac{\Theta_1 - \Theta_2}{\ln(r_2/r_1)}.$$

Rearranging this equation, we obtain

$$\Theta = \Theta_1 - \frac{\Theta_1 - \Theta_2}{\ln(r_2/r_1)} \ln\left(\frac{r}{r_1}\right).$$

(b) Using the expression for Θ derived in part (a), the temperature at radius $r = 0.007\,\mathrm{m}$ is

$$\begin{aligned}\Theta &= 353.2 - \frac{353.2 - 293.2}{\ln(0.0075/0.0065)} \ln\left(\frac{0.007}{0.0065}\right)\\ &= 322.13\,\mathrm{K}.\end{aligned}$$

So the temperature at a radius of 7 mm in the pipe is predicted to be 322.13 K, or 48.93°C.

(Note that the temperature does not depend linearly on the radius. Note also that the same result is obtained if the Celsius rather than the absolute scale is used in evaluating Θ.)

2.7 Using Equation (2.7) with $\kappa = 1.0\,\mathrm{W\,m^{-1}\,K^{-1}}$ (from Table 2.1), $A = 2\,\mathrm{m^2}$, $\Theta_1 = 20°\mathrm{C}$, $\Theta_2 = 10°\mathrm{C}$ and $b = 0.004\,\mathrm{m}$, we have

$$\begin{aligned}q &= \frac{\kappa A(\Theta_1 - \Theta_2)}{b}\\ &= \frac{1.0 \times 2 \times (20 - 10)}{0.004}\\ &= 5000\,\mathrm{W}.\end{aligned}$$

So the rate of transfer of heat energy by conduction through the window is 5000 W.

2.8 We denote the variables and parameters by the symbols given in the following table.

Quantity	Symbol
Inner radius of tea-urn	r_1
Outer radius of tea-urn	r_2
Height of tea-urn	h
Thickness of sides and lid of tea-urn	b
Thermal conductivity of stainless steel	κ
Temperature at inner surface of tea-urn	Θ_1
Temperature at outer surface of tea-urn	Θ_2
Rate of loss of heat energy through cylindrical sides of tea-urn	q_1
Rate of loss of heat energy through lid of tea-urn	q_2
Total rate of loss of heat energy from tea-urn	q

From the data given in the question and Table 2.1, $r_1 = 0.172\,\text{m}$, $r_2 = 0.175\,\text{m}$, $h = 0.515\,\text{m}$, $b = 0.003\,\text{m}$, $\kappa = 150\,\text{W}\,\text{m}^{-1}\,\text{K}^{-1}$, $\Theta_1 = 100°\text{C}$ and $\Theta_2 = 20°\text{C}$.

(a) Using Equation (2.11), the rate of transfer of heat energy by conduction through the cylindrical sides of the tea-urn is estimated to be

$$q_1 = \frac{2\pi\kappa h(\Theta_1 - \Theta_2)}{\ln(r_2/r_1)} = \frac{2\pi \times 150 \times 0.515 \times (100 - 20)}{\ln(0.175/0.172)} = 2.246 \times 10^6\,\text{W}.$$

(b) Using Equation (2.7), the rate of loss of heat energy by conduction through the lid is estimated to be

$$q_2 = \frac{\kappa(\pi r_1^2)(\Theta_1 - \Theta_2)}{b} = \frac{150 \times \pi \times 0.172^2 \times (100 - 20)}{0.003} = 3.718 \times 10^5\,\text{W}.$$

(We use r_1 rather than r_2 because only the part of the lid in contact with the water is the part inside the cylinder.)

(c) Assuming that there is no loss of heat energy through the base of the tea-urn, the total rate of loss of heat energy by conduction from the tea-urn is estimated to be

$$q = q_1 + q_2 = 2.617 \times 10^6\,\text{W},$$

i.e. the total rate of loss of heat energy by conduction from the tea-urn is estimated to be 2617 kW.

A typical tea-urn has a 3 kW heating element. If this estimate were correct, it would mean that water heated in a tea-urn would never boil, as the predicted rate of heat energy loss far exceeds the rate of heat energy supplied by the element. The reason for this discrepancy is the incorrect assumption that the temperatures of the surfaces of the tea-urn are the same as the temperatures of the fluids with which they are in contact.

2.9 **(a)** The temperature at any point in the wall is determined solely by its distance from the centre of the sphere and the heat transfer from the inside to the outside of the sphere takes place radially. Hence the temperature gradient in the steady state is $d\Theta/dr$, where Θ is the temperature at a point whose distance from the centre of the sphere is r. Using Equation (2.2) (the general form of Fourier's law), the rate of heat transfer by conduction through the entire spherical area at distance r from the centre is

$$q = -\kappa \times 4\pi r^2 \times \frac{d\Theta}{dr}.$$

Hence

$$\frac{d\Theta}{dr} = -\frac{q}{4\pi\kappa r^2} = -\frac{q}{4\pi\kappa}\frac{1}{r^2}.$$

In the steady state, q is a constant, so this equation can be solved by direct integration to give the general solution

$$\Theta = \frac{q}{4\pi\kappa}\frac{1}{r} + C,$$

where C is a constant.

Thus, since $\Theta = \Theta_1$ when $r = r_1$ and $\Theta = \Theta_2$ when $r = r_2$, we have

$$\Theta_1 = \frac{q}{4\pi\kappa}\frac{1}{r_1} + C, \quad \Theta_2 = \frac{q}{4\pi\kappa}\frac{1}{r_2} + C,$$

and, subtracting the second equation from the first,

$$\Theta_1 - \Theta_2 = \frac{q}{4\pi\kappa}\left(\frac{1}{r_1} - \frac{1}{r_2}\right),$$

so

$$q = 4\pi\kappa\left(\frac{1}{r_1} - \frac{1}{r_2}\right)^{-1}(\Theta_1 - \Theta_2).$$

(b) As r_2 increases, the heat transfer rate derived in part (a) decreases, to a limiting value of

$$4\pi\kappa\left(\frac{1}{r_1}\right)^{-1}(\Theta_1 - \Theta_2) = 4\pi\kappa r_1(\Theta_1 - \Theta_2).$$

For the given data (and taking κ for mild steel to be $63\,\text{W}\,\text{m}^{-1}\,\text{K}^{-1}$, from Table 2.1), this gives a heat transfer rate of 395.8 W. Thus the heat transfer rate for conduction cannot be kept below 395 W.

Section 3

3.1 My list is:

(a) the area of the surface;

(b) the shape of the surface;

(c) the temperature of the surface;

(d) the temperature of the fluid;

(e) the nature of the fluid motion;

(f) the thermal properties of the fluid (e.g. its specific heat and its thermal conductivity);

(g) the mechanical properties of the fluid (e.g. its density and its viscosity).

3.2 From Equation (3.1),

$$h = \frac{q}{A(\Theta_1 - \Theta_2)} = \frac{750}{0.04 \times (200 - 20)} = 104.2\,\mathrm{W\,m^{-2}\,K^{-1}}.$$

3.3 According to Equation (3.5), the rate of transfer of heat energy q is directly proportional to the surface area A of the slab and to the overall temperature difference $\Theta_{\text{in}} - \Theta_{\text{out}}$. So as A and $\Theta_{\text{in}} - \Theta_{\text{out}}$ increase, so does q, which is what one would expect intuitively. As h_{out} increases, h_{out}^{-1} decreases, so U^{-1} decreases and U increases. Hence, as h_{out} increases, Equation (3.5) predicts that q also increases. One situation when h_{out} increases is when a calm day turns into a windy day; in such a situation, the rate of heat energy loss from a house through the walls increases. So Equation (3.5) predicts the behaviour that one would expect intuitively.

3.4 **(a)** From Equation (3.6), and using Table 2.1,

$$U = \left(\frac{1}{h_{\text{in}}} + \frac{b}{\kappa} + \frac{1}{h_{\text{out}}}\right)^{-1} = \left(\frac{1}{10} + \frac{0.21}{0.6} + \frac{1}{150}\right)^{-1} = 2.190\,\mathrm{W\,m^{-2}\,K^{-1}}.$$

(This calculated U-value agrees surprisingly well with the experimental value of about $2.1\,\mathrm{W\,m^{-2}\,K^{-1}}$, even though we have ignored any effects due to radiation and there are uncertainties in the values of the convective heat transfer coefficients.)

(b) Using Equation (3.5), we have

$$\frac{q}{A} = U(\Theta_{\text{in}} - \Theta_{\text{out}}) = 2.190 \times (18 - 10) = 17.52\,\mathrm{W\,m^{-2}}.$$

Thus the model predicts that the rate of heat transfer per square metre of wall surface when convection is taken into account is $17.52\,\mathrm{W\,m^{-2}}$, compared with the value of $22.86\,\mathrm{W\,m^{-2}}$ obtained in Solution 2.4(a) when we assumed that the temperatures at the wall surfaces were the same as those of the surrounding air.

(You may find this decrease in the rate of heat transfer surprising. This decrease is because the air-film close to the surface of the wall acts very effectively as a layer of insulation. Notice also that this new estimate is reasonably close to the value $16.8\,\mathrm{W\,m^{-2}}$ found experimentally, which is comforting.)

(c) The equation for heat transfer by convection at the inner surface of the wall is $q = h_{\text{in}}A(\Theta_{\text{in}} - \Theta_1)$, so

$$\Theta_1 = \Theta_{\text{in}} - \frac{q}{h_{\text{in}}A} = 18 - \frac{17.52}{10} = 16.25^\circ\mathrm{C}.$$

Similarly, the equation for heat transfer by convection at the outer surface of the wall is $q = h_{\text{out}}A(\Theta_2 - \Theta_{\text{out}})$, so

$$\Theta_2 = \Theta_{\text{out}} + \frac{q}{h_{\text{out}}A} = 10 + \frac{17.52}{150} = 10.12^\circ\mathrm{C}.$$

Therefore the temperatures of the inner and outer surfaces of the wall are 16.25°C and 10.12°C, respectively.

(Note that the Celsius or absolute scales can be used in these calculations. Note also that Equation (2.7) can be used as a check on the calculations.)

3.5 Using the method of Example 3.1 and the usual notation, the U-value is given by

$$U = \left(\frac{1}{h_{\text{in}}} + \frac{b}{\kappa} + \frac{1}{h_{\text{c}}} + \frac{b}{\kappa} + \frac{1}{h_{\text{out}}}\right)^{-1} = \left(\frac{1}{10} + \frac{0.105}{0.6} + \frac{1}{1.75} + \frac{0.105}{0.6} + \frac{1}{150}\right)^{-1} = 0.9727\,\mathrm{W\,m^{-2}\,K^{-1}}.$$

Thus the rate of heat transfer per square metre of wall surface is

$$\frac{q}{A} = U(\Theta_{\text{in}} - \Theta_{\text{out}}) = 0.9727 \times (18 - 10) = 7.781\,\mathrm{W\,m^{-2}}.$$

This is less than half the value obtained in Solution 2.4, so introducing a cavity into the wall has more than halved the predicted rate of heat energy losses.

(You will see in Section 4 that this prediction needs to be nearly doubled when the effects of radiation are included.)

3.6 From Table 3.3, the U-value for a pitched felted roof with 100 mm of insulation is $0.3\,\mathrm{W\,m^{-2}\,K^{-1}}$. So, using Equation (3.5), the rate of loss of heat energy through the roof is

$$q = UA(\Theta_{\text{in}} - \Theta_{\text{out}}) = 0.3 \times 50 \times (20 - 6) = 210\,\mathrm{W}.$$

3.7 Using Equation (3.8),

$$\begin{aligned} q &= 2\pi l\left(\frac{1}{h_{\text{in}}r_1} + \frac{1}{\kappa}\ln\left(\frac{r_2}{r_1}\right) + \frac{1}{h_{\text{out}}r_2}\right)^{-1}(\Theta_{\text{in}} - \Theta_{\text{out}}) \\ &= 2\pi \times 1 \\ &\quad \times \left(\tfrac{1}{1000\times 0.0065} + \tfrac{1}{385}\ln\left(\tfrac{0.0075}{0.0065}\right) + \tfrac{1}{10\times 0.0075}\right)^{-1} \\ &\quad \times (80 - 20) \\ &= 27.95\,\mathrm{W}. \end{aligned}$$

So the rate of heat transfer by conduction and convection through a one-metre length of the pipe is predicted to be 27.95 W.

Including the effects of convection reduces the estimate of the rate of heat transfer for a one-metre length of pipe from 1014 kW, which was the solution to Exercise 2.5, to 27.95 W, which is a much more realistic result.

3.8 **(a)** Using Equation (3.6), the U-value for the window is

$$U = \left(\frac{1}{h_{\text{in}}} + \frac{b}{\kappa} + \frac{1}{h_{\text{out}}}\right)^{-1} = \left(\frac{1}{10} + \frac{0.004}{1.0} + \frac{1}{150}\right)^{-1} = 9.036\,\mathrm{W\,m^{-2}\,K^{-1}}.$$

(b) Using Equation (3.5),

$$q = UA(\Theta_{\text{in}} - \Theta_{\text{out}}) = 9.036 \times 2 \times (20 - 10) = 180.7\,\mathrm{W}.$$

So taking into account the effects of convection at the surfaces of the window, the rate of heat energy loss through the window is predicted to be 180.7 W. In Exercise 2.7 we assumed that there was perfect transfer of heat energy from the surfaces of the window to the air and obtained the unrealistic prediction of 5000 W. The huge discrepancy between the two predictions illustrates the importance of modelling the effects of convection in this type of situation.

(c) If the temperatures at the inside and outside surfaces of the window are Θ_1 and Θ_2, then Equation (3.1) for convective transfer of heat energy at the window surfaces gives

$$q = h_{\text{in}}A(\Theta_{\text{in}} - \Theta_1) \quad \text{and} \quad q = h_{\text{out}}A(\Theta_2 - \Theta_{\text{out}}).$$

Therefore

$$\Theta_1 = \Theta_{\text{in}} - \frac{q}{h_{\text{in}}A} = 20 - \frac{180.7}{10 \times 2} = 10.96^\circ\text{C},$$

$$\Theta_2 = \Theta_{\text{out}} + \frac{q}{h_{\text{out}}A} = 10 + \frac{180.7}{150 \times 2} = 10.60^\circ\text{C}.$$

So the temperatures at the inside and outside surfaces of the window are 10.96°C and 10.60°C, respectively.

(Note that the Celsius or absolute scales can be used in these calculations. Note also that Equation (2.7) can be used as a check on the calculations.)

3.9 **(a)** We denote the temperatures at the four glass surfaces by Θ_1, Θ_2, Θ_3 and Θ_4, as shown below.

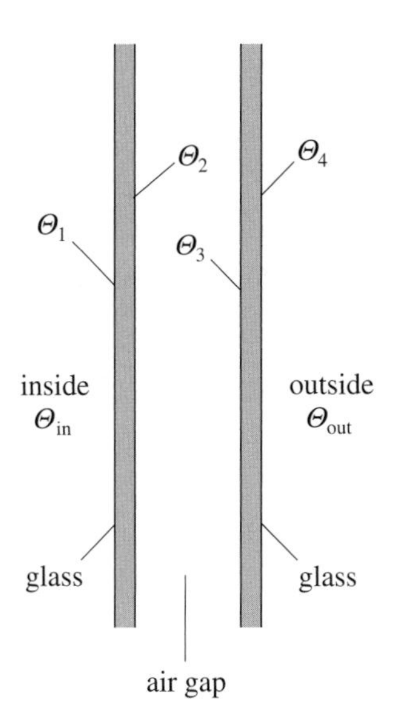

Using the method of Example 3.1 and the usual notation, the U-value is given by

$$U = \left(\frac{1}{h_{\text{in}}} + \frac{b}{\kappa} + \frac{1}{h_{\text{c}}} + \frac{b}{\kappa} + \frac{1}{h_{\text{out}}}\right)^{-1}.$$

(Note that, as the thickness of the air gap is 20 mm, we have used Equation (3.7) for the heat transfer across the gap.) So, using the given data and Table 2.1,

$$U = \left(\frac{1}{10} + \frac{0.004}{1.0} + \frac{1}{1.75} + \frac{0.004}{1.0} + \frac{1}{150}\right)^{-1}$$
$$= 1.458\,\text{W}\,\text{m}^{-2}\,\text{K}^{-1}.$$

(b) The rate of transfer of heat energy through the window is predicted to be

$$q = UA(\Theta_{\text{in}} - \Theta_{\text{out}}) = 1.458 \times 2 \times (20 - 10)$$
$$= 29.15\,\text{W}.$$

Hence, by double-glazing the window, the predicted rate of heat transfer through the window has been reduced from 180.7 W to 29.15 W.

3.10 **(a)** We denote the temperatures at the liquid–pipe, pipe–lagging and lagging–air surfaces by Θ_1, Θ_2 and Θ_3, as shown below.

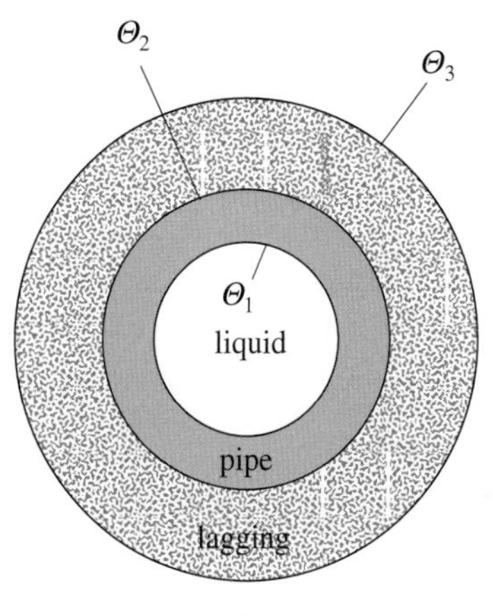

The equations for heat transfer through the walls of the lagged pipe are

$$q = 2\pi h_{\text{in}} r_1 l(\Theta_{\text{in}} - \Theta_1),$$

$$q = \frac{2\pi\kappa l(\Theta_1 - \Theta_2)}{\ln(r_2/r_1)},$$

$$q = \frac{2\pi\kappa_{\text{lag}} l(\Theta_2 - \Theta_3)}{\ln(r_3/r_2)},$$

$$q = 2\pi h_{\text{out}} r_3 l(\Theta_3 - \Theta_{\text{out}}).$$

Rearranging these equations, the temperature differences are

$$\Theta_{\text{in}} - \Theta_1 = \frac{q}{2\pi h_{\text{in}} r_1 l},$$

$$\Theta_1 - \Theta_2 = \frac{q\ln(r_2/r_1)}{2\pi\kappa l},$$

$$\Theta_2 - \Theta_3 = \frac{q\ln(r_3/r_2)}{2\pi\kappa_{\text{lag}} l},$$

$$\Theta_3 - \Theta_{\text{out}} = \frac{q}{2\pi h_{\text{out}} r_3 l}.$$

Since, in the steady state, q takes the same constant value at each stage of the heat transfer process, adding these equations gives

$$\Theta_{\text{in}} - \Theta_{\text{out}} = \frac{q}{2\pi l}\left(\frac{1}{h_{\text{in}} r_1} + \frac{\ln(r_2/r_1)}{\kappa} + \frac{\ln(r_3/r_2)}{\kappa_{\text{lag}}} + \frac{1}{h_{\text{out}} r_3}\right).$$

Hence

$$q = 2\pi l\left(\frac{1}{h_{\text{in}} r_1} + \frac{\ln(r_2/r_1)}{\kappa} + \frac{\ln(r_3/r_2)}{\kappa_{\text{lag}}} + \frac{1}{h_{\text{out}} r_3}\right)^{-1} \times (\Theta_{\text{in}} - \Theta_{\text{out}}).$$

(b) For the unlagged pipe,

$$q = 2\pi l \left(\frac{1}{h_{in} r_1} + \frac{\ln(r_2/r_1)}{\kappa} + \frac{1}{h_{out} r_2} \right)^{-1} (\Theta_{in} - \Theta_{out})$$

$$= 2\pi \times 1 \times \left(\frac{1}{1000 \times 0.004} + \frac{\ln(0.005/0.004)}{50} + \frac{1}{10 \times 0.005} \right)^{-1} \times (50 - 20)$$

$$= 9.306\,\mathrm{W}.$$

So the rate of transfer of heat energy through the walls of a one-metre length of the unlagged pipe is predicted to be 9.306 W.

(c) For the lagged pipe,

$$q = 2\pi l \left(\frac{1}{h_{in} r_1} + \frac{\ln(r_2/r_1)}{\kappa} + \frac{\ln(r_3/r_2)}{\kappa_{lag}} + \frac{1}{h_{out} r_3} \right)^{-1} (\Theta_{in} - \Theta_{out})$$

$$= 2\pi \times 1 \times \left(\frac{1}{1000 \times 0.004} + \frac{\ln(0.005/0.004)}{50} + \frac{\ln(r_3/0.005)}{0.1} + \frac{1}{10 r_3} \right)^{-1} \times (50 - 20).$$

For $r_3 = 0.02\,\mathrm{m}$ we obtain $q = 9.860\,\mathrm{W}$, whereas for $r_3 = 0.03\,\mathrm{m}$ we obtain $q = 8.765\,\mathrm{W}$. So the heat transfer rate for a lagged pipe can be greater or less than that for an unlagged pipe.

(d) We wish to find the value of r_3 for which q is a maximum. Now q is a maximum when

$$R = \frac{1}{h_{in} r_1} + \frac{\ln(r_2/r_1)}{\kappa} + \frac{\ln(r_3/r_2)}{\kappa_{lag}} + \frac{1}{h_{out} r_3}$$

is a minimum. Now

$$\frac{dR}{dr_3} = \frac{1}{\kappa_{lag} r_3} - \frac{1}{h_{out} r_3^2},$$

so $dR/dr_3 = 0$ when $r_3 = \kappa_{lag}/h_{out}$.

When $r_3 = \kappa_{lag}/h_{out}$, we have

$$\frac{d^2R}{dr_3^2} = -\frac{1}{\kappa_{lag} r_3^2} + \frac{2}{h_{out} r_3^3} = -\frac{h_{out}^2}{\kappa_{lag}^3} + \frac{2h_{out}^2}{\kappa_{lag}^3} = \frac{h_{out}^2}{\kappa_{lag}^3} > 0,$$

so $r_3 = \kappa_{lag}/h_{out}$ gives a minimum value of R and hence the maximum rate of heat energy loss.

In the case under consideration, $r_3 = 0.1/10 = 0.01\,\mathrm{m}$. So an estimate of the thickness of lagging that gives the maximum rate of heat energy loss is $0.01 - 0.005 = 0.005\,\mathrm{m}$. (For this thickness, the rate of heat transfer for a one-metre length of pipe is predicted to be 10.97 W.)

(The radius $r_3 = \kappa_{lag}/h_{out}$ is called the **critical radius** of insulation. If the radius of the unlagged pipe is less than the critical radius, then the heat transfer rate q increases with the addition of lagging, until q reaches a maximum at $r_3 = \kappa_{lag}/h_{out}$. Then any further addition of insulation decreases the heat transfer rate.)

Section 4

4.1 The (curved) surface area of the cylindrical element is

$$A = 2\pi \times 0.005 \times 0.3 = 0.009\,425\,\mathrm{m}^2.$$

By Equation (4.1), the rate of heat energy emitted from the element is $q = \varepsilon\sigma A\Theta^4$, so

$$\Theta^4 = \frac{q}{\varepsilon\sigma A} = \frac{2000}{1 \times 5.670 \times 10^{-8} \times 0.009\,425} = 3.743 \times 10^{12}.$$

Hence $\Theta = 1391\,\mathrm{K}$, and the temperature of the element is predicted to be 1391 K (or about 1118°C).

4.2 **(a)** Using Equation (4.3), the rate of transfer of radiation (per square metre) between the two walls is

$$\frac{q}{A} = \frac{\sigma(\Theta_1^4 - \Theta_2^4)}{\frac{1}{\varepsilon_1} + \frac{1}{\varepsilon_2} - 1} = \frac{5.670 \times 10^{-8} \times (298.2^4 - 278.2^4)}{\frac{1}{0.9} + \frac{1}{0.9} - 1} = 88.95\,\mathrm{W\,m^{-2}}.$$

(b) Denoting the temperature of the shield by Θ_s and its emissivity by ε_s, the rates of heat transfer (per unit area) on each side of the sheet are modelled by

$$\frac{q}{A} = \frac{\sigma(\Theta_1^4 - \Theta_s^4)}{\frac{1}{\varepsilon_1} + \frac{1}{\varepsilon_s} - 1} \quad \text{and} \quad \frac{q}{A} = \frac{\sigma(\Theta_s^4 - \Theta_2^4)}{\frac{1}{\varepsilon_s} + \frac{1}{\varepsilon_2} - 1}.$$

Therefore, since the rate of heat transfer is the same at either side of the sheet,

$$\frac{\sigma(\Theta_1^4 - \Theta_s^4)}{\frac{1}{\varepsilon_1} + \frac{1}{\varepsilon_s} - 1} = \frac{\sigma(\Theta_s^4 - \Theta_2^4)}{\frac{1}{\varepsilon_s} + \frac{1}{\varepsilon_2} - 1}.$$

Since $\varepsilon_1 = \varepsilon_2$, this leads to

$$\Theta_1^4 - \Theta_s^4 = \Theta_s^4 - \Theta_2^4,$$

so

$$2\Theta_s^4 = \Theta_1^4 + \Theta_2^4 = 298.2^4 + 278.2^4.$$

Hence $\Theta_s = 288.7\,\mathrm{K}$, and an estimate of the temperature of the aluminium radiation shield is 288.7 K (or about 15.5°C). Substituting this value into the first equation for q/A above, we obtain

$$\frac{q}{A} = \frac{\sigma(\Theta_1^4 - \Theta_s^4)}{\frac{1}{\varepsilon_1} + \frac{1}{\varepsilon_s} - 1} = \frac{5.670 \times 10^{-8} \times (298.2^4 - 288.7^4)}{\frac{1}{0.9} + \frac{1}{0.05} - 1} = 2.703\,\mathrm{W\,m^{-2}}.$$

So the insertion of the radiation shield has reduced the predicted rate of transfer of radiation from $88.95\,\mathrm{W\,m^{-2}}$ to $2.703\,\mathrm{W\,m^{-2}}$. (This reduction is largely due to the low emissivity of aluminium. However, even if the shield was a perfect emitter, the predicted rate would have been reduced to $49.01\,\mathrm{W\,m^{-2}}$.)

(The effect of a radiation shield is utilised in an Aga oven by the use of the cold plain shelf, which allows the use of the roasting oven for baking items that require a more moderate temperature.)

4.3 Equation (4.2) gives

$$q_{\text{exact}}/\left((\varepsilon_1^{-1}+\varepsilon_2^{-1}-1)^{-1}\sigma A\right)=\Theta_1^4-\Theta_2^4,$$

whereas Equation (4.3) gives

$$q_{\text{approx}}/\left((\varepsilon_1^{-1}+\varepsilon_2^{-1}-1)^{-1}\sigma A\right)=4\Theta_{\text{mean}}^3(\Theta_1-\Theta_2)$$

where $\Theta_{\text{mean}}=\frac{1}{2}(\Theta_1+\Theta_2)$.

The values of $q_{\text{exact}}/\left((\varepsilon_1^{-1}+\varepsilon_2^{-1}-1)^{-1}\sigma A\right)$ and $q_{\text{approx}}/\left((\varepsilon_1^{-1}+\varepsilon_2^{-1}-1)^{-1}\sigma A\right)$ are summarized in the following table for $\Theta_2=283.2\,\text{K}$, $\Theta_1=288.2$, 293.2, 303.2, 313.2, 333.2, 353.2 and 373.2 K.

Θ_1	$q_{\text{exact}}/\left((\varepsilon_1^{-1}+\varepsilon_2^{-1}-1)^{-1}\sigma A\right)$	Θ_{mean}	$q_{\text{approx}}/\left((\varepsilon_1^{-1}+\varepsilon_2^{-1}-1)^{-1}\sigma A\right)$
288.2	4.664×10^8	285.7	4.664×10^8
293.2	9.578×10^8	288.2	9.575×10^8
303.2	2.019×10^9	293.2	2.016×10^9
313.2	3.190×10^9	298.2	3.182×10^9
333.2	5.894×10^9	308.2	5.855×10^9
353.2	9.130×10^9	318.2	9.021×10^9
373.2	1.297×10^{10}	328.2	1.273×10^{10}

The above calculations suggest that the linear approximation can be used with confidence for temperature differences of up to 100°C.

4.4 The rate of loss of heat energy from the spaceship is modelled by Equation (4.2). So

$$\begin{aligned}\frac{q}{A}&=\varepsilon\sigma(\Theta^4-\Theta_{\text{sur}}^4)\\&=0.1\times5.670\times10^{-8}\times(278.2^4-0^4)\\&=33.96\,\text{W}.\end{aligned}$$

So the rate of loss of heat energy per unit area from the surface of the spaceship is 33.96 W.

4.5 **(a)** When the gap is filled with air, heat energy is transferred by convection and conduction, which is given by Equation (3.7), and by radiation, which is given by Equation (4.3). So

$$\begin{aligned}\frac{q}{A}&=h_c(\Theta_1-\Theta_2)+\frac{\sigma(\Theta_1^4-\Theta_2^4)}{\dfrac{1}{\varepsilon_1}+\dfrac{1}{\varepsilon_2}-1}\\&=1.75\times(288.2-278.2)\\&\quad+\frac{5.670\times10^{-8}(288.2^4-278.2^4)}{\frac{1}{0.9}+\frac{1}{0.9}-1}\\&=17.5+42.16\\&=59.66\,\text{W}\,\text{m}^{-2}.\end{aligned}$$

So the rate of heat transfer per unit surface area is $59.66\,\text{W}\,\text{m}^{-2}$. (Note the dominant effect of radiation in the transfer of heat energy across the air gap.)

(b) When the gap is filled with foam, the only mode of heat transfer is conduction. Using Equation (2.6),

$$\begin{aligned}\frac{q}{A}=\frac{\kappa}{b}(\Theta_1-\Theta_2)&=\frac{0.026}{0.03}(288.2-278.2)\\&=8.667\,\text{W}\,\text{m}^{-2}.\end{aligned}$$

So the rate of transfer of heat energy per unit area is $8.667\,\text{W}\,\text{m}^{-2}$. (Notice that by inserting foam in the gap we have reduced the rate of heat energy loss by a factor of more than six.)

UNIT 16 Interpretation of mathematical models

Study guide for Unit 16

The process of mathematical modelling was introduced in MST121 *Chapter A1*. In this unit we shall reintroduce and extend these ideas in order to give you an appreciation of the mathematical modelling which underlies the models which you have met earlier in this course, particularly in Block 2 and the earlier units of this block.

The discussion of the modelling process in Section 1 uses as illustration the models for an object falling from the Clifton Suspension Bridge which we discussed in *Unit 6*, the motion of a projectile from *Unit 14*, and the oscillation of a pendulum from *Units 8* and *13*. The case study in Sections 4 and 5 depends heavily on the models for heat transfer which were discussed in *Unit 15*, especially the model for convection.

Ideally you should study the material in the order in which it is presented. However, Sections 2 and 3 are largely self-contained and could be studied at any time, although there are a few exercises in Section 4 which depend on this material. You will need access to your computer for Section 5.

Sections 2 and 3 are shorter than the other sections and could sensibly be studied together in one study session. You should plan to spend one study session on each of the other three sections.

Introduction

As you know, one of the main aims of this course is to help you to develop your appreciation of the role of mathematics in understanding and predicting the behaviour of the real world (as opposed to the world of mathematical theories). This process is called *mathematical modelling.*

There was a time when the application of mathematics was restricted more or less to physics and engineering; but those days are long gone, and now mathematics turns up all over the place. In case you need to be convinced that this is the case, you may like to consider the following list of titles of some of the conferences organized in 1998 by the UK Institute of Mathematics and its Applications.

- Modelling Permeable Rocks
(the modelling of spatial patterns in geology, with applications in the oil industry, groundwater hydrology and nuclear waste disposal)
- Mathematics in Transport Planning and Control
(topics include the analysis of traffic at congested roundabouts)
- Mathematical Models in Maintenance
(topics include the asset management of vehicle fleets, high-rise buildings, housing estates, rolling stock and ships, as well as logistic support and human resource models)
- Mathematics in Heat Transfer
(topics include combustion and geothermal applications; condensation, boiling and evaporation; convective heat transfer)
- Mathematical Theory of Biological Systems
(covering epidemiology and immunology of infectious diseases, developmental biology, morphogenesis, physiological and medical systems, ecology, genetics and evolution)
- The Mathematics of Surfaces
(with applications in computer-aided design and machining, computer inspection of manufactured parts, geographic information systems)
- Control
(with applications in aerospace, automotive systems, biomedical systems, environmental and safety systems, heating and ventilation, marine systems, robotics and transport)
- Cardiovascular Flow Modelling and Measurement with Application to Clinical Medicine
(topics include fluid modelling, blood rheology (mixing), flow patterns in the circulation, development and treatment of cardiovascular disease)
- Image Processing: Mathematical Methods, Algorithms and Applications
(focusing on compression, transformations and neural networks)
- Mathematics in Communications
(topics include error-correcting codes, radio propagation models, network traffic modelling, queuing theory)

Although these diverse uses of mathematics call on different aspects of the subject, there is a range of skills that is common to all of them: these are the skills that together constitute the craft of mathematical modelling.

You may have been introduced to the process of mathematical modelling in *Chapter A1* of the prerequisite course MST121. This process is summarized in Figure 0.1.

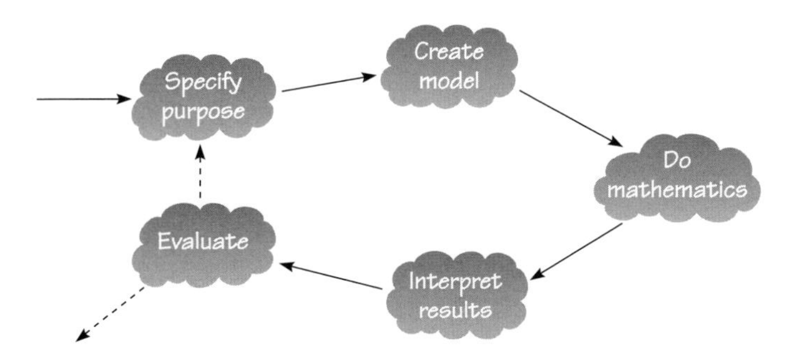

Figure 0.1 The mathematical modelling process (or cycle)

In the first section of this unit we discuss the five key stages of the mathematical modelling process in more detail, using some of the models that you have met in earlier units as illustrations. In the next two sections we look at the dimensions and units of physical quantities, and see how they can be used to predict and check the outcomes of the modelling process. Finally, the last two sections are devoted to a case study in which we shall see how the models developed in *Unit 15* for steady-state heat transfer can be applied to a situation which is not steady-state, namely the cooling of a cup of hot tea. This case study will show our progression around the modelling cycle shown in Figure 0.1.

Some words of warning are necessary. Firstly, mathematical modelling is unlike other branches of mathematics. Mathematical models depend critically on the problem a model is intended to help solve, and on the simplifying assumptions made about the system being modelled. You may disagree profoundly with the assumptions that I make in this unit (and assumptions made about other models in other units of this course). There are many ways of tackling any modelling problem, and none can be expected to yield an exact solution. If your assumptions differ from mine, then your model may be just as valid, or indeed better, than mine. Secondly, we may need to go round the modelling cycle in Figure 0.1 several times, improving our model each time. Finally, and most importantly, the modelling process *never* conforms to the rigid structure suggested by Figure 0.1 and expanded in Section 1. For example, in Stage 2 of the modelling process we 'state assumptions' and 'choose variables and parameters'. However, at a later stage, we might realize that there are other assumptions we require and other variables or parameters we need to define. Nevertheless, the modelling process shown in Figure 0.1 provides an invaluable framework to assist in the modelling of real-world situations.

1 An overview of mathematical modelling

This section presents the process of mathematically formulating and solving problems in the real world. In this course we do *not* expect you to master this process of mathematical modelling. Rather, we provide sufficient background so that you can appreciate the process involved in formulating the models that we have presented and their limitations. In order to further develop your skills of mathematical modelling, you would need to study another course which has this as one of its aims.

The *mathematical modelling process* starts with a problem in the 'real world', which is translated into a mathematical model whose solution enables us to provide solutions to the real-world problem. For example, in *Unit 6* we asked how long it takes a marble dropped from the Clifton Suspension Bridge in Bristol to reach the River Avon below, and what is its speed as it hits the water. While thinking about this problem, other questions might have passed through your mind, possibly including the following.

See *Unit 6*, Sections 3 and 4.

- Would a larger marble reach the River Avon more quickly or more slowly than a smaller marble?
- Would a marble of polystyrene, rather than glass, reach the River Avon in a shorter or longer time?
- How does the time to reach the River Avon compare to the time taken to reach half-way?
- How sensitive are the time and final speed to the fact that the River Avon is tidal (so the distance between the bridge and the river varies slightly)?
- How sensitive are the time and final speed to the possibility that the initial horizontal and vertical components of the velocity of the marble may not be zero?

Our mathematical model of the physical situation should help us to answer these questions as well as the problem originally posed. The key stages in the mathematical modelling process are as follows.

See MST121, *Chapter A1*, Section 7.

1. **Specify the purpose:**
   define the problem;
   decide which aspects of the problem to investigate.
2. **Create the model:**
   simplify the problem;
   state assumptions;
   choose variables and parameters;
   formulate mathematical relationships.
3. **Do the mathematics:**
   solve equations;
   draw graphs;
   derive results.
4. **Interpret the results:**
   collect relevant data;
   describe the mathematical solution in words;
   decide what results to compare with reality.
5. **Evaluate the outcomes:**
   test the model by comparing its predictions with reality;
   criticize the model;
   decide if it is necessary to adjust the model and enter the cycle again.

The diagram in Figure 1.1 may help you to remember the five key stages in the mathematical modelling process.

The mathematical modelling process is sometimes referred to as the *mathematical modelling cycle*.

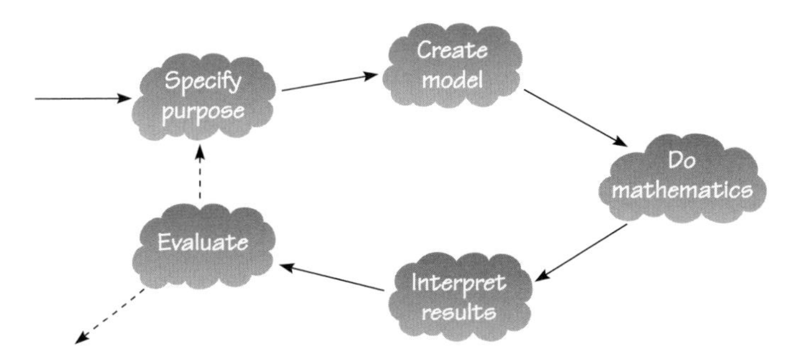

Figure 1.1 The mathematical modelling process (or cycle)

In developing a mathematical model, you may need to go round the loop in Figure 1.1 several times, improving your model each time. (In Section 3 of *Unit 6* we developed a first model of the Clifton Suspension Bridge problem which neglected the effects of air resistance; in Section 4 we developed the model by including air resistance. For light objects, we might need to go round the modelling loop again in order to include the effects of buoyancy, for example.) When you start to create a mathematical model for a real problem, you should begin with a simple model, in order to get a feel for the problem. In fact, it is often the case that a simple model that gives a reasonable approximation to the real world is more useful than a complicated model; a more complex model may give a better fit to the available data, but the key processes that are being modelled may be more difficult to identify. If, in evaluating a model, you find that it is not satisfactory for its purpose, you need to identify why it is deficient and try to include additional features that address those deficiencies in your next pass through the modelling loop.

In the remainder of this section we shall discuss each of the stages of the modelling process in more detail, using the Clifton Suspension Bridge problem for illustration.

1.1 Specify the purpose

In mathematical modelling, problems are rarely posed in a way that can be translated directly into mathematical form. For example, the Clifton Suspension Bridge problem might have been originally stated in the form

> 'How long does it take something to fall from the Clifton Suspension Bridge?'

It is important to establish at the outset a clear statement of the purpose of the model. In clarifying the statement of this problem, some of the questions which went through my mind were as follows.

- What is the object being dropped? For example, is it a feather or a brick?
- How is the object being dropped? Is it dropped from rest or is it thrown?
- What is the end point of the fall? Is it when the object hits the water or when the object finally comes to rest on the bed of the river?

Other questions may have occurred to you. At this stage it is also very helpful to get a 'feel' for the physical situation. In our case, this might involve actually dropping different types of objects from the Clifton Suspension Bridge. Such a test would also enable us to assess whether external physical phenomena, such as cross-winds, are sufficiently common that they ought to be taken into account when formulating our model.

After clarifying the precise problem being posed, the statement of the problem might become

> 'How long does it take a marble dropped from rest from the Clifton Suspension Bridge in still air to reach the surface of the river below?'

Exercise 1.1

A manufacturer of tin cans asks you: 'What is the best shape for a can of baked beans?'

(a) What questions might you ask the manufacturer in order to clarify this problem?

(b) Try to formulate a clear statement of a suitable modelling problem for this situation, based on possible answers to the questions you posed in part (a).

It is also worth bearing in mind that some models, created for a specific purpose, might be useful in answering different questions about the same situation and, furthermore, may be applicable in other situations. For example, our model for the Clifton Suspension Bridge problem might be used to predict the final speed of the marble just before it enters the river, or even the time and speed of the marble at different heights above the river. Almost certainly our model could be used for falling objects other than marbles, and for locations other than the Clifton Suspension Bridge! It is possible that the model could be used, possibly after some modifications, for objects dropped with an initial velocity and for objects dropped through mediums other than air, such as water.

Exercise 1.2

In *Unit 14* we considered the problem of how far one can put a shot. Suggest other situations where the model developed there could be used, possibly with some modifications.

1.2 Create the model

There are a number of skills that are needed in building a sensible model that approximates a real situation.

Simplify the problem

Usually you cannot hope to develop and solve a mathematical model which encompasses *all* the factors which influence the behaviour of a physical situation under investigation. So it is important to identify the key features when developing a model, at least initially. For example, when developing our first model of the marble dropped from the Clifton Suspension Bridge, we assumed that the marble could be modelled as a particle, that the initial velocity of the marble was zero, and that air resistance could be ignored.

Exercise 1.3

What simplifying assumptions would you make if you wanted to find the best shape for a cylindrical tin can made to contain a specified quantity of baked beans?

State assumptions

In modelling a physical situation you should always look for a model which is as simple as possible consistent with the salient features of the problem. But it is important to be clear about the simplifying assumptions that have been made in order to arrive at that model. This is necessary to ensure that anyone who may be interested can follow how the model has been derived. Furthermore, if you have an explicit list of assumptions you have made, and you wish to improve your model, you have an obvious place to start: review the assumptions, and ask yourself which can and should be modified or relaxed. For example, for the problem of the marble dropped from the Clifton Suspension Bridge, you might decide to improve the first model by taking into account air resistance: in the revised model, you might assume air resistance which depends linearly or quadratically on the marble's speed.

Exercise 1.4

Looking at the list of assumptions in Solution 1.3 for the tin can problem, which assumption do you think should be modified in a revised model?

Exercise 1.5

(a) List the assumptions which were used in developing the model of the pendulum given in *Unit 8*.

(b) Which of these assumptions do you think should be modified in a revised model?

Choose variables and parameters

In the falling marble problem, the things which vary are the height and speed of the marble, which are functions of time. So we can identify our key variables as height, h, speed, v, and time, t. Our problem might be summarized as: find h and v as functions of time t.

At this stage, it is important to decide on the units in which the variables are measured: for example, we might measure height in metres, speed in metres per second, and time in seconds. It is sensible to use units of measurement which are appropriate to the problem under consideration: for example, for the Clifton Suspension Bridge problem, it would be silly to measure the height in millimetres and the time in years. It is also a good idea to use units which are consistent: it would not be sensible to measure height in metres, time in seconds and speed in miles per hour!

It is good practice to keep a list of all your variables and parameters, to ensure that all of them have been consistently defined and used. It pays to be careful in defining variables to avoid confusion later. For example, 'time since the marble was dropped' is far clearer and less open to misinterpretation than just 'time'.

Exercise 1.6

For the Clifton Suspension Bridge problem, give a clear definition of height.

The list of the variables used should include a note of the symbol used to represent each one, and the units used in its measurement, as well as its definition. For example, our list of the variables for the Clifton Suspension Bridge problem might be as follows:

- h is the height of the marble above the River Avon, measured in metres;
- v is the speed of the marble, measured in $\mathrm{m\,s^{-1}}$;
- t is the time since the marble was dropped, measured in seconds.

As the model is developed, it might be necessary to add further variables and parameters to the list. Most probably we shall have to add

- g is the magnitude of the acceleration due to gravity, measured in $\mathrm{m\,s^{-2}}$

to the above list.

It is worthwhile giving some thought to the choice of symbol used to represent a variable, and choosing something memorable. It is very annoying to have to continually refer back to find the meaning of a symbol, so it is sensible to use the symbol h to represent *h*eight, and t to represent *t*ime. The obvious choice of symbol to represent *s*peed is s. Unfortunately, the symbol s is often used to represent distance (I don't know why!), so this choice might be confusing to readers. We might instead choose the symbol v, as in everyday speech *v*elocity is synonymous with speed. One final word about the choice of symbol: you should *not* use the same symbol to represent two different variables in the same model.

Formulate mathematical relationships

The core differential equation in the Clifton Suspension Bridge problem arose from the use of Newton's second law. Indeed, most models of mechanical systems involve the use of Newton's laws, though the use may be hidden, such as use of the law of conservation of mechanical energy, or use of the relationships between speed, distance and time for constant acceleration. In heat energy transfer problems, we shall probably use Fourier's law. In Section 4 of this unit, we shall develop a model for the cooling of a cup of tea which uses both Fourier's law and the input–output principle.

See *Unit 6*, Section 2.

See *Unit 15*, Subsection 2.2.

Exercise 1.7

In *Unit 14*, a mathematical model of putting the shot is discussed. Describe how the equation of motion is obtained.

---

*Exercise 1.8

A shopping centre is surrounded by car parks, as shown in Figure 1.2.

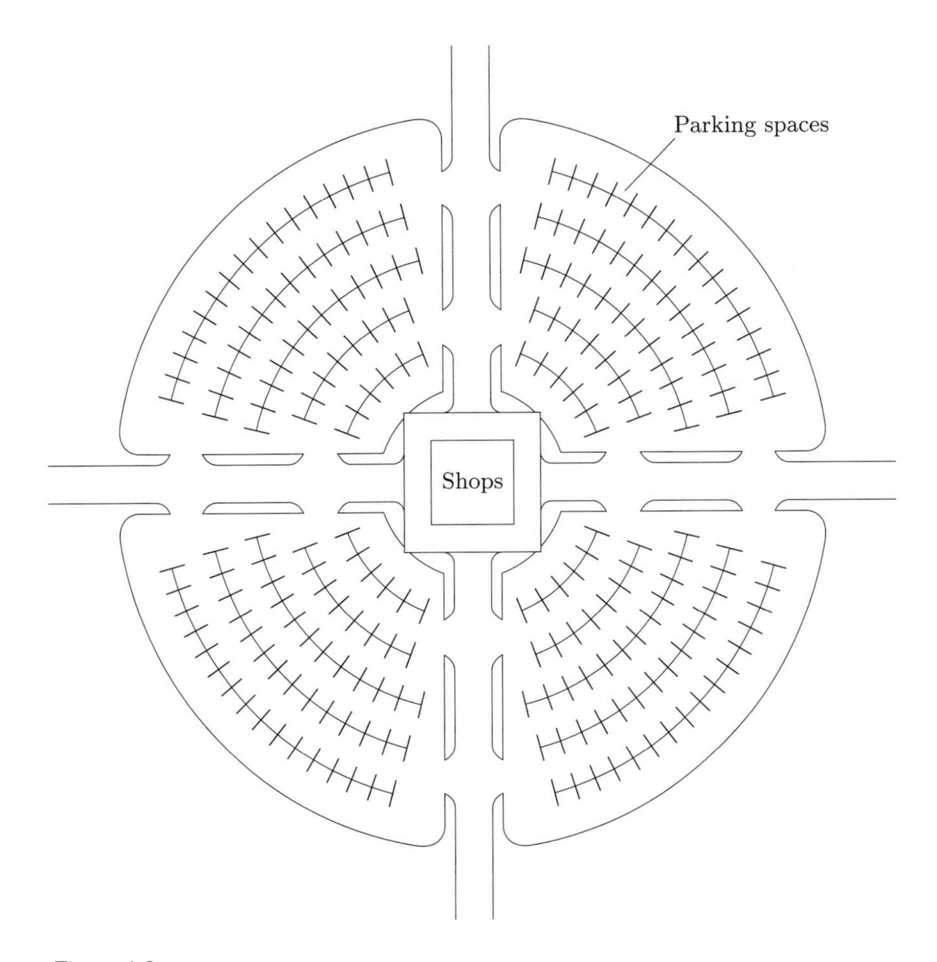

Figure 1.2

The problem is to decide on the best parking space to use when doing your shopping. The problem arises because the closer to the centre you go, more time will be spent driving around looking for a vacant parking space; if you park your car far away from the centre, however, you will have to spend more time walking to and from the shops. The following is one way of resolving this difficulty.

- Find how the time between arriving at the car park (including time to find a parking space and walking to and from the shops) is dependent on where you park your car.
- Work out how far away you need to park to minimize this time.

Let t be the time, in seconds, between arriving at the car park and getting to the shops, plus the time spent walking back to the car, and let x be the walking distance, in metres, between your car and the shops. The time it takes to find somewhere to park is a decreasing function of x: suppose that, based on empirical evidence, it may reasonably be modelled as being inversely proportional to x.

Formulate a relationship between t and x that could be used as a model for solving the problem.

1.3 Do the mathematics

The majority of this course, and most other courses in mathematics, is about 'doing the mathematics', so we shall not add anything further in this unit!

Exercise 1.9

Consider the tin can modelling problem formulated in part (b) of Solution 1.1, using the assumptions given in Solution 1.3. Outline in words the strategy you would use to 'do the mathematics'. (You are not expected to actually solve the problem.)

1.4 Interpret the results

Obtaining a solution to a mathematical modelling problem is not the end of the modelling process. The solution needs to be interpreted in terms of the original problem posed, and a number of checks need to be made. In this subsection we shall outline some of the techniques used to interpret the solution and, in the next subsection, to check its reliability.

The main point to emphasize is that the answer to the original problem should be given in words. For example, the answer to the question 'How long does it take a marble to drop from the Clifton Suspension Bridge?' should be 'It takes approximately 4 seconds for the marble to hit the water when dropped from the Clifton Suspension Bridge', rather than just '$t \simeq 3.962$'. When expressing the answer in words, it is important to remember the expected audience. For example, if you were posed the problem of how to space the lines which are often painted across the road before a road junction in order to slow down approaching vehicles, your answer to the Chief Engineer would probably be different in form to that given to the workforce who actually paint the lines!

When giving numerical answers, it is important to give them to an appropriate accuracy. For example, for most purposes 4 seconds is probably an appropriate answer for the time of fall for the marble falling from the Clifton Suspension Bridge, although in other situations a more accurate answer might be appropriate. In particular, you need to consider the accuracy of the data. The height of the Clifton Suspension Bridge above the River Avon was assumed to be 77 metres, an accuracy of 2 significant figures, and the value of g was assumed to be $9.81\,\mathrm{m\,s^{-2}}$, an accuracy of 3 significant figures. So in quoting our final answer for the time of fall, we are justified in an accuracy of only 2 significant figures (at most).

Exercise 1.10

Consider the problem of finding the amount of the monthly repayment for a loan of £200 000 over a period of 25 years, at a fixed interest rate of 5% per annum which is charged annually (rather than on a daily basis, for example). This problem can be modelled by the recurrence relation

$$u_{r+1} = 1.05u_r - 12M,$$

with the initial condition

$$u_0 = 200\,000,$$

where u_r is the amount owed after r years and M is the monthly repayment in £.

The mathematical solution to the problem is

$$M = 1182.540\,955\ldots.$$

Express the solution to the problem in words, giving the amount of the monthly repayment to an appropriate accuracy.

In some situations, you might consider giving your answer in the form of a graph or a table. For example, the formula

$$t = cm^{2/3}$$

is given in the book by Philip Harben, *The Grammar of Cookery* (Penguin, 1962) as a model for the cooking time t of food, such as a turkey, of weight m. This formula would not be very helpful for most cooks, and the same information might be better expressed in the form of Table 1.1.

Here we are using 'weight' in its everyday sense and measuring it in kg. Strictly speaking we should be using the word 'mass'.

Table 1.1 Cooking time for turkeys

Weight of turkey	Cooking time
4 kg	1 h 55 min
$4\frac{1}{2}$ kg	2 h
5 kg	2 h 10 min
$5\frac{1}{2}$ kg	2 h 20 min
6 kg	2 h 30 min
$6\frac{1}{2}$ kg	2 h 35 min
7 kg	2 h 45 min
$7\frac{1}{2}$ kg	2 h 50 min
8 kg	3 h
$8\frac{1}{2}$ kg	3 h 5 min
9 kg	3 h 15 min
$9\frac{1}{2}$ kg	3 h 20 min
10 kg	3 h 30 min

In the above table, the times are rounded to the nearest 5 minutes, which seems appropriate to the situation. Looking at the table, it is clear why most cookery books use a linear model for cooking times!

*Exercise 1.11

The time t (in seconds) taken for an object to fall from a height h (in metres) is modelled by the formula

$$t = \sqrt{\frac{2h}{g}},$$

where g is the magnitude of the acceleration due to gravity measured in $\mathrm{m\,s^{-2}}$. Present the outcome of this model for heights between 0 and 100 metres in the form of a table and in the form of a graph.

What do you think are the advantages and disadvantages of these two methods of presenting the outcome for this problem?

1.5 Evaluate the outcomes

Test the outcomes of the model with reality

Here there are several points to be emphasized. It is usually worth checking that the model predicts the kind of results that one would expect from common sense and from experience. If possible, one should validate the model by comparing its predictions with data from an experiment or other reliable source.

For example, in the Clifton Suspension Bridge problem, we could actually time how long it takes a marble dropped from the bridge to hit the water below (in an experiment this was 4.1 seconds), and compare it with our prediction (in our first model this was 3.96 seconds). Even better would be to time the fall for different objects from different heights. It is good practice to try to reformulate the results so that this check turns into something simple such as drawing a straight line. Ignoring air resistance, for falling objects, the time of fall t for different heights h is modelled by

$$t^2 = \frac{2}{g}h.$$

So if we plot t^2 against h, we should obtain a straight line through the origin with slope $2/g$ if our model is satisfactory. Such a plot is shown in Figure 1.3.

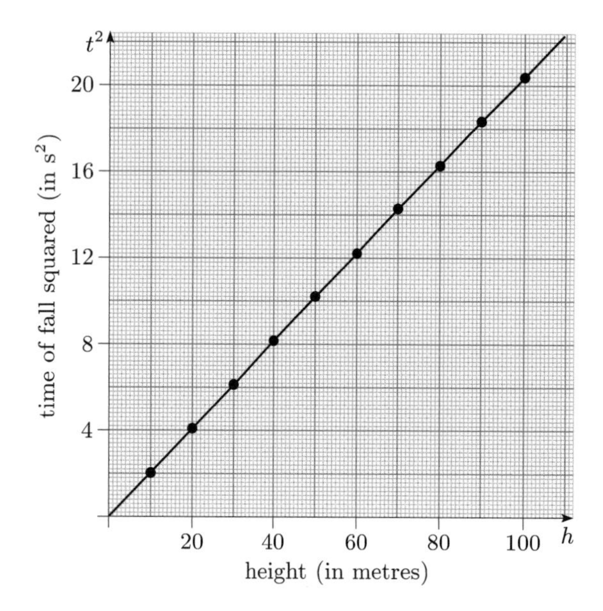

Figure 1.3

Exercise 1.12

Joints of beef of similar shapes were roasted in an oven. A meat thermometer inserted into the centre of a joint was used to decide when the joint was cooked. The following roasting times were found.

Again we are using 'weight' in its everyday sense and measuring it in kg.

Table 1.2 Roasting times

Weight of joint	Roasting time
1 kg	27 min
$1\frac{1}{4}$ kg	31 min
$1\frac{1}{2}$ kg	35 min
$1\frac{3}{4}$ kg	39 min
2 kg	42 min

(a) A model for the roasting time t for a joint of weight m is the linear equation

$$t = a + bm$$

('roast for a minutes plus b minutes per kg'). By plotting t against m for the above data, decide if the linear model is satisfactory, and find values for the parameters a and b.

(b) An alternative model for roasting times is

$$t = cm^{2/3}.$$

By plotting t against $m^{2/3}$ for the above data, decide if the two-thirds power model is a satisfactory model, and find the value of the parameter c.

As well as using data to validate the model, you may also require experimental data to find numerical values for parameters in the model. For example, in Exercise 1.12, we used the experimental data not only to verify the models, but also to find values for the parameters a, b and c.

Adjust the model

If a model is found to be unsatisfactory, the simplifying assumptions which were used in developing the model can be reconsidered. In our initial model of the Clifton Suspension Bridge problem, the effects of air resistance were ignored. We might now decide to include these.

*Exercise 1.13

In the Clifton Suspension Bridge problem, an initial model is proposed in which velocity-dependent forces are ignored. This model is superseded by one in which such forces are taken into account. What is the likely effect of this on the result?

Our improved model may, in its turn, be found to be not completely satisfactory. Our first model for the Clifton Suspension Bridge problem assumed that gravity was the only force acting; the second also took air resistance into account. However, objects which are sufficiently light will rise when released in a fluid, rather than fall, due to pressure variation within the fluid. Thus a hollow rubber ball immersed in water will rapidly rise to the surface when released; the same effect is put to use for the purpose of flight in a hot-air balloon. The motion of such an object may be modelled more satisfactorily by allowing for the presence of a third force in addition to gravity and air (or other fluid) resistance. This is known as *Archimedes' buoyancy force*, and its magnitude is equal to the weight of fluid displaced by the object. The effect of this force is not significant for the Clifton Suspension Bridge problem, but may be significant for other situations. Further effects due to the motion of the fluid may also need to be considered in certain circumstance, such as a falling feather, but fluid dynamics is beyond the scope of this course.

Exercise 1.14

Consider again the model of the tin can problem based on the assumptions in Exercise 1.3. In Solution 1.4, we suggested that this initial model should be modified by allowing for wastage when cutting the circular ends. What effect do you think this would have on the shape of the can?

---

2 Dimensional consistency and change of units

2.1 Dimensional consistency

In modelling, we attempt to establish relationships between variables by using assumptions to develop equations. In this subsection we shall investigate a technique used to verify that these equations make sense, in that they are *dimensionally consistent*. Such an analysis can never establish that an equation is correct, but it provides a useful check and can sometimes tell us that an equation is wrong.

For example, suppose you are cooking a meringue nest using egg whites and sugar. In order to determine the mass, m, of the meringue, you would first need to determine the mass, m_1, of an egg white and the mass, m_2, of the sugar, all measured in the same SI units. Then, assuming that no mass is lost during the cooking process, the mass of a meringue using n egg whites is given by $m = nm_1 + m_2$. Each additive term on the right-hand side of this equation (nm_1 and m_2) is a mass, and the equation makes sense only if each of these terms is measured in the same SI units, giving the overall mass m in the same SI units. This is the essence of dimensional consistency.

In reality, the mass of an egg white varies slightly from egg to egg.

Now, the choice of unit of measurement does not affect the physical quantity being measured. For example, the width of this page is the same irrespective of whether we measure it in millimetres or inches. Similarly, no matter what units we use, speed must always be expressed as length divided by time. To measure speed we could use metres per second, centimetres per hour, or yards per day, but it has to be a unit-of-length per unit-of-time. In terms of dimensional consistency, the important property of volume is that it is length cubed, and the important property of speed is that it is length divided by time. In these examples, we can think of length and time as being fundamental properties, referred to as *base dimensions*.

Definition

Mass, length, time and temperature are fundamental properties and are referred to as **base dimensions**. The base dimension mass is denoted by M, length by L, time by T, and temperature by Θ.

Θ is the Greek capital letter theta.

The dimensions of all physical quantities (in this course) can be expressed in terms of these four base dimensions. For example, the dimensions of speed, length divided by time, are $\mathrm{L\,T^{-1}}$. To write this more succinctly, we introduce square brackets to mean 'the dimensions of', and write

$$[\text{speed}] = \mathrm{L\,T^{-1}}.$$

This is read as 'the dimensions of speed are $\mathrm{L\,T^{-1}}$'. Similarly,

$$[\text{volume}] = \mathrm{L^3}.$$

The dimensions of other physical quantities can be expressed in terms of M, L, T and Θ by working from their units of measurement.

Example 2.1

Find the dimensions of the magnitude of acceleration, of the magnitude of force and of kinetic energy.

Solution

The SI unit for the magnitude of acceleration is $\mathrm{m\,s^{-2}}$, so

$$[\text{acceleration}] = \mathrm{L\,T^{-2}}.$$

We use [acceleration] here as a shorthand for 'the dimensions of the magnitude of acceleration'.

The SI unit for the magnitude of force is the newton, where $1\,\mathrm{N} = 1\,\mathrm{kg\,m\,s^{-2}}$, therefore

$$[\text{force}] = \mathrm{M\,L\,T^{-2}}.$$

The kinetic energy of a particle is $\frac{1}{2}mv^2$, where m is its mass and v is its speed. Mass has dimensions M, and speed has dimensions $\mathrm{L\,T^{-1}}$. The number $\frac{1}{2}$ has no dimensions; it is a **dimensionless quantity**, and we denote this by writing $[\frac{1}{2}] = 1$. Therefore we have

$$\begin{aligned}[\text{kinetic energy}] &= [\tfrac{1}{2}]\,[\text{mass}]\,[\text{speed}]^2 \\ &= 1 \times \mathrm{M} \times (\mathrm{L\,T^{-1}})^2 = \mathrm{M\,L^2\,T^{-2}}. \quad \blacksquare\end{aligned}$$

As Example 2.1 has illustrated, we can multiply, divide and take powers of dimensions using the usual rules of arithmetic and algebra.

**Exercise 2.1*

(a) What are the dimensions of area?

(b) Given that, in SI units, density is measured in $\mathrm{kg\,m^{-3}}$, what are the dimensions of density?

(c) Find the dimensions of the gravitational potential energy of a particle, mgh, where m is its mass in kilograms, g is the magnitude of the acceleration due to gravity in $\mathrm{m\,s^{-2}}$, and h is its height above the datum in metres.

(d) The size of an angle θ, measured in radians, can be determined by assuming that the angle lies at the centre of a circle and that the two lines defining the angle are radii of the circle, as shown in Figure 2.1. If the radii have length r and the arc defined by θ has length l, then $\theta = l/r$. What are the dimensions of angle?

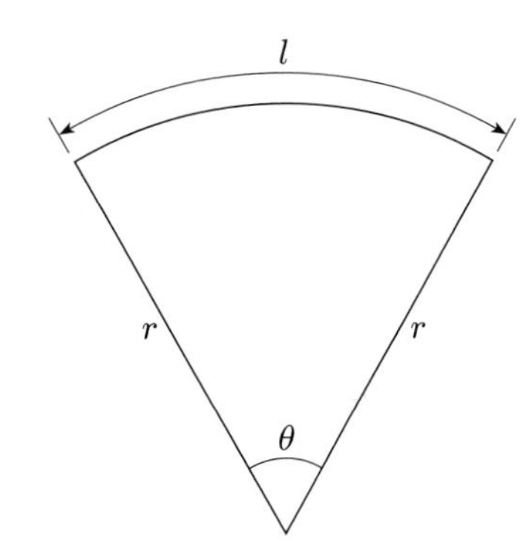

Figure 2.1

The dimensions of some of the physical quantities used in this course are given in Table 2.1, where dimensions of 1 indicate that the quantity is dimensionless.

For vector quantities we give the dimensions of the *magnitude* of the vector.

Table 2.1

Physical quantity	Dimensions
number	1
angle	1
mass	M
length	L
time	T
temperature	Θ
area	L^2
volume	L^3
speed	$L\,T^{-1}$
acceleration	$L\,T^{-2}$
force	$M\,L\,T^{-2}$
energy	$M\,L^2\,T^{-2}$
torque	$M\,L^2\,T^{-2}$
density	$M\,L^{-3}$

Note that energy and torque have the same dimensions although they are different physical quantities.

In modelling, any equation must be **dimensionally consistent**: the dimensions must be the same for each of the additive terms on either side of the equation. If they are, then our confidence in the model is increased; if they are not, then we know that we have made a mistake somewhere in deriving the equation.

Example 2.2

The period τ of small oscillations of a particle of mass m suspended from a fixed point by a light inextensible string of length l is given by

$$\tau = 2\pi\sqrt{\frac{l}{g}}.$$

Show that this equation is dimensionally consistent.

Solution

The period τ has dimensions T. For the right-hand side of the equation we have

$$\left[2\pi\sqrt{l/g}\right] = [2\pi]\,([l]/[g])^{1/2} = 1 \times (L/(L\,T^{-2}))^{1/2} = (T^2)^{1/2} = T.$$

So both sides of the equation have dimensions T, and the equation is dimensionally consistent. ■

Example 2.3

In Solution 1.8 the total time taken to park and walk to the shops and back was modelled as

$$t = \frac{k}{x} + \frac{2x}{v}.$$

Determine the dimensions for k that ensure that this equation is dimensionally consistent.

Solution

All three terms in the equation, t, k/x and $2x/v$, must have the same dimensions if the equation is to be dimensionally consistent. We have

$$[t] = \mathrm{T} \quad \text{and} \quad [2x/v] = [2]\,[x]/[v] = 1 \times \mathrm{L}/(\mathrm{L\,T^{-1}}) = \mathrm{T},$$

so dimensional consistency is assured if $[k/x] = [k]/[x] = \mathrm{T}$. Since $[x] = \mathrm{L}$, this means that we must have $[k] = \mathrm{L\,T}$ for dimensional consistency. ■

Example 2.3 illustrates that when checking for dimensional consistency, each additive term must be checked separately: although we can multiply, divide and take powers of dimensions, we can add or subtract only terms which have the same dimensions. It also shows how dimensional consistency can be used to determine the units of parameters of models.

*Exercise 2.2

Show that the equation

$$v^2 = u^2 + 2ax,$$

which relates the speed of something moving with constant acceleration a to the distance x travelled, is dimensionally consistent.

Exercise 2.3

A mathematical model of pollution in a lake leads to the differential equation

$$\frac{dm}{dt} = -k\,m(t),$$

where $m(t)$ is the mass of pollutant in the lake at time t, and $k = r/V$, where r is the volume flow rate of water through the lake and V is the volume of water in the lake. Show that this equation is dimensionally consistent.

Hint: A derivative is essentially a ratio, or fraction, so its dimensions are those of its numerator divided by those of its denominator.

*Exercise 2.4

The magnitude R of the air resistance force on an object can be modelled, in certain circumstances, as

See *Unit 6*, Subsection 4.2.

$$R = c_2 D^2 v^2,$$

where c_2 is a constant, D is the effective diameter of the object and v is its speed. Use dimensional consistency to determine the dimensions of the constant c_2. What SI units would be used to measure c_2?

We have seen how to check for dimensional consistency in equations where the additive terms involve multiplying, dividing or taking powers. But many of the models you have seen in the course involve functions such as exp, ln, sin, cos, and so on. How does one check for dimensional consistency in such cases? For example, the solution of the differential equation $dm/dt = -k\,m(t)$ in the lake pollution model is

$$m(t) = m(0)\,e^{-kt}, \tag{2.1}$$

where $m(0)$ is the initial mass of pollutant. To be able to check for dimensional consistency in this equation, we need to be able to find the dimensions of e^{-kt}. Now we know that exp, ln, sin, cos, and so on, all have real numbers as their domains and image sets. Therefore, for dimensional consistency, the argument x of the function must be dimensionless, and we can take e^x, $\ln x$, $\sin x$, $\cos x$, and so on, to be dimensionless. So the key to checking for dimensional consistency in equations involving such functions is to ensure that their arguments are dimensionless. In the above case, we know from the equation $k = r/V$ given in Exercise 2.3 that $[k] = [r/V] = [r][V]^{-1} = (L^3T^{-1}) \times (L^3)^{-1} = \mathrm{T}^{-1}$, so $[-kt] = 1$. Hence $[e^{-kt}] = 1$, and Equation (2.1) is dimensionally consistent, since $[m(t)] = [m(0)] = \mathrm{M}$.

Sometimes, however, the arguments of such functions are *not* dimensionless. For example, in obtaining Equation (2.1), one might have begun by using the separation of variables method to solve the differential equation $dm/dt = -k\,m(t)$ and obtained

$$\ln m(t) = -kt + C, \tag{2.2}$$

where C is an arbitrary constant. Now $m(t)$ is not dimensionless (it has dimensions M), so we cannot determine the dimensions of $\ln m(t)$. However, putting $t = 0$ into Equation (2.2) gives $C = \ln m(0)$, and this enables us to rewrite Equation (2.2) as

$$\ln\left(\frac{m(t)}{m(0)}\right) = -kt, \tag{2.3}$$

where $[m(t)/m(0)] = \mathrm{M}/\mathrm{M} = 1$. So now the argument of ln *is* dimensionless, and it is an easy matter to check for dimensional consistency (both sides of Equation (2.3) have dimensions 1).

Very often, if the argument of a function in an equation is not dimensionless, some simple manipulation of the equation can render it so and hence enable dimensional consistency to be checked.

Exercise 2.5

The solution to a simple harmonic motion problem may be written as

$$x(t) = A\cos(\omega t + \phi),$$

where $x(t)$ measures the displacement from the equilibrium position at time t, and ϕ is the phase angle. What dimensions for A and ω will ensure dimensional consistency?

2.2 Change of units

There is now almost universal acceptance of the SI system in professional scientific and engineering circles. This system is based on seven **base units**, of which the following four are used in this course.

Table 2.2

Physical quantity	Unit	Abbreviation
length	metre	m
mass	kilogram	kg
time	second	s
temperature	kelvin	K

The other three base units are the ampere (the unit of electric current), the candela (the unit of luminous intensity), and the mole (the unit of the amount of substance).

In addition, there are various **derived units** in common use, which can be formed by combining the above base units. For example, we have already introduced the *newton* (N) as the unit of force and the *joule* (J) as the unit of energy. In terms of the base units, $1\,\mathrm{N} = 1\,\mathrm{kg\,m\,s^{-2}}$ and $1\,\mathrm{J} = 1\,\mathrm{kg\,m^2\,s^{-2}}$.

To avoid very large or very small numbers, we also use multiple or fractional units. For example, the distance between London and Edinburgh is more conveniently expressed as 665 km (kilometres), rather than 6.65×10^5 m. Similarly, the thickness of copper used in a central heating pipe is usually stated to be 1 mm (millimetres), rather than 1×10^{-3} m. The most important prefixes for forming these units are given in Table 2.3.

Table 2.3

Multiplication factor	Prefix	Symbol
$10^9 = 1\,000\,000\,000$	giga	G
$10^6 = 1\,000\,000$	mega	M
$10^3 = 1\,000$	kilo	k
$10^{-2} = 0.01$	centi	c
$10^{-3} = 0.001$	milli	m
$10^{-6} = 0.000\,001$	micro	μ
$10^{-9} = 0.000\,000\,001$	nano	n

For example, the pressure of the atmosphere, which is about $10^5\,\mathrm{N\,m^{-2}}$, is sometimes written $100\,\mathrm{kN\,m^{-2}}$, i.e. 100 kilonewtons per square metre. The conversion between such alternative units is quite straightforward but does need some care! For example, if we wish to convert 6 kilometres into metres, we know that

$$1\,\mathrm{km} = 10^3\,\mathrm{m},$$

so the conversion factor from kilometres to metres is

$$\frac{10^3\,\mathrm{m}}{1\,\mathrm{km}} \quad (=1).$$

Using this conversion factor, we have

$$6\,\mathrm{km} = 6\,\mathrm{km} \times \left(\frac{10^3\,\mathrm{m}}{1\,\mathrm{km}}\right) = 6 \times 10^3\,\mathrm{m}.$$

This example may seem trivial, but the method used here can be used in more complicated problems.

In this calculation we have, in essence, treated the units in a similar way to algebraic quantities and 'cancelled' the 'km' between the numerator and denominator.

Example 2.4

The speed of a car is $50\,\mathrm{km\,h^{-1}}$. Express this speed in the SI units of $\mathrm{m\,s^{-1}}$.

Solution

We have

$$1\,\mathrm{km} = 10^3\,\mathrm{m}$$

and

$$1\ \mathrm{h} = 60\,\mathrm{min} = 60 \times 60\,\mathrm{s}.$$

So

$$\begin{aligned} 50\,\mathrm{km\,h^{-1}} &= 50\,\mathrm{km\,h^{-1}} \times \left(\frac{10^3\,\mathrm{m}}{1\,\mathrm{km}}\right) \times \left(\frac{60 \times 60\,\mathrm{s}}{1\ \mathrm{h}}\right)^{-1} \\ &= 50 \times 10^3 \times 60^{-1} \times 60^{-1}\,\mathrm{m\,s^{-1}} \\ &= 13.89\,\mathrm{m\,s^{-1}}. \end{aligned}$$

So the speed of the car is $13.89\,\mathrm{m\,s^{-1}}$. ■

*Exercise 2.6

The density of mercury is $13.546\,\mathrm{g\,cm^{-3}}$. Express this density in the SI units of $\mathrm{kg\,m^{-3}}$.

Unfortunately, the metric system of units is not the one in everyday use everywhere, particularly in the United Kingdom and in the United States of America, where lengths may be measured in inches, feet and miles, masses in ounces, pounds and tons, and temperatures in degrees Fahrenheit. The method we have used above can equally be used to convert between such units and SI units. However, when converting between imperial and metric systems of units, the conversion factors are not 'nice round numbers'. For example,

$$1\,\mathrm{lb} = 0.453\,592\,37\,\mathrm{kg}.$$

Some of the common conversion factors between imperial and SI units are given in Table 2.4.

Table 2.4

Imperial unit	SI unit
1 in	$2.54 \times 10^{-2}\,\mathrm{m}$
1 ft	$0.304\,8\,\mathrm{m}$
1 mile	$1.609\,344 \times 10^{3}\,\mathrm{m}$
1 pint	$5.682\,613 \times 10^{-4}\,\mathrm{m^3}$
1 gallon	$4.546\,09 \times 10^{-3}\,\mathrm{m^3}$
1 oz	$2.834\,952 \times 10^{-2}\,\mathrm{kg}$
1 lb	$0.453\,592\,37\,\mathrm{kg}$
1 ton	$1.016\,047 \times 10^{3}\,\mathrm{kg}$

Example 2.5

The speed of a car is 30 miles per hour. Express this speed in SI units.

Solution

We have

$$1\text{ mile} = 1.609\,344 \times 10^{3}\,\mathrm{m}$$

and

$$1\text{ hour} = 60 \times 60\,\mathrm{s}.$$

So

$$\begin{aligned} 30\text{ miles hour}^{-1} &= 30\text{ miles hour}^{-1} \times \left(\frac{1.609\,344 \times 10^{3}\,\mathrm{m}}{1\text{ mile}}\right) \times \left(\frac{60 \times 60\,\mathrm{s}}{1\text{ hour}}\right)^{-1} \\ &= 30 \times 1.609\,344 \times 10^{3} \times 60^{-1} \times 60^{-1}\,\mathrm{m\,s^{-1}} \\ &= 13.41\,\mathrm{m\,s^{-1}}. \quad \blacksquare \end{aligned}$$

*Exercise 2.7

The pressure on a piston is 61.00 lb per square inch. Express this pressure (to 4 s.f.) in the SI units of $\mathrm{kg\,m^{-2}}$.

In the SI system, pressure is *force* per unit area, not *mass* per unit area. To convert our answer here to the correct units, we would have to multiply it by g.

End-of-section Exercises

*Exercise 2.8

One term in the following equation is in error:

$$\frac{p}{\rho} + \tfrac{1}{2}u - gz = \text{constant},$$

where p is the pressure of a fluid, ρ is its density, u is its speed, g is the magnitude of the acceleration due to gravity, and z is the height above some datum. By checking the dimensions of each term of the equation, find which term is in error, and suggest how it might be made dimensionally correct. (The dimensions of pressure are $\mathrm{M\,L^{-1}\,T^{-2}}$.)

Exercise 2.9

Before a recent holiday to South America, I was unable to buy local currency in the UK. So I bought US dollars in the UK, the exchange rate being £1 = \$1.75. In Bolivia, I exchanged my dollars for the local currency, the rate of exchange being \$1 = 7.75 boliviano. How much was 1 boliviano worth in £?

3 The method of dimensional analysis

In the last section, we used the base dimensions of physical quantities to check the consistency of equations and to find the dimensions of parameters in equations. However, the fact that an equation must be dimensionally consistent can be used to *suggest* the possible form of the relationship between the physical quantities involved in modelling a situation. This process is called the method of **dimensional analysis**.

We shall illustrate the method by considering the example of a projectile, which we have met previously in *Unit 14*, Section 2. Our aim is to find the form of the formula for the range of a projectile thrown on horizontal ground in terms of the parameters involved in the situation. If we assume that the projectile is thrown from ground level and neglect any effects due to air resistance, the principal quantities involved in the situation are those listed in Table 3.1.

In this case we already know the formula, but this example illustrates the general method in a situation with which we are already familiar.

Table 3.1

Physical quantity	Symbol	Dimensions
Range of projectile	R	L
Mass of projectile	m	M
Launch speed of projectile	u	$\mathrm{L\,T^{-1}}$
Launch angle of projectile	θ	1
Magnitude of acceleration due to gravity	g	$\mathrm{L\,T^{-2}}$

Our aim is to find the range R as a function of the four parameters. In other words, we are looking for a function f of four variables such that

$$R = f(m, u, \theta, g).$$

We shall begin by assuming that

$$R = k\, m^{\alpha}\, u^{\beta}\, \theta^{\gamma}\, g^{\delta}, \tag{3.1}$$

where k is a (dimensionless) real number, and the powers α, β, γ and δ are to be found.

For this equation to be dimensionally consistent, we must have

$$\begin{aligned}[R] &= [k\, m^{\alpha}\, u^{\beta}\, \theta^{\gamma}\, g^{\delta}] \\ &= [k]\, [m]^{\alpha}\, [u]^{\beta}\, [\theta]^{\gamma}\, [g]^{\delta}.\end{aligned}$$

In terms of the base dimensions, we have

$$\begin{aligned}\mathrm{L} &= \mathrm{M}^{\alpha}\, (\mathrm{L\,T^{-1}})^{\beta}\, (\mathrm{L\,T^{-2}})^{\delta} \\ &= \mathrm{M}^{\alpha}\, \mathrm{L}^{\beta+\delta}\, \mathrm{T}^{-\beta-2\delta},\end{aligned}$$

as k and θ are dimensionless. Equating powers of M, L and T on both sides of this equation, we have

$$0 = \alpha, \quad 1 = \beta + \delta, \quad 0 = -\beta - 2\delta.$$

Solving these equations for α, β, γ and δ gives

$$\alpha = 0, \quad \beta = 2, \quad \delta = -1.$$

So the requirement that the equation must be dimensionally consistent has given us values of α, β and δ. Because the parameter θ is dimensionless, the method cannot give us a value for γ.

We have shown that

$$R = k\, u^2\, g^{-1}\, \theta^{\gamma}$$

is dimensionally consistent for any value of the power γ. We can take a linear combination of such expressions (and still be dimensionally consistent), so the best we can deduce is that

$$R = k(\theta)\, u^2\, g^{-1} = k(\theta)\, \frac{u^2}{g}. \tag{3.2}$$

As the launch angle θ is dimensionless, the function $k(\theta)$ is also dimensionless, and Equation (3.2) is dimensionally consistent. Dimensional analysis can tell us nothing further about the form of the function $k(\theta)$. In order to find this function, we would have to use Newton's second law to determine it analytically, as we did in *Unit 14*, finding that

$$k(\theta) = \sin 2\theta,$$

or we would have to use a suitable experiment to find it numerically.

In the following exercise, we shall find the form of the relationship for the period of a pendulum. From *Unit 8*, Section 2 we already know this relationship for *small* oscillations of the pendulum, where we can use the approximation $\sin\theta \simeq \theta$ throughout the oscillations, but here we shall consider the case of *large* oscillations.

*Exercise 3.1

A pendulum is oscillating in a vertical plane. Use dimensional analysis to find a possible form for the expression for the period τ of the pendulum in terms of the mass m of the bob, the length l of the pendulum stem, the angular amplitude Φ of the oscillations, and g, the magnitude of the acceleration due to gravity.

In this exercise we neglect air resistance.

In Exercise 3.1, we derived the result

$$\tau = k(\Phi)\sqrt{\frac{l}{g}} \tag{3.3}$$

for the period of a pendulum. You may have been disappointed in this result, in that we have not been able to determine the function $k(\Phi)$. But in fact the result is very powerful. First, it shows that the period of oscillations of the pendulum is independent of the mass of the bob — a fact that we can easily verify by experiment in situations where air resistance is small. Secondly, it implies that for given angular amplitude, the period is proportional to $\sqrt{l/g}$. So if we determine the period of oscillations for one known length of pendulum stem for a particular angular amplitude, say $\Phi = \frac{1}{4}\pi$, then we can deduce the period of oscillation of any pendulum, no matter what its length is, for this amplitude, even if the pendulum is on Mars!

Let us now return to our initial assumption that the relationship between the parameters involves their powers, such as in Equation (3.1). You might think that the relationship could involve transcendental functions such as exp, ln, sin, cos, tan, and so on. However, as we remarked in Section 2, the argument of any such function must be dimensionless. In our previous example of the simple pendulum, if we ignore air resistance, there is no dimensionless combination of the parameters m, l and g, so the only possible transcendental function involved is in the term $k(\Phi)$.

So far we have discussed situations where there is only one possible combination of the parameters with the required dimensions. We shall now discuss a situation where this is not the case. We consider again our investigation of the range of a projectile, but include air resistance. Now the important parameters are R, m, u, θ, g (as before) and air resistance F. (Of course, air resistance is a function of speed, not a parameter, but we can define F to be the magnitude of the air resistance at a typical speed, such as the launch speed u). These parameters are listed in Table 3.2, together with their dimensions.

Table 3.2

Physical quantity	Symbol	Dimensions
Range of projectile	R	L
Mass of projectile	m	M
Launch speed	u	$\mathrm{L\,T^{-1}}$
Launch angle	θ	1
Acceleration due to gravity	g	$\mathrm{L\,T^{-2}}$
Typical air resistance	F	$\mathrm{M\,L\,T^{-2}}$

Again, we shall assume a relationship between these parameters of the form

$$R = k\, m^{\alpha}\, u^{\beta}\, \theta^{\gamma}\, g^{\delta}\, F^{\varepsilon}, \tag{3.4}$$

where k is a dimensionless number. For this equation to be dimensionally consistent, we must have

$$\begin{aligned}[R] &= [k\, m^{\alpha}\, u^{\beta}\, \theta^{\gamma}\, g^{\delta}\, F^{\varepsilon}] \\ &= [k]\,[m]^{\alpha}\,[u]^{\beta}\,[\theta]^{\gamma}\,[g]^{\delta}\,[F]^{\varepsilon}.\end{aligned}$$

In terms of the base dimensions M, L and T, we have

$$\begin{aligned}\mathrm{L} &= \mathrm{M}^{\alpha}\,(\mathrm{L\,T^{-1}})^{\beta}\,(\mathrm{L\,T^{-2}})^{\delta}\,(\mathrm{M\,L\,T^{-2}})^{\varepsilon} \\ &= \mathrm{M}^{\alpha+\varepsilon}\,\mathrm{L}^{\beta+\delta+\varepsilon}\,\mathrm{T}^{-\beta-2\delta-2\varepsilon},\end{aligned}$$

as k and θ are dimensionless. Equating powers of M, L and T on both sides of this equation, we have

$$\alpha+\varepsilon = 0, \quad \beta+\delta+\varepsilon = 1, \quad -\beta-2\delta-2\varepsilon = 0.$$

As before, the constant γ remains indeterminate. By adding twice the second of these three equations to the third, we deduce that $\beta = 2$. But we still have two equations, namely

$$\alpha+\varepsilon = 0, \quad \delta+\varepsilon = -1,$$

in the three unknowns α, δ and ε.

To proceed, we choose to write two of these unknowns in terms of the third. If we let $\varepsilon = a$, where a is an unknown parameter, then we have $\alpha = -a$ and $\delta = -1-a$. Equation (3.4) becomes

$$\begin{aligned}R &= k\, m^{-a}\, u^{2}\, \theta^{\gamma}\, g^{-1-a}\, F^{a} \\ &= k\,\frac{u^2}{g}\,\theta^{\gamma}\left(\frac{F}{mg}\right)^{a}.\end{aligned}$$

Each choice of values of the parameters γ and a gives a possible expression for the range R, as does a linear combination of these possibilities. More generally, we can write

$$R = \frac{u^2}{g}\, f\!\left(\theta, \frac{F}{mg}\right), \tag{3.5}$$

where f is a function of two variables. The two quantities θ and F/mg are dimensionless.

You may be wondering whether we would have arrived at a different result if, when solving the equations $\alpha+\varepsilon = 0$, $\delta+\varepsilon = -1$, we had made a different choice than $\varepsilon = a$ for the unknown parameter. Suppose that we let $\delta = b$ instead. Then the solution of the equations is $\alpha = 1+b$ and $\varepsilon = -1-b$. So Equation (3.4) becomes

$$\begin{aligned}R &= k\, m^{1+b}\, u^{2}\, \theta^{\gamma}\, g^{b}\, F^{-1-b} \\ &= k\,\frac{mu^2}{F}\,\theta^{\gamma}\left(\frac{mg}{F}\right)^{b},\end{aligned}$$

and we deduce that the general expression for the range is

$$R = \frac{mu^2}{F}\, h\!\left(\theta, \frac{mg}{F}\right),$$

where h is a function of two variables.

At first sight this appears different from Equation (3.5). However,

$$\begin{aligned}\frac{mu^2}{F}h\left(\theta,\frac{mg}{F}\right) &= \frac{u^2}{g}\frac{mg}{F}h\left(\theta,\frac{mg}{F}\right)\\ &= \frac{u^2}{g}f\left(\theta,\frac{F}{mg}\right),\end{aligned}$$

where

$$f(x,y) = \frac{1}{y}h\left(x,\frac{1}{y}\right).$$

(Similarly, if we had made a third possible choice, and let $\alpha = c$, we would again have arrived at an expression for the range R which is equivalent to Equation (3.5).)

Dimensionless combinations of physical quantities, such as F/mg in Equation (3.5), are called **dimensionless groups**. These are particularly important in situations where we cannot find an analytical solution to our model. For example, in the case of the range of a projectile with air resistance, Equation (3.5) means that we have reduced the problem to finding, either numerically or by experiment, an unknown function of two dimensionless groups, namely θ and F/mg, so we do not have to consider the effect of varying every individual parameter involved in the model.

The above discussion of the range of a projectile, taking into account the effects of air resistance, illustrates the method of dimensional analysis which is summarized in the following box.

The method of dimensional analysis

1. List the parameters $y, x_1, x_2, \dots, x_n$ which represent the important features involved in the situation being modelled, and determine their dimensions.
2. Assume a relationship involving the powers of these parameters, namely
$$y = k\,x_1^\alpha\,x_2^\beta\,x_3^\gamma\,\cdots\,x_n^\nu,$$
where k is a dimensionless constant.
3. Use the principle of dimensional consistency to write
$$[y] = [x_1]^\alpha\,[x_2]^\beta\,[x_3]^\gamma\,\cdots\,[x_n]^\nu,$$
and equate the powers of M, L, T and Θ on both sides of this equation.
4. Solve the four simultaneous equations obtained in Step 3 for the powers $\alpha, \beta, \dots, \nu$. This solution will usually involve unknown parameters.
5. Substitute for the powers in the expression in Step 2, and rewrite it in terms of dimensionless groups. Hence write down a general expression for y, which will usually involve an unknown function of these dimensionless groups.

*Exercise 3.2

Use dimensional analysis to find an expression for the drag force F acting on a sphere moving through a viscous fluid, assuming that it depends on only the speed v of the sphere, the radius r of the sphere, the density ρ of the fluid, and the viscosity μ of the fluid. (The dimensions of viscosity are $\mathrm{M\,L^{-1}\,T^{-1}}$.)

End-of-section Exercises

Exercise 3.3

Use dimensional analysis to find an expression for the frequency Ω of vibration of a guitar string, assuming that it depends on only the mass m of the string, the length l of the string, and the tension H of the string.

Exercise 3.4

Consider water flowing through a horizontal smooth pipe. Use dimensional analysis to find an expression for the speed u of the water in the pipe, assuming that it depends on only the pressure difference p between the two ends of the pipe, the length l of the pipe, the diameter d of the pipe, the density ρ of water, and the viscosity μ of water. (The dimensions of pressure are $\mathrm{M\,L^{-1}\,T^{-2}}$ and the dimensions of viscosity are $\mathrm{M\,L^{-1}\,T^{-1}}$.)

4 A case study of modelling: Transient heat transfer 1 — Creating the model

In the first three sections of this unit we have introduced the modelling cycle and discussed some of the skills required in modelling. In this section we see how the modelling cycle can be applied to a problem which you probably face every day, although you might not have thought of using your mathematical skills to solve it!

In *Unit 15* we considered *steady-state* heat transfer by conduction and convection. In this section we shall see how the ideas we have developed can be applied to situations in which the temperature varies with time.

Specify the purpose

In particular, we are going to explore the following problem.

> Immediately after a cup of tea is poured out, it is usually too hot to drink. How long does it have to be left to cool before it is drinkable? More generally, how does the temperature of the cooling tea vary with time?

This is not, on the face of it, a terribly important problem. However, there are many different situations in which cooling plays a significant role, some of which are of considerable importance — particularly in industry. Analogous domestic situations include the cooling of a hot-water tank and the warming of a cool box. The problem of the cooling of a cup of tea has been chosen because it is a familiar and simple example which involves the principles that apply in most cooling problems.

At this stage it would be sensible to conduct an experiment by making a cup of tea, resisting the temptation to drink it, and measuring its temperature at regular intervals. The data I collected in such an experiment are presented in the next section. As you might expect:

The data are given in Table 5.1.

- the temperature of the tea decreased with time;
- the rate of decrease of temperature was greater at higher temperatures.

This type of experiment allows us to get a 'feel' for the situation being modelled, and provides data which we can use to validate the model we develop.

Create the model

The cooling of the tea occurs through conduction, convection and radiation. Also, when the tea is hot, steam rises from its surface, so it is likely that evaporation plays a role in the cooling process. However, to keep the modelling simple, initially we shall consider just one form of heat loss: convection from the surface of the tea. As with all modelling, it is better to develop a simple model first, which you can be reasonably confident will produce an answer. Improvements can be made gradually, but only if you have something that actually works on which to improve.

The outside of a cup containing hot tea is a lot cooler than the tea itself: after all, one reason why china, for example, is used to make cups is that it is a good insulator. So heat is probably lost much more slowly by conduction through the cup than it is by convection through the surface of the tea. As a first model, it therefore seems sensible to ignore all forms of heat loss except convection from the surface of the tea.

In *Unit 15*, Section 3, we used the formula

$$q = hA(\Theta_1 - \Theta_2) \tag{4.1}$$

This is Equation (3.1) in *Unit 15*, Section 3.

to model steady-state convective heat transfer. Here, there are two convective heat transfers at the surface of the tea: one from the tea itself to the surface, and one from the surface to the air. If we denote the ambient temperature of the tea by Θ_{tea} and the temperature of the surface by Θ_1, then the convective heat transfer from the tea to the surface is modelled as

$$q = h_{\text{tea}}A(\Theta_{\text{tea}} - \Theta_1), \tag{4.2}$$

where q is the rate of loss of heat energy from the cup of tea, h_{tea} is the convective heat transfer coefficient between the tea and the surface, and A is the area of the surface of the tea.

Similarly, the convective heat transfer from the surface to the air is modelled as

$$q = h_{\text{air}} A(\Theta_1 - \Theta_{\text{air}}), \tag{4.3}$$

where h_{air} is the convective heat transfer coefficient between the surface and the air, and Θ_{air} is the ambient temperature of the air.

*Exercise 4.1

Eliminate Θ_1 from Equations (4.2) and (4.3) to obtain an equation modelling the rate of convective heat transfer from the tea to the air.

In the solution to Exercise 4.1 we showed that the heat loss from the tea to the air is given by

$$q = UA(\Theta_{\text{tea}} - \Theta_{\text{air}}), \tag{4.4}$$

where

$$U = \left(\frac{1}{h_{\text{tea}}} + \frac{1}{h_{\text{air}}}\right)^{-1}. \tag{4.5}$$

U is the U-value for the loss of heat energy from the tea to the air.

Now Equation (4.1) applies only when the temperature differences remain constant in time. This is definitely not true of the situation under consideration — indeed, the whole point is to find how the temperature of the tea *varies* with time. But we can get round this by assuming that over a short interval of time the temperature of the tea remains effectively constant. We can then, for a short time interval, use the steady-state result given by Equation (4.1) as an approximation, which improves as the time interval gets shorter and shorter. Therefore, using this assumption, in a short time interval $[t, t + \delta t]$, the *rate* of loss of heat energy by convection from the surface of the tea can be approximated as

This sort of assumption is a standard modelling device. You met versions of it in modelling a population in *Unit 2*.

$$q(t) \simeq UA(\Theta_{\text{tea}}(t) - \Theta_{\text{air}}).$$

Note that we now consider q and Θ_{tea} to be functions of time t.

The *quantity* of heat energy lost over the time interval can therefore be approximated as

$$q(t)\,\delta t \simeq UA(\Theta_{\text{tea}}(t) - \Theta_{\text{air}})\,\delta t.$$

At the beginning of the time interval, the temperature of the tea is $\Theta_{\text{tea}}(t)$, whereas at the end of the interval it is $\Theta_{\text{tea}}(t + \delta t)$. Hence, using Equation (1.1) of *Unit 15*, the 'accumulation' δE of heat energy in the tea over the interval is

In this case the 'accumulation' is negative.

$$\delta E = mc\left(\Theta_{\text{tea}}(t + \delta t) - \Theta_{\text{tea}}(t)\right),$$

where m is the mass of the tea and c is its specific heat capacity. We now apply the **input–output principle**

$$\boxed{\text{accumulation}} = \boxed{\text{input}} - \boxed{\text{output}}$$

to the amount of heat energy in the cup of tea over the time interval $[t, t + \delta t]$. Since there is no input of heat energy to the tea, we obtain

$$mc\left(\Theta_{\text{tea}}(t + \delta t) - \Theta_{\text{tea}}(t)\right) \simeq 0 - UA(\Theta_{\text{tea}}(t) - \Theta_{\text{air}})\,\delta t.$$

Rearranging this equation, we obtain

$$\frac{\Theta_{\text{tea}}(t + \delta t) - \Theta_{\text{tea}}(t)}{\delta t} \simeq -\frac{UA}{mc}(\Theta_{\text{tea}}(t) - \Theta_{\text{air}}).$$

This approximation gets more and more accurate as δt gets smaller, so taking the limit as $\delta t \to 0$ gives the differential equation

$$\frac{d\Theta_{\text{tea}}}{dt} = -\lambda(\Theta_{\text{tea}}(t) - \Theta_{\text{air}}), \tag{4.6}$$

Notice that this differential equation is of a familiar form (see *Unit 2*).

where $\lambda = UA/(mc)$. This model of the cooling process is usually referred to as **Newton's law of cooling**.

Exercise 4.2

Show that Equation (4.6) is dimensionally consistent.

This completes the second stage (create the model) of the modelling process outlined in Section 1. You will recall that the second stage involves stating assumptions, choosing variables and parameters, and formulating mathematical relationships. We have clearly formulated mathematical relationships, culminating in Equation (4.6), and we have defined our variables and parameters at various points in this section and in *Unit 15*. But we have not explicitly listed the assumptions made in deriving the model.

****Exercise 4.3***

Make a list of the assumptions made in deriving the above model for the cooling of a cup of tea.

Do the mathematics

Our aim is to find how the temperature Θ_{tea} of the tea changes with time t. We can do this by solving Equation (4.6). But before doing so, it is worth asking whether it predicts the right kind of behaviour for Θ_{tea}.

Exercise 4.4

(a) Qualitatively, how would you expect the rate of change of temperature $d\Theta_{\text{tea}}/dt$ to depend on the temperature Θ_{tea} of the tea?

(b) Is Equation (4.6) consistent with what you would expect?

Having confirmed that the differential equation predicts the right kind of behaviour for Θ_{tea}, our next task is to solve it, assuming that we know the initial temperature Θ_0 of the tea.

*Exercise 4.5

Find the particular solution of the differential equation

$$\frac{d\Theta_{\text{tea}}}{dt} = -\lambda(\Theta_{\text{tea}} - \Theta_{\text{air}})$$

that satisfies the initial condition $\Theta_{\text{tea}}(0) = \Theta_0$, assuming that Θ_{air} is a constant.

From Exercise 4.5, the required particular solution of the differential equation is

$$\Theta_{\text{tea}}(t) = \Theta_{\text{air}} + (\Theta_0 - \Theta_{\text{air}})e^{-\lambda t}, \quad \text{where } \lambda = \frac{UA}{mc}. \tag{4.7}$$

This formula agrees with common sense. For $\Theta_0 > \Theta_{\text{air}}$, the temperature Θ_{tea} decreases with time and tends to Θ_{air} in the long term. The temperature difference $\Theta_{\text{tea}} - \Theta_{\text{air}}$ decreases exponentially with time and so decreases at a slower rate for smaller temperature differences. The temperature will fall more quickly if the surface area A is increased: that seems right, because in that case there will be more surface area from which the heat energy can dissipate. Indeed, to make her tea cool more quickly to a drinkable temperature, my grandmother used to pour her tea into the saucer, thus increasing the surface area A (and decreasing the mass m). Similarly, the rate of decrease of temperature will increase if the U-value U is increased, which again seems intuitively correct — my grandmother also used to blow on her tea, which increased the value of h_{air} and so U. On the other hand, if we have more tea (keeping A and U constant), it will cool more slowly: a greater mass will hold more heat energy, and the loss of a given amount of heat energy will result in a smaller drop in temperature.

It remains to answer the original specific question: how long will it be before the tea is drinkable? Mathematically, it is simply a matter of setting $\Theta_{\text{tea}}(t)$ equal to the temperature at which tea becomes drinkable, say Θ_T, and solving for t. Suppose that $\Theta_{\text{tea}}(t) = \Theta_T$ at time $t = T$, i.e. $\Theta_{\text{tea}}(T) = \Theta_T$. Using Equation (4.7) gives

$$\Theta_T - \Theta_{\text{air}} = (\Theta_0 - \Theta_{\text{air}})e^{-\lambda T}, \quad \text{so} \quad \frac{\Theta_T - \Theta_{\text{air}}}{\Theta_0 - \Theta_{\text{air}}} = e^{-\lambda T},$$

hence

$$T = \frac{1}{\lambda}\ln\left(\frac{\Theta_0 - \Theta_{\text{air}}}{\Theta_T - \Theta_{\text{air}}}\right) = \frac{mc}{UA}\ln\left(\frac{\Theta_0 - \Theta_{\text{air}}}{\Theta_T - \Theta_{\text{air}}}\right). \tag{4.8}$$

Exercise 4.6

Show that Equation (4.8) is dimensionally consistent.

Interpret the results

In order to obtain an explicit numerical answer, the values of the various parameters in Equation (4.8) need to be known. Table 4.1 shows values I obtained for a cup of tea I made while writing this unit, where in each case I have indicated how I found that value.

Table 4.1

Parameter	Value	How obtained
m	$0.25\,\text{kg}$	Weigh a full and an empty cup
c	$4190\,\text{J kg}^{-1}\,\text{K}^{-1}$	Use value for water given in Table 1.1 of *Unit 15*
U	$9.804\,\text{W m}^{-2}\,\text{K}^{-1}$	Use Equation (4.5) and Table 3.2 of *Unit 15*
A	$0.004\,07\,\text{m}^2$	Measure diameter of top of cup
Θ_0	$80°\text{C}$	Measure with thermometer
Θ_{air}	$17.5°\text{C}$	Measure with thermometer
Θ_T	$60°\text{C}$	Sample, then measure with thermometer

The values $h_{\text{air}} = 10\,\text{W m}^{-2}\,\text{K}^{-1}$ and $h_{\text{tea}} = 500\,\text{W m}^{-2}\,\text{K}^{-1}$ obtained from Table 3.2 of *Unit 15* were used to calculate U.

The ambient temperature of the air decreased from 18°C to 17°C during the cooling period, so the average 17.5°C is used here.

With these values we obtain $\lambda = 3.809 \times 10^{-5}\,\text{s}^{-1}$ and $T = 10\,120\,\text{s}$ (rounded to the nearest ten seconds). In other words, the time taken for the tea to cool enough to be drinkable is estimated to be about 2 hours 50 minutes!

Evaluate the outcomes

How does the model compare with reality? Well, you will not be surprised that my cup of tea took considerably less time, namely 12 minutes 50 seconds, to cool from 80°C to 60°C. So the estimate provided by our model compares very badly with reality. Nevertheless, the qualitative prediction of an exponential decrease of temperature, given by Equation (4.7), may compare well with reality, at least for a different value of λ. We shall explore and extend this comparison with reality in the next section, using Mathcad.

End-of-section Exercises

Below we have linked the parts of the exercises to the five stages of the modelling process which we introduced in Section 1.

*Exercise 4.7

Specify the purpose

When I go on holiday, I use a small travel immersion heater, placed in a cup of water, to make an early morning cup of tea. While the heater is heating up the water in the cup, the water is itself losing heat to the surroundings. You are asked to develop a model for this situation.

Create the model

For the sake of simplicity, assume that the loss of heat energy from the water is due only to convection from the surface area A of the water. Denote the mass of water by m, the specific heat capacity of water by c, the U-value for the convective heat transfer from the water to the air by U, and the temperature of the water at time t by $\Theta_{\text{water}}(t)$. Assume that the heater in the water supplies heat energy at a constant rate Q.

(a) What is the accumulation of heat energy in the cup of water over a short time interval $[t, t+\delta t]$? What is the amount of heat energy supplied to the cup of water by the heater in that time interval? What is the amount of heat energy lost from the cup of water by convection from the surface of the water in that time interval?

(b) By using the input–output principle applied to the heat energy of the water in the time interval $[t, t+\delta t]$, show that the temperature of the cup of water satisfies the differential equation

$$\frac{d\Theta_{\text{water}}}{dt} = \frac{Q}{mc} - \lambda(\Theta_{\text{water}} - \Theta_{\text{air}}), \quad \text{where } \lambda = \frac{UA}{mc}.$$

(c) Find the particular solution of the above differential equation that satisfies the initial condition $\Theta_{\text{water}}(0) = \Theta_{\text{air}}$.

Do the mathematics

(d) Sketch the graph of the particular solution you found in part (c). Does this graph correspond with what you would expect from a cup of water while it is being heated?

Interpret the results

(e) Find an expression for the time T it takes for the water to reach boiling point, based on this model.

(f) Use the data in Table 4.1 to estimate the time it takes to boil the water in the cup, starting from water at a room temperature of 17°C, given that the heater has a power rating of 350 W.

(g) Comment on your estimate, given that when I used my heater to boil water in my cup, starting at 17°C, it took about 4 minutes 25 seconds.

Evaluate the outcomes

Exercise 4.8

In this exercise, you are asked to estimate the time taken to heat the water in a full tea-urn from room temperature to boiling point. The tea-urn is cylindrical, with diameter 350 mm and height 515 mm. It has a circular lid and stands on a wooden table. The capacity of the tea-urn is 30 litres, and it is fitted with a 3 kW heating element.

Specify the purpose

Assume that 1 litre of water has mass 1 kilogram.

The tea-urn is constructed from a thin sheet of metal which is a good conductor of heat energy. It seems reasonable, therefore, to assume that the outside metal surface of the tea-urn has the same temperature as the water inside the tea-urn. This assumption means that if we ignore the effects of radiation and any heat energy loss from the bottom of the tea-urn, the only mode of heat transfer is by convection from the curved sides and from the lid of the tea-urn.

Create the model

(a) By analogy with Exercise 4.7, write down the differential equation that models the variation of the temperature of the water in the tea-urn.

(b) Find the particular solution of this differential equation such that the initial temperature of the water is equal to the room temperature. Find also an expression for the time it takes for the water to reach a given temperature Θ_T, based on this model.

Do the mathematics

(c) If the room temperature is 20°C and the convective heat transfer coefficient between the surfaces of the tea-urn and the surrounding air is $10\,\text{W}\,\text{m}^{-2}\,\text{K}^{-1}$, according to the model how long will it take for the water in the tea-urn to reach boiling point?

(d) Comment on your answer to part (c), given that the publicity brochure for the tea-urn quotes a boiling time of 70 minutes.

Interpret the results

Evaluate the outcomes

5 A case study of modelling: Transient heat transfer 2 — Evaluating and revising the model

In the previous section we developed a model for the cooling of a cup of tea which resulted in Equation (4.7), namely

$$\Theta_{\text{tea}}(t) = \Theta_{\text{air}} + (\Theta_0 - \Theta_{\text{air}})e^{-\lambda t}, \quad \text{where } \lambda = \frac{UA}{mc}. \tag{5.1}$$

We saw that this predicted that it would take 2 hours 50 minutes for the cup of tea to become drinkable, whereas in reality it took only 12 minutes 50 seconds! Our model assumed that the tea cooled principally by convection from its surface, and convective heat transfer coefficients are not known with any accuracy. It is possible that this lack of accuracy in one of the main parameters in our model could explain the gross discrepancy between our prediction of the cooling time and the actual time. If this is the case, our prediction of an exponential decrease of temperature, given by Equation (5.1) should compare well with reality for *some* value of λ.

In Table 5.1 I have tabulated the temperature of my cup of tea over a period of 90 minutes — my tea was practically cold by the time I got round to drinking it! A plot of these data is shown in Figure 5.1. From this graph, it would certainly appear that the data might fit well with a decreasing exponential function.

Table 5.1

Time (minutes)	Temperature of tea (°C)
0	80
1	77
2	75
3	$73\frac{1}{2}$
4	72
5	$70\frac{1}{2}$
6	69
7	$67\frac{1}{2}$
8	66
9	65
10	$63\frac{1}{2}$
12	61
14	59
16	57
18	55
20	53
25	$49\frac{1}{2}$
30	46
35	$43\frac{1}{2}$
40	41
45	39
60	$34\frac{1}{2}$
75	$30\frac{1}{2}$
90	$27\frac{1}{2}$

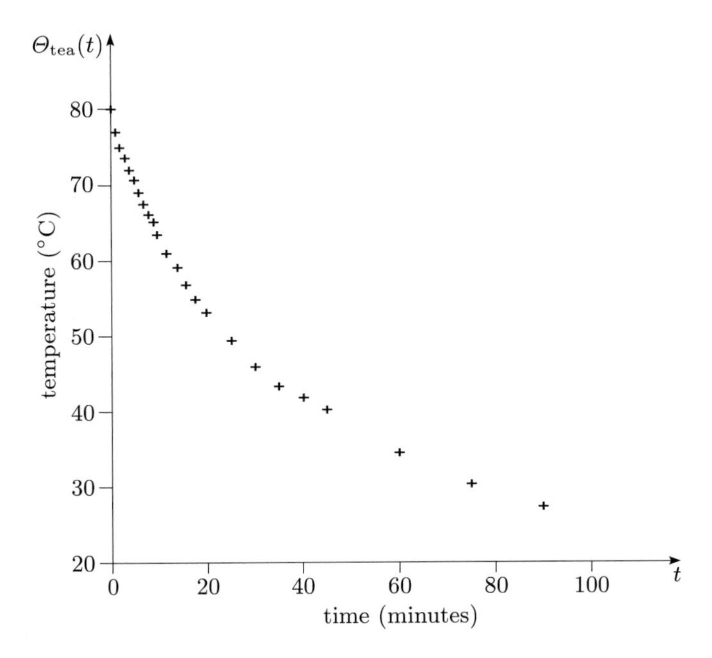

Figure 5.1 Graph of temperature against time for the cooling of a cup of tea

In the following Mathcad Activity you are asked to investigate an exponential model

$$\Theta(t) = \Theta_{\text{air}} + Ce^{-\lambda t} \qquad (5.2)$$

with the experimental data given in Table 5.1. The worksheet automatically calculates the parameters C and λ which best fit the data, but you are asked to:

- plot the experimental data and the best-fit exponential model, in order to assess how good the model is;
- use a solve block to find the time predicted by the model for the tea to cool to 60°C.

Note that the worksheet uses units of min^{-1} for the value of λ, rather than the SI units of s^{-1}.

Use your computer to complete the following activities.

*Activity 5.1

Investigate the exponential model

$$\Theta(t) = \Theta_{\text{air}} + Ce^{-\lambda t}$$

for the temperature of a cooling cup of tea.

(a) Plot the experimental data and the values predicted by the model.

(b) Find the time predicted by the model for the temperature of the tea to cool to 60°C.

Exercise 5.1

Using the best-fit exponential model to the data given in Figure 5.1, we saw in Activity 5.1 that the value of λ is $0.023\,\text{min}^{-1}$, or $3.911 \times 10^{-4}\,\text{s}^{-1}$, which differs from the value obtained using Table 4.1 by a factor of ten. Calculate the value of U that would result in this value for λ, assuming that the other data values in Table 4.1 are correct. Assuming that $h_{\text{tea}} = 500\,\text{W m}^{-2}\,\text{K}^{-1}$, as before, what is the corresponding value of h_{air}?

From Activity 5.1, it is clear that my experimental data for the cooling of a cup of tea cannot be well fitted by an exponential model. So my cup of tea did not cool exponentially: either its initial rate of cooling was too great, or its final rate of cooling was too small, or both.

In order to improve the model, we need to reconsider the assumptions we made in setting up our model. In the solution to Exercise 5.1 we saw that, to predict the actual rate of cooling, a convective heat transfer coefficient from the tea surface to the air of approximately $126\,\text{W m}^{-2}\,\text{K}^{-1}$ would be required, assuming that all the other data values are correct. This value is over ten times larger than the value given in Table 3.2 of *Unit 15*, and is outside the range of typical convective heat transfer coefficients for gases given in Table 3.1 of *Unit 15*. This suggests that the discrepancy in the value of λ may not be solely due to uncertainties in the value of U.

In fact, better results can be obtained if we revise the model to include the heat energy losses by conduction and convection through the sides of the cup. The revised model does result in a much larger value of λ, but one that is still not very close to the experimental value. Also, the revised model still does not match the non-exponential cooling demonstrated by the experimental data. In order to predict non-exponential cooling, our model would need to incorporate cooling processes other than conduction and convection, such as radiation and evaporation.

An alternative mechanism that we have not yet explored is that initially hot tea is poured into a cold cup. So the heat energy of the tea is used initially to heat up the material of the cup until tea and cup have almost the same temperature. This is borne out by measuring the temperature of the outside of the cup. Immediately after pouring the tea, this temperature is the ambient air temperature. But then the temperature of the outside of the cup increases until it is similar to that of the tea. The temperature then begins to decrease in parallel with that of the tea. In no phase, however, are the temperatures of the tea and the cup the same — the cup heats up and cools down more slowly than the tea itself.

All these three mechanisms — radiation, evaporation and the heating of the cup — would be more important for the initial higher temperatures, and would result in a rate of cooling initially faster than that predicted by my first model. We shall not pursue the modelling of any of these possibilities here.

What we shall do, however, is to assume that the cooling of a cup of tea is the sum of two exponential decays, i.e.

$$\Theta_{\text{tea}} = \Theta_{\text{air}} + C_1 e^{-\lambda_1 t} + C_2 e^{-\lambda_2 t}. \tag{5.3}$$

This is the sort of behaviour I would expect from a revised model which incorporates the heating of the cup, and possibly from a model incorporating evaporation. I would expect more complicated behaviour from a model incorporating radiation, as such a model would be non-linear.

Activity 5.2

Investigate the model

$$\Theta(t) = \Theta_{\text{air}} + C_1 e^{-\lambda_1 t} + C_2 e^{-\lambda_2 t}$$

for the temperature of a cooling cup of tea.

(a) Plot the experimental data and the values predicted by the model.

(b) Find the time predicted by the model for the temperature of the tea to cool to 60°C.

Outcomes

After studying this unit you should be able to:

- identify the steps in the modelling process, given an example of a piece of mathematical modelling;
- write down the simplifying assumptions that underpin a model;
- check that mathematical relationships between variables and parameters are dimensionally consistent;
- convert the values of physical quantities from one system of units to another;
- use dimensional analysis to find the possible forms of the relationship between physical quantities;
- use the input–output principle to apply steady-state models for heat transfer to situations where the temperatures are varying;
- use Mathcad to draw graphs;
- use a solve block in Mathcad to solve an equation with one unknown.

Solutions to the exercises

Section 1

1.1 **(a)** The sorts of questions I would ask the manufacturer are as follows.

> It all depends on what you mean by 'best'. Do you mean best for transporting to the supermarket? Do you mean best for stacking on the supermarket shelf? Or do you mean using the least tin-plate when manufacturing the cans?
>
> Do you have any preferences as to the shape of the can (cylindrical, box-shaped, ...)?
>
> What capacity of can(s) do you want to produce?

You might have other questions, but I think these are the important ones.

(b) The formulation will depend on the answers to the questions posed in part (a). But a possible formulation might be as follows.

> Find the height and diameter of a cylindrical can containing a specified volume of baked beans which uses the minimum area of tin-plate in its manufacture.

1.2 Finding the maximum range of a projectile has a number of military applications; for example, working out whether a ship is within the range of a gun or missile. There are applications in sports such as football, cricket, golf and basketball, where finding the maximum range of the ball might be important, and in the long jump, triple jump, hammer, discus and javelin events in athletics.

1.3 My list of assumptions is as follows.

(a) The baked beans completely fill the tin can with no air-gap.

(b) The surfaces of the can are smooth, with no ridges or furrows, so that the can is a perfect cylinder.

(c) One can ignore the area of tin-plate required to make the seams of the can.

(d) There is no wastage resulting from cutting the circular pieces for the ends of the can from sheet material.

1.4 I think that the most important deficiency in the model which would result from the assumptions in Solution 1.3 is due to the fourth assumption: there would be significant wastage resulting from the cutting of the circular ends. The wastage is 27% of the tin-plate used if the circles are stamped in the rectangular pattern shown in the next diagram, although there are more efficient patterns of stamping. So I would modify assumption (d) in order to allow for the wastage.

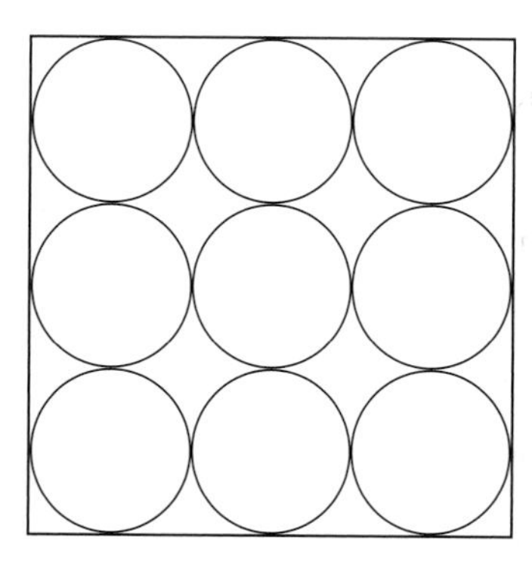

1.5 **(a)** The principal assumptions which were made in *Unit 8* are as follows.

(i) The pendulum bob can be modelled as a particle.

(ii) The pendulum rod is weightless.

(iii) We can neglect any effects due to air resistance.

(iv) The motion is confined to a vertical plane.

(v) We can use the law of conservation of mechanical energy.

(vi) The oscillations are so small that we can apply the approximation $\sin\theta \simeq \theta$ throughout the motion.

(b) The main deficiency of the model developed in *Unit 8* is that it predicts that the pendulum oscillates forever. So I would modify the third assumption. In fact, in my revised model, I would assume *linear* air resistance in order that the resulting differential equation could still be solved analytically. In its turn, this means that we will have modify assumption (v) to 'We can use Newton's Law of Motion'.

(In fact, in *Unit 13*, Section 4, we modified assumptions (iii) and (vi). However, we could then no longer solve the resulting differential equation analytically, and had to use the phase diagram to describe the motion qualitatively.)

1.6 The height h is the (vertical) height of the marble above the surface of the River Avon vertically below the Clifton Suspension Bridge.

In making this definition, there are some hidden assumptions:

- the marble can be treated as a point;
- the surface of the River Avon is horizontal and its height does not change, at least over the period of time under consideration.

1.7 The total force on the shot is calculated. In our first model, this is just the weight of the shot, although in a revised model you might want to also include air resistance. This total force is then substituted into Newton's second law, resulting in a second-order (vector) differential equation.

1.8 To express t in terms of x, we must work out the time taken to find a parking space, and the time taken to walk to and from the shops, and add the two together. The time taken to find a parking space is assumed to be inversely proportional to x, so it can be written as k/x, where k is a constant. To walk to and from the shops you have to walk a distance $2x$ at a constant speed of (say) v, which takes a time $2x/v$. The total time is therefore given by

$$t = \frac{k}{x} + \frac{2x}{v}.$$

All quantities here could be measured in appropriate SI units or in any other consistent system of units. (Yards and minutes might be considered more suitable than metres and seconds.) The constant of proportionality k must have units of m s in the SI system.

The question asks only for the formulation of the problem, but it is easy to find the value of x which minimizes t, and it turns out to be $\sqrt{\frac{1}{2}kv}$. (Note that the units make sense: since k has units m s and v has units $\mathrm{m\,s^{-1}}$, the units of the answer $\sqrt{\frac{1}{2}kv}$ are metres, as required.) You know your walking speed v, or can easily measure it. The difficulty with this model will be to estimate the value of k. One reason for this is that although it is stated that k is a constant, it will actually vary from day to day, and even during the day. In fact, k will depend on how much competition there is for parking spaces, i.e. on how many other people want to go shopping at the same time as you do.

1.9 First, find a formula for the area of tin-plate required to make a cylindrical can in terms of the dimensions of the can (its height and its diameter). Secondly, find a formula for the volume of the can in terms of its dimensions. We are concerned with cans of given volume, so we can use the expression for the volume to eliminate one of the variables (either the height or the diameter of the can) from the formula for the area, so expressing the area in terms of just one variable. We can then use calculus to find the value of the variable which minimizes the area. Finally, we can use the expression for the volume to find the value of the other variable.

1.10 The data given are (presumably) fully accurate, so we have to consider only an appropriate accuracy for the answer. The lowest denomination of currency in circulation in the UK is 1 penny (£0.01), which suggests that an appropriate accuracy for the answer is £1182.54. However, this would mean that the loan would not be fully repaid after 25 years, although the outstanding debt would be only £0.55. So a more appropriate repayment amount might be £1182.55, which would mean that the account would be £5.18 in credit after 25 years. So my solution to the problem would be as follows.

> In order to repay the loan over 25 years, the repayment amount should be £1182.55 per month.

1.11 From the question, it is not clear who are the 'audience' for the answer. The time for the object to fall 100 metres is less than 5 seconds, so in the table below I have decided to use an accuracy of 0.01 seconds for the answers, and to give answers for intervals of 10 metres in the height. The accuracy (of at most 3 significant figures) in the answers is consistent with the accuracy of $9.81\,\mathrm{m\,s^{-2}}$ used for the value of g.

Height (in metres)	Time of fall (in seconds)
10	1.43
20	2.02
30	2.47
40	2.86
50	3.19
60	3.50
70	3.78
80	4.04
90	4.28
100	4.52

The outcome of the model is shown as a graph below.

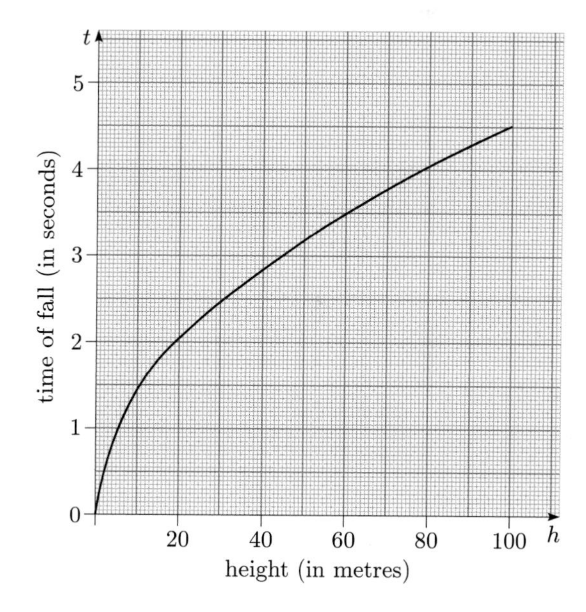

The table would be more appropriate for an audience who are less numerate. Also, the answers given in the table are more accurate, but are given only for 10-metre intervals. The graph can be used for the time of fall for any height, but the answers are less accurate (at most to 2 significant figures). The graph also shows more clearly that the time taken to fall through each 10-metre interval decreases with height — in other words, that the speed of fall increases with height.

1.12 (a)

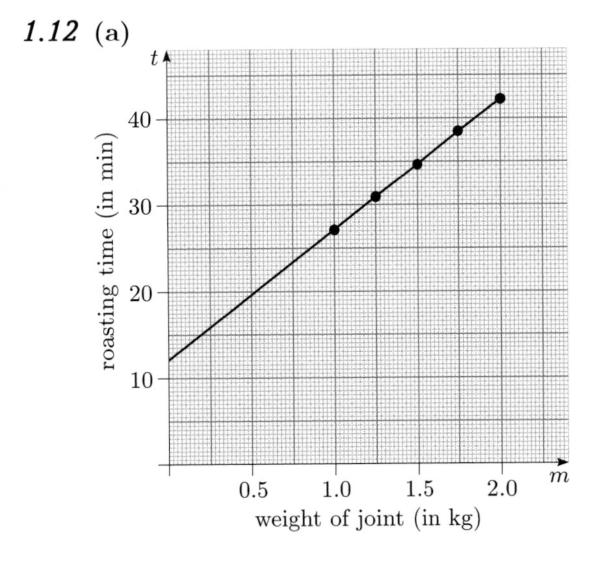

From the graph above, it is clear that the data points are well-fitted by the straight line

$$t = 12 + 15.2m.$$

So the cooking instructions might be 'roast for 12 minutes plus 15 minutes per kg'.

(b)

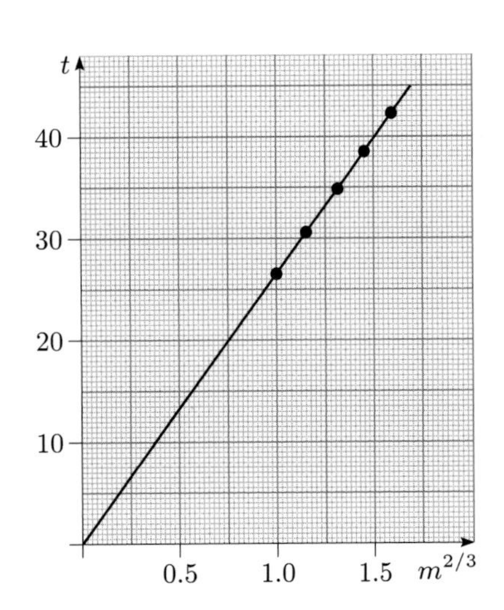

From the graph, it is clear that the data points are well-fitted by a straight line through the origin. The graph shows the straight line

$$t = 26.7m^{2/3},$$

which is a good fit, although you might have found a slightly different value for c.

It is intriguing that the same data can be fitted well by both a linear model and a two-thirds power model. Which one to use really depends on the purpose of the model: I certainly would not use the linear model for a very small joint.

1.13 The effect of air resistance is to decrease the magnitude of the total force acting on the object, so decreasing the magnitude of its acceleration. I would therefore expect the inclusion of air resistance to increase the time of fall.

1.14 In the revised model, the amount of tin-plate required for a cylindrical end of given diameter is increased, so I would expect the optimum shape for the can to be slightly taller than that given by the first model.

Section 2

2.1 **(a)** $[\text{area}] = \mathrm{L}^2$

(b) $[\text{density}] = \mathrm{M\,L^{-3}}$

(c) The dimensions of mass m are M, the dimensions of the magnitude g of the acceleration due to gravity are $\mathrm{L\,T^{-2}}$, and the dimensions of height h are L. Hence

$$\begin{aligned}[\text{gravitational potential energy}] &= \mathrm{M} \times (\mathrm{L\,T^{-2}}) \times \mathrm{L} \\ &= \mathrm{M\,L^2\,T^{-2}}.\end{aligned}$$

Note that these are the same dimensions as for kinetic energy (derived in Example 2.1), as they should be.

(d) $[\theta] = [l/r] = [l]\,[r]^{-1} = \mathrm{L} \times (\mathrm{L})^{-1} = 1.$

So angle is a dimensionless quantity, and radians are dimensionless units.

2.2 The symbol v represents a speed, so

$$[v^2] = [v]^2 = (\mathrm{L\,T^{-1}})^2 = \mathrm{L^2\,T^{-2}}.$$

Similarly, u is a speed, so u^2 has dimensions $\mathrm{L^2\,T^{-2}}$. The final term in the equation has dimensions

$$[2ax] = [2]\,[a]\,[x] = 1 \times (\mathrm{L\,T^{-2}}) \times \mathrm{L} = \mathrm{L^2\,T^{-2}}$$

also. Hence the equation is dimensionally consistent.

2.3 The left-hand side of the equation, dm/dt, has the same dimensions as m/t, namely $\mathrm{M\,T^{-1}}$. The right-hand side of the equation has dimensions

$$\begin{aligned}[-km] &= \left[-\frac{r}{V}m\right] \\ &= [-1]\,[r]\,[V]^{-1}\,[m] \\ &= 1 \times (\mathrm{L^3\,T^{-1}}) \times (\mathrm{L^3})^{-1} \times \mathrm{M} = \mathrm{M\,T^{-1}}.\end{aligned}$$

Hence the equation is dimensionally consistent.

2.4 We require the dimensions of

$$c_2 = \frac{R}{D^2v^2}.$$

R is the magnitude of a force and so has dimensions $\mathrm{M\,L\,T^{-2}}$. D is a length and has dimensions L. v is a speed and has dimensions $\mathrm{L\,T^{-1}}$. For dimensional consistency we must have

$$\begin{aligned}[c_2] &= \left[\frac{R}{D^2v^2}\right] \\ &= [R]\,[D]^{-2}\,[v]^{-2} \\ &= (\mathrm{M\,L\,T^{-2}}) \times (\mathrm{L})^{-2} \times (\mathrm{L\,T^{-1}})^{-2} = \mathrm{M\,L^{-3}}.\end{aligned}$$

Hence, in SI units, c_2 would be measured in $\mathrm{kg\,m^{-3}}$.

2.5 First let us consider the argument $\omega t + \phi$ of the cosine function. Since ϕ is an angle, $[\phi] = 1$. So for dimensional consistency, we need $[\omega t] = 1$. Since $[t] = \mathrm{T}$, we must have $[\omega] = \mathrm{T}^{-1}$.

The argument of the cosine function is dimensionless, so $[\cos(\omega t + \phi)] = 1$. Now $[x] = \mathrm{L}$, so the equation is dimensionally consistent if $[A] = \mathrm{L}$.

(The above results are consistent with the symbol A representing an amplitude and ω representing an angular frequency.)

2.6 We have

$$1\,\mathrm{kg} = 10^3\,\mathrm{g}$$

and

$$1\,\mathrm{cm} = 10^{-2}\,\mathrm{m}.$$

Hence

$$\begin{aligned} 13.546\,\mathrm{g\,cm^{-3}} &= 13.546\,\mathrm{g\,cm^{-3}} \times \left(\frac{1\,\mathrm{kg}}{10^3\,\mathrm{g}}\right) \times \left(\frac{1\,\mathrm{cm}}{10^{-2}\,\mathrm{m}}\right)^3 \\ &= 13.546 \times 10^{-3} \times 10^6\,\mathrm{kg\,m^{-3}} \\ &= 1.3546 \times 10^4\,\mathrm{kg\,m^{-3}}. \end{aligned}$$

So the density of mercury is $1.3546 \times 10^4\,\mathrm{kg\,m^{-3}}$.

2.7 We have

$$1\,\mathrm{lb} = 0.453\,592\,\mathrm{kg}$$

and

$$1\,\mathrm{in} = 2.54 \times 10^{-2}\,\mathrm{m}.$$

Hence

$$\begin{aligned} 61.00\,\mathrm{lb\,in^{-2}} &= 61.00\,\mathrm{lb\,in^{-2}} \times \left(\frac{0.453\,592\,\mathrm{kg}}{1\,\mathrm{lb}}\right) \times \left(\frac{2.54 \times 10^{-2}\,\mathrm{m}}{1\,\mathrm{in}}\right)^{-2} \\ &= \frac{61.00 \times 0.453\,592}{(2.54 \times 10^{-2})^2}\,\mathrm{kg\,m^{-2}} \\ &= 4.289 \times 10^4\,\mathrm{kg\,m^{-2}}. \end{aligned}$$

So the pressure on the piston is $42\,890\,\mathrm{kg\,m^{-2}}$.

As mentioned in the marginal note, in the SI system, pressure is *force* per unit area, not *mass* per unit area — this arises because of the difference between mass and weight. So we should multiply the above answer by g, the magnitude of the acceleration due to gravity, to give a pressure of $4.289 \times 9.81 \times 10^4\,\mathrm{kg\,m^{-1}\,s^{-2}} = 420\,800\,\mathrm{kg\,m^{-1}\,s^{-2}}$.

2.8 Consider the dimensions of the terms on the left-hand side of the equation one-by-one:

$$\left[\frac{p}{\rho}\right] = \frac{[p]}{[\rho]} = \frac{\mathrm{M\,L^{-1}\,T^{-2}}}{\mathrm{M\,L^{-3}}} = \mathrm{L^2\,T^{-2}},$$

$$\left[\tfrac{1}{2}u\right] = [u] = \mathrm{L\,T^{-1}},$$

$$[gz] = [g]\,[z] = (\mathrm{L\,T^{-2}}) \times \mathrm{L} = \mathrm{L^2\,T^{-2}}.$$

The equation is dimensionally inconsistent because the second term has different dimensions from the other two. It therefore seems likely that the second term is incorrect, and that its dimensions should be $\mathrm{L^2\,T^{-2}}$. One form that would be consistent is $\frac{1}{2}u^2$, rather than $\frac{1}{2}u$.

Note that the 'constant' on the right-hand side of this equation is not dimensionless.

2.9 We have

$$1 \text{ boliviano} = 1 \text{ boliviano} \times \left(\frac{\$1}{7.75 \text{ boliviano}}\right) \times \left(\frac{£1}{\$1.75}\right) = £0.074.$$

I approximated this exchange rate as 10 boliviano $= £\frac{3}{4}$. For example, I bought a memory card for my digital camera for 830 boliviano. I approximated this cost in £ as $84 \times \frac{3}{4} = £63$ (84 being divisible by 4). (The cost on my credit card bill was £61.59.)

Section 3

3.1 The dimensions of the quantities assumed to be involved are listed in the table below.

Physical quantity	Symbol	Dimensions
Time taken for one complete oscillation	τ	T
Mass of bob	m	M
Length of pendulum stem	l	L
Angular amplitude of oscillations	Φ	1
Acceleration due to gravity	g	$\mathrm{L\,T^{-2}}$

We wish to find an expression for the period τ in terms of the other quantities. We assume that this expression takes the form

$$\tau = k\,m^\alpha\,l^\beta\,\Phi^\gamma\,g^\delta,$$

where k is a dimensionless constant. For this equation to be dimensionally consistent, we must have

$$[\tau] = [k]\,[m]^\alpha\,[l]^\beta\,[\Phi]^\gamma\,[g]^\delta.$$

Hence

$$\mathrm{T} = \mathrm{M}^\alpha\,\mathrm{L}^\beta\,(\mathrm{L\,T^{-2}})^\delta = \mathrm{M}^\alpha\,\mathrm{L}^{\beta+\delta}\,\mathrm{T}^{-2\delta}.$$

Equating powers of M, L and T on both sides of this equation leads to

$$0 = \alpha, \quad 0 = \beta + \delta, \quad 1 = -2\delta.$$

Solving these equations gives

$$\alpha = 0, \quad \beta = \tfrac{1}{2}, \quad \delta = -\tfrac{1}{2}.$$

Hence

$$\tau = k\,l^{1/2}\,g^{-1/2}\,\Phi^\gamma.$$

We conclude that

$$\tau = k(\Phi)\,l^{1/2}\,g^{-1/2} = k(\Phi)\sqrt{\frac{l}{g}},$$

where $k(\Phi)$ is an (undetermined) function of Φ.

3.2 The dimensions of the quantities involved in the situation are listed in the table below.

Physical quantity	Symbol	Dimensions
Drag force on sphere	F	$\mathrm{M\,L\,T^{-2}}$
Speed of sphere	v	$\mathrm{L\,T^{-1}}$
Radius of sphere	r	L
Density of fluid	ρ	$\mathrm{M\,L^{-3}}$
Viscosity of fluid	μ	$\mathrm{M\,L^{-1}\,T^{-1}}$

We wish to find an expression for the drag force F in terms of the other quantities. We assume that this expression takes the form

$$F = k\,v^\alpha\,r^\beta\,\rho^\gamma\,\mu^\delta,$$

where k is a dimensionless constant. For this to be dimensionally consistent, we must have

$$[F] = [k]\,[v]^\alpha\,[r]^\beta\,[\rho]^\gamma\,[\mu]^\delta.$$

Hence

$$\begin{aligned}\mathrm{M\,L\,T^{-2}} &= (\mathrm{L\,T^{-1}})^\alpha\,\mathrm{L}^\beta\,(\mathrm{M\,L^{-3}})^\gamma\,(\mathrm{M\,L^{-1}\,T^{-1}})^\delta\\ &= \mathrm{M}^{\gamma+\delta}\,\mathrm{L}^{\alpha+\beta-3\gamma-\delta}\,\mathrm{T}^{-\alpha-\delta}.\end{aligned}$$

Equating powers of M, L and T on both sides of this equation gives

$$1 = \gamma+\delta, \quad 1 = \alpha+\beta-3\gamma-\delta, \quad -2 = -\alpha-\delta.$$

We have three equations in the four unknowns α, β, γ and δ. If we let $\delta = a$, where a is an unknown parameter, then the solution to these equations is

$$\alpha = 2-a, \quad \beta = 2-a, \quad \gamma = 1-a, \quad \delta = a.$$

Hence

$$\begin{aligned}F &= k\,v^{2-a}\,r^{2-a}\,\rho^{1-a}\,\mu^a\\ &= k\,v^2\,r^2\,\rho\left(\frac{\mu}{vr\rho}\right)^a.\end{aligned}$$

We deduce that the general expression for the drag force is

$$F = v^2\,r^2\,\rho\,f\left(\frac{\mu}{vr\rho}\right),$$

where f is an undetermined function.

(Some alternative equivalent answers which you may have obtained are

$$F = \frac{\mu^2}{\rho}\,f\left(\frac{vr\rho}{\mu}\right) \quad \text{and} \quad F = vr\mu\,f\left(\frac{vr\rho}{\mu}\right).)$$

3.3 The dimensions of the quantities involved in the situation are listed below.

Physical quantity	Symbol	Dimensions
Frequency of vibration of string	Ω	$\mathrm{T^{-1}}$
Mass of string	m	M
Length of string	l	L
Tension of string	H	$\mathrm{M\,L\,T^{-2}}$

We wish to find an expression for the frequency Ω in terms of the other quantities. We assume that this expression takes the form

$$\Omega = k\,m^\alpha\,l^\beta\,H^\gamma,$$

where k is a dimensionless constant. For this equation to be dimensionally consistent, we must have

$$[\Omega] = [k]\,[m]^\alpha\,[l]^\beta\,[H]^\gamma,$$

or

$$\mathrm{T^{-1}} = \mathrm{M}^\alpha\,\mathrm{L}^\beta\,(\mathrm{M\,L\,T^{-2}})^\gamma = \mathrm{M}^{\alpha+\gamma}\,\mathrm{L}^{\beta+\gamma}\,\mathrm{T}^{-2\gamma}.$$

Equating powers of M, L and T on both sides of this equation leads to

$$0 = \alpha+\gamma, \quad 0 = \beta+\gamma, \quad -1 = -2\gamma.$$

The solution to these equations is

$$\alpha = -\tfrac{1}{2}, \quad \beta = -\tfrac{1}{2}, \quad \gamma = \tfrac{1}{2}.$$

Hence

$$\begin{aligned}\Omega &= k\,m^{-1/2}\,l^{-1/2}\,H^{1/2}\\ &= k\sqrt{\frac{H}{ml}},\end{aligned}$$

where k is a dimensionless constant.

3.4 The dimensions of the quantities involved in the situation are listed below.

Physical quantity	Symbol	Dimensions
Speed of water	u	$\mathrm{L\,T^{-1}}$
Pressure difference across the pipe	p	$\mathrm{M\,L^{-1}\,T^{-2}}$
Length of pipe	l	L
Diameter of pipe	d	L
Density of water	ρ	$\mathrm{M\,L^{-3}}$
Viscosity of water	μ	$\mathrm{M\,L^{-1}\,T^{-1}}$

We wish to find an expression for the speed u in terms of the other quantities. We assume that this expression takes the form

$$u = k\,p^\alpha\,l^\beta\,d^\gamma\,\rho^\delta\,\mu^\varepsilon,$$

where k is a dimensionless constant. For this equation to be dimensionally consistent, we must have

$$[u] = [k]\,[p]^\alpha\,[l]^\beta\,[d]^\gamma\,[\rho]^\delta\,[\mu]^\varepsilon,$$

or

$$\begin{aligned}\mathrm{L\,T^{-1}} &= (\mathrm{M\,L^{-1}\,T^{-2}})^\alpha\,\mathrm{L}^\beta\,\mathrm{L}^\gamma\,(\mathrm{M\,L^{-3}})^\delta\,(\mathrm{M\,L^{-1}\,T^{-1}})^\varepsilon\\ &= \mathrm{M}^{\alpha+\delta+\varepsilon}\,\mathrm{L}^{-\alpha+\beta+\gamma-3\delta-\varepsilon}\,\mathrm{T}^{-2\alpha-\varepsilon}.\end{aligned}$$

Equating powers of M, L and T on both sides of this equation leads to

$$0 = \alpha + \delta + \varepsilon, \quad 1 = -\alpha + \beta + \gamma - 3\delta - \varepsilon,$$
$$-1 = -2\alpha - \varepsilon.$$

We have three equations in the five unknowns α, β, γ, δ and ε. If we let $\gamma = a$ and $\varepsilon = b$, where a and b are unknown parameters (obviously, other choices are possible), the equations become

$$\alpha + \delta = -b, \quad -\alpha + \beta - 3\delta = 1 - a + b,$$
$$-2\alpha = -1 + b.$$

The solution to these equations is

$$\alpha = \tfrac{1}{2} - \tfrac{1}{2}b, \quad \beta = -a - b, \quad \gamma = a,$$
$$\delta = -\tfrac{1}{2} - \tfrac{1}{2}b, \quad \varepsilon = b.$$

Hence

$$\begin{aligned} u &= k\, p^{(1-b)/2}\, l^{-a-b}\, d^a\, \rho^{(-1-b)/2}\, \mu^b \\ &= k\, p^{1/2}\rho^{-1/2}\,(l^{-1}d)^a\,(p^{-1/2}l^{-1}\rho^{-1/2}\mu)^b \\ &= k\sqrt{\frac{p}{\rho}}\left(\frac{d}{l}\right)^a\left(\frac{\mu}{l\sqrt{p\rho}}\right)^b, \end{aligned}$$

where a and b are arbitrary constants. We deduce that the general expression for the speed is

$$u = \sqrt{\frac{p}{\rho}}\, f\!\left(\frac{d}{l}, \frac{\mu}{l\sqrt{p\rho}}\right),$$

where f is an undetermined function of two variables.

There are many alternative equivalent answers. The important factors in these answers are that:

- the two variables of the undetermined function are both dimensionless;
- the factor multiplying the function has the same dimensions as u, namely $\mathrm{L\,T^{-1}}$.

Section 4

4.1 Rearranging the two equations, the temperature differences are

$$\Theta_{\text{tea}} - \Theta_1 = \frac{q}{h_{\text{tea}}A} \quad \text{and} \quad \Theta_1 - \Theta_{\text{air}} = \frac{q}{h_{\text{air}}A}.$$

In order to eliminate Θ_1, we add these two equations to obtain

$$\Theta_{\text{tea}} - \Theta_{\text{air}} = \frac{q}{A}\left(\frac{1}{h_{\text{tea}}} + \frac{1}{h_{\text{air}}}\right).$$

Hence

$$q = UA(\Theta_{\text{tea}} - \Theta_{\text{air}}), \quad \text{where } U = \left(\frac{1}{h_{\text{tea}}} + \frac{1}{h_{\text{air}}}\right)^{-1}.$$

4.2 The dimensions of $\lambda = UA/(mc)$ are

$$\begin{aligned} [\lambda] &= [UA/(mc)] \\ &= [U]\,[A]\,[m]^{-1}\,[c]^{-1} \\ &= (\mathrm{M\,T^{-3}\,\Theta^{-1}}) \times \mathrm{L^2} \times \mathrm{M^{-1}} \times (\mathrm{L^2\,T^{-2}\,\Theta^{-1}})^{-1} \\ &= \mathrm{T^{-1}}, \end{aligned}$$

recalling that a U-value U is measured in $\mathrm{W\,m^{-2}\,K^{-1}}$, and a specific heat capacity c is measured in $\mathrm{J\,kg^{-1}\,K^{-1}}$. So the dimensions of the right-hand side of Equation (4.6) are

$$[\lambda]\,[\Theta_{\text{tea}} - \Theta_{\text{air}}] = \mathrm{T^{-1}} \times \Theta = \mathrm{T^{-1}}\,\Theta.$$

The dimensions of the left-hand side of the equation are

$$[\Theta_{\text{tea}}]/[t] = \Theta \times \mathrm{T^{-1}} = \mathrm{T^{-1}}\,\Theta,$$

so the equation is dimensionally consistent.

4.3 My list of the assumptions is as follows.

(a) The change in the heat energy of the tea is given by Equation (1.1) of *Unit 15*, with c effectively constant over the range of temperatures considered.

(b) We neglect any heat losses due to radiation.

(c) We neglect any heat losses due to conduction and convection through the sides and the bottom of the cup.

(d) The transfer of heat energy by convection can be modelled by Equation (4.1).

(e) The tea (apart from a thin layer close to the surface) has a uniform temperature.

(f) The surrounding air (apart from a thin layer close to the surface of the tea) has a uniform, constant temperature. (The assumption that the room temperature is constant is not actually necessary for our model until we solve the differential equation in Exercise 4.5.)

(g) Over a short time interval, the steady-state model given by Equation (4.1) provides a good approximation of the rate of heat energy loss, and this approximation improves as the time interval gets shorter.

4.4 **(a)** If $\Theta_{\text{tea}} > \Theta_{\text{air}}$, I would expect the temperature of the tea to be decreasing, i.e. $d\Theta_{\text{tea}}/dt < 0$. If $\Theta_{\text{tea}} < \Theta_{\text{air}}$ (for example, if I were drinking iced tea), I would expect $d\Theta_{\text{tea}}/dt > 0$. If $\Theta_{\text{tea}} = \Theta_{\text{air}}$, I would not expect the temperature of the tea to be changing, so $d\Theta_{\text{tea}}/dt = 0$. Furthermore, I would expect the magnitude $|d\Theta_{\text{tea}}/dt|$ of the rate of change of temperature to increase as a result of any increase in the magnitude $|\Theta_{\text{tea}} - \Theta_{\text{air}}|$ of the temperature difference.

(b) Equation (4.6) says that the rate of change of temperature $d\Theta_{\text{tea}}/dt$ is proportional to the temperature difference $(\Theta_{\text{tea}} - \Theta_{\text{air}})$, with a *negative* constant of proportionality. So this equation is consistent with all the statements in part (a).

4.5 The differential equation can be solved by using the integrating factor method or the separation of variables method from *Unit 2*. Using the integrating factor method, we first rewrite the equation in the form

$$\frac{d\Theta_{\text{tea}}}{dt} + \lambda\Theta_{\text{tea}}(t) = \lambda\Theta_{\text{air}}.$$

The integrating factor is $p = \exp(\int \lambda\, dt) = e^{\lambda t}$, and this leads to

$$e^{\lambda t}\,\Theta_{\text{tea}}(t) = \int \lambda\,\Theta_{\text{air}}\,e^{\lambda t}\,dt = \Theta_{\text{air}}\,e^{\lambda t} + C,$$

where C is an arbitrary constant. Rearranging gives

$$\Theta_{\text{tea}}(t) = \Theta_{\text{air}} + Ce^{-\lambda t}.$$

Putting $t = 0$ and using the initial condition $\Theta_{\text{tea}}(0) = \Theta_0$, we obtain $C = \Theta_0 - \Theta_{\text{air}}$. Hence the required particular solution of the differential equation is

$$\Theta_{\text{tea}}(t) = \Theta_{\text{air}} + (\Theta_0 - \Theta_{\text{air}})e^{-\lambda t}.$$

4.6 The argument of the logarithm function on the right-hand side of the equation is dimensionless, as both the numerator and denominator of the fraction are temperature differences and so have the same dimensions. So the dimensions of the right-hand side are

$$\left[\frac{mc}{UA}\right] = [\lambda^{-1}] = [\lambda]^{-1} = (\mathrm{T}^{-1})^{-1} = \mathrm{T},$$

using the calculation for the dimensions of λ in Exercise 4.2. The dimensions of the left-hand side of the equation are

$$[T] = \mathrm{T},$$

so the equation is dimensionally consistent.

Note that if Equation (4.8) had been written in the form

$$T = \lambda^{-1}\left(\ln(\Theta_0 - \Theta_{\text{air}}) - \ln(\Theta_T - \Theta_{\text{air}})\right),$$

we would not have been able to test for dimensional consistency because the arguments of the logarithm functions are no longer dimensionless.

4.7 **(a)** Using Equation (1.1) of *Unit 15*, the accumulation of heat energy in the cup over the time interval is

$$\text{accumulation} = mc\left(\Theta_{\text{water}}(t+\delta t) - \Theta_{\text{water}}(t)\right).$$

The heater supplies energy at rate Q. So, over a time interval of length δt, the amount of energy supplied is

$$\text{input} = Q\,\delta t.$$

Over a short time interval, the temperature of the water is approximately constant, so we can use the steady-state formula $q = UA(\Theta_{\text{water}} - \Theta_{\text{air}})$ for the rate of loss of heat energy by convection from the surface of the water. So, over the time interval, the approximate heat energy loss is

$$\text{output} \simeq q(t)\,\delta t \simeq UA(\Theta_{\text{water}}(t) - \Theta_{\text{air}})\,\delta t.$$

(b) The input–output principle applied to the heat energy of the cup of water over the time interval $[t, t+\delta t]$ gives

$$mc\left(\Theta_{\text{water}}(t+\delta t) - \Theta_{\text{water}}(t)\right) \simeq Q\,\delta t - UA(\Theta_{\text{water}}(t) - \Theta_{\text{air}})\,\delta t.$$

Hence

$$\frac{\Theta_{\text{water}}(t+\delta t) - \Theta_{\text{water}}(t)}{\delta t} \simeq \frac{Q}{mc} - \frac{UA}{mc}(\Theta_{\text{water}}(t) - \Theta_{\text{air}}),$$

and taking the limit as $\delta t \to 0$ gives

$$\frac{d\Theta_{\text{water}}}{dt} = \frac{Q}{mc} - \lambda(\Theta_{\text{water}} - \Theta_{\text{air}}),$$

where $\lambda = UA/(mc)$.

(c) Solving the differential equation by the integrating factor method, for example, gives the general solution

$$\Theta_{\text{water}}(t) = \Theta_{\text{air}} + \frac{Q}{\lambda mc} + Ce^{-\lambda t},$$

where C is a constant. The initial condition $\Theta_{\text{water}}(0) = \Theta_{\text{air}}$ gives $C = -Q/(\lambda mc)$, and the corresponding particular solution is

$$\Theta_{\text{water}}(t) = \Theta_{\text{air}} + \frac{Q}{\lambda mc}(1 - e^{-\lambda t}).$$

(d)

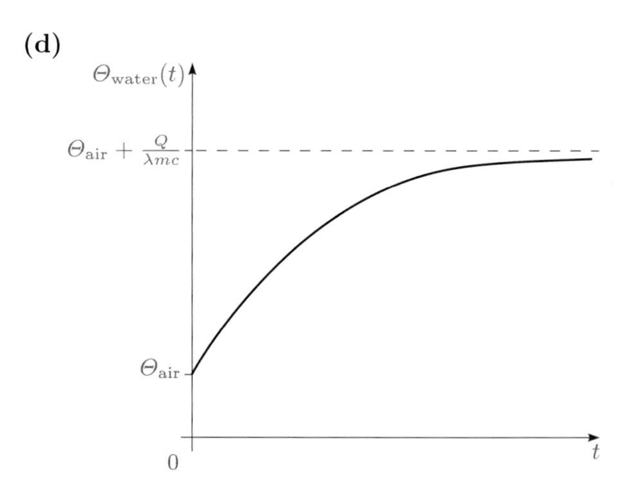

The temperature increases from its initial value Θ_{air} and asymptotically approaches the value

$$\Theta_{\text{air}} + \frac{Q}{\lambda mc}.$$

This is in line with what I would have expected. The asymptotic value is the equilibrium temperature, at which the heat energy supplied by the heater just balances the heat energy lost by the cup of water to the surroundings.

(e) If it takes T seconds to reach a temperature of $\Theta_T = 100°\text{C}$, then we have

$$\Theta_T = \Theta_{\text{air}} + \frac{Q}{\lambda mc}(1 - e^{-\lambda T}).$$

Rearranging this gives

$$T = -\frac{1}{\lambda}\ln\left(1 - \frac{\lambda mc}{Q}(\Theta_T - \Theta_{\text{air}})\right) = -\frac{mc}{UA}\ln\left(1 - \frac{UA}{Q}(\Theta_T - \Theta_{\text{air}})\right),$$

since $\lambda = UA/(mc)$.

(f) Using the given data, we have

$$T = -\frac{0.25 \times 4190}{9.804 \times 0.004\,07} \times \ln\left(1 - \frac{9.804 \times 0.004\,07}{350}(100 - 17)\right) = 249.6 \text{ seconds}.$$

So the model predicts that it will take about 4 minutes 10 seconds to boil the water in the cup.

(g) The estimate from the model and the experimental value differ by only fifteen seconds. So it looks as though we may have a reasonably good model this time.

4.8 **(a)** This situation is analogous to that considered in Exercise 4.7, except that here we are assuming that the only mode of heat energy loss is convection from the surfaces of the tea-urn, so we need to replace U by the convective heat transfer coefficient h between the surfaces of the tea-urn and the surrounding air. Furthermore, the value of the area A must include the area of the curved sides of the tea-urn as well as the area of the lid. So the differential equation that models the variation of the temperature of the tea-urn is

$$\frac{d\Theta_{\text{water}}}{dt} = \frac{Q}{mc} - \lambda(\Theta_{\text{water}}(t) - \Theta_{\text{air}}),$$

where $\lambda = hA/(mc)$.

(b) Using Solution 4.7, the required solution is

$$\Theta_{\text{water}}(t) = \Theta_{\text{air}} + \frac{Q}{\lambda mc}(1 - e^{-\lambda t}).$$

If the time to reach a temperature Θ_T is T, then we have

$$T = -\frac{mc}{hA} \ln\left(1 - \frac{hA}{Q}(\Theta_T - \Theta_{\text{air}})\right).$$

(c) The area of the curved sides of a cylinder of height H and radius r is $2\pi rH$, and the area of the top of the cylinder is πr^2. Hence

$$A = 2\pi rH + \pi r^2.$$

Here, $r = 0.175\,\text{m}$ and $H = 0.515\,\text{m}$, so

$$A = 2\pi \times 0.175 \times 0.515 + \pi \times 0.175^2 = 0.6625\,\text{m}^2.$$

Also, we have

$$m = 30\,\text{kg}, \quad c = 4190\,\text{J}\,\text{kg}^{-1}\,\text{K}^{-1},$$
$$h = 10\,\text{W}\,\text{m}^{-2}\,\text{K}^{-1}, \quad Q = 3000\,\text{W},$$
$$\Theta_{\text{air}} = 20^\circ\text{C}, \quad \Theta_T = 100^\circ\text{C}.$$

Using these data,

$$T = -\frac{30 \times 4190}{10 \times 0.6625} \ln\left(1 - \frac{10 \times 0.6625}{3000}(100 - 20)\right)$$
$$= 3688 \text{ seconds}.$$

So the model predicts that it will take about 3688 seconds, i.e. 1 hour 1 minute and 28 seconds, for the water in the tea-urn to reach boiling point.

(d) This prediction is slightly less than the value given in the brochure, but not too much less. The discrepancy could be because the effects of radiation and heat loss through the base of the tea-urn have been neglected, and also perhaps because the value of the convective heat transfer coefficient may not be accurate.

Section 5

5.1 We have $\lambda = UA/(mc)$, so

$$U = \frac{\lambda mc}{A} = \frac{3.911 \times 10^{-4} \times 0.25 \times 4190}{0.004\,07}$$
$$= 100.7\,\text{W}\,\text{m}^{-2}\text{K}^{-1}.$$

Also,

$$\frac{1}{U} = \frac{1}{h_{\text{air}}} + \frac{1}{h_{\text{tea}}},$$

so

$$\frac{1}{h_{\text{air}}} = \frac{1}{U} - \frac{1}{h_{\text{tea}}} = \frac{1}{100.7} - \frac{1}{500} = 0.007\,935.$$

Hence $h_{\text{air}} = 126.0\,\text{W}\,\text{m}^{-2}\,\text{K}^{-1}$.

Therefore the experimental value for λ would arise from a value for the convective heat transfer coefficient from the tea to the air of $100.7\,\text{W}\,\text{m}^{-2}\,\text{K}^{-1}$, which corresponds to a convective heat transfer coefficient from the tea surface to the air of $126.0\,\text{W}\,\text{m}^{-2}\,\text{K}^{-1}$, which is outside the range of values given in Table 3.1 of *Unit 15*.

Index